BIFURCATION THEORY AND NONLINEAR EIGENVALUE PROBLEMS

MATHEMATICS LECTURE NOTE SERIES

E. Artin and J. Tate	CLASS FIELD THEORY
Michael Atiyah	K-THEORY
Hyman Bass	ALGEBRAIC K-THEORY
Melvyn S. Berger Marion S. Berger	PERSPECTIVES IN NONLINEARITY
Paul J. Cohen	SET THEORY AND THE CONTINUUM HYPOTHESIS
Eldon Dyer	COHOMOLOGY THEORIES
Walter Feit	CHARACTERS OF FINITE GROUPS
William Fulton	ALGEBRAIC CURVES
Marvin J. Greenberg	LECTURES ON ALGEBRAIC TOPOLOGY
Marvin J. Greenberg	LECTURES ON FORMS IN MANY VARIABLES
Robin Hartshorne	FOUNDATIONS OF PROJECTIVE GEOMETRY
J. F. P. Hudson	PIECEWISE LINEAR TOPOLOGY
Irving Kaplansky	RINGS OF OPERATORS
K. Kapp and H. Schneider	COMPLETELY O-SIMPLE SEMIGROUPS
Joseph B. Keller Stuart Antman	BIFURCATION THEORY AND NONLINEAR EIGENVALUE PROBLEMS
Serge Lang	ALGEBRAIC FUNCTIONS
Serge Lang	RAPPORT SUR LA COHOMOLOGIE DES GROUPES
Ottmar Loos	SYMMETRIC SPACES I: GENERAL THEORY II: COMPACT SPACES AND CLASSIFICATION
I. G. Macdonald	ALGEBRAIC GEOMETRY: INTRODUCTION TO SCHEMES
George W. Mackey	INDUCED REPRESENTATIONS OF GROUPS AND QUANTUM MECHANICS

Andrew Ogg	MODULAR FORMS AND DIRICHLET SERIES
Richard Palais	FOUNDATIONS OF GLOBAL NON-LINEAR ANALYSIS
William Parry	ENTROPY AND GENERATORS IN ERGODIC THEORY
D. S. Passman	PERMUTATION GROUPS
Walter Rudin	FUNCTION THEORY IN POLYDISCS
Jean-Pierre Serre	ABELIAN *l*-ADIC REPRESENTATIONS AND ELLIPTIC CURVES
Jean-Pierre Serre	ALGEBRES DE LIE SEMI-SIMPLE COMPLEXES
Jean-Pierre Serre	LIE ALGEBRAS AND LIE GROUPS
Sholmo Sternberg	CELESTIAL MECHANICS

A Note from the Publisher

This volume was printed directly from a typescript prepared by the editors, who take full responsibility for its content and appearance. The Publisher has not performed his usual functions of reviewing, editing, typesetting, and proofreading the material prior to publication.

The Publisher fully endorses this informal and quick method of publishing conference proceedings, and he wishes to thank the editors for preparing the material for publication.

BIFURCATION THEORY AND NONLINEAR EIGENVALUE PROBLEMS

Edited by

JOSEPH B. KELLER AND STUART ANTMAN

New York University

W. A. BENJAMIN, INC.

New York 1969 Amsterdam

BIFURCATION THEORY
AND
NONLINEAR EIGENVALUE PROBLEMS

Library of Congress Catalog Card Number 76-78857
Manufactured in the United States of America
12345 MR 32109

*The manuscript was put into production on January 15, 1969;
this volume was published on March 1, 1969*

W. A. BENJAMIN, INC.
New York, New York 10016

PREFACE

A seminar on Bifurcation Theory and Nonlinear Eigenvalue Problems, was held during 1966-1967 at the Courant Institute of Mathematical Sciences, New York University. This seminar, organized by Professors J.B. Keller and E.L. Reiss, consisted of fifteen lectures. Notes based on these lectures and related material were prepared by the speakers and edited by J.B. Keller and S. Antman. Since these notes are intended for readers with diverse backgrounds, each lecture contains introductory and background material together with statements of definitions and theorems of an advanced or specialized nature. References to proofs of such theorems are also included. Each lecture, except Lecture VII, can be read independently of the others. Some of the lectures are primarily expository, but most of them present recent research results. Together they represent a wide variety of techniques for treating nonlinear problems. Although many of the lectures treat examples from physics or engineering, the emphasis is on the analysis of the corresponding nonlinear problems.

The editors wish to thank the Army Reseach Office, Durham,and the Office of Naval Research for their support of this work.

CONTENTS

	Preface	vii
	Introduction	xi
I.	Column Buckling--An Elementary Example of Bifurcation EDWARD L. REISS, New York University	1
II.	Bifurcation Theory for Ordinary differential Equations JOSEPH B. KELLER, New York University	17
III.	Existence of Buckled States of Circular Plates Via the Schauder Fixed Point Theorem JAY H. WOLKOWISKY, University of Colorado	49
IV.	Buckled States of Elastic Rings I. TADJBAKHSH, I.B.M. Corporation	69
	Appendix: The Case n = 1 STUART ANTMAN, New York University	93
V.	A Bifurcation Problem in Superconductivity F. ODEH, I.B.M. Corporation	99
VI.	A Bifurcation Theory for Nonlinear Elliptic Partial Differential Equations and Related Systems MELVYN S. BERGER, University of Minnesota	113
VII.	A Bifurcation Theory for Nonlinear Elliptic Partial Differential Equations (continued) MELVYN S. BERGER, University of Minnesota	191
VIII.	Some Positone Problems Suggested by Nonlinear Heat Generation H.B. KELLER, California Institute of Technology	217

IX. Bifurcation Phenomena in Surface Wave Theory 257
J.J. STOKER, New York University

X. Perturbation Theory of Quasiperiodic Solutions of Differential Equations 283
J. MOSER, New York University

XI. Some Buckling Problems in Nonlinear Elasticity 309
C. SENSENIG, New York University

XII. Equilibrium States of Nonlinearly Elastic Rods 331
STUART ANTMAN, New York University

XIII. Nonuniqueness of Rectangular Solutions of the Bénard Problem 359
PAUL H. RABINOWITZ, Stanford University

XIV. Exchange of Stability in Couette Flow 395
H.F. WEINBERGER, University of Minnesota

XV. Perturbation Solutions of Some Nonlinear Boundary Value Problems 411
M. MILLMAN, New York University

INTRODUCTION

By a nonlinear eigenvalue problem we mean the problem of finding appropriate solutions of a nonlinear equation of the form

$$F(u,\lambda) = 0. \tag{1}$$

Here F is a nonlinear operator, depending upon the parameter λ, which operates on the unknown function or vector u. One of the first questions to be answered is whether or not (1) has any solution u for a given value of λ. If it does, the question of how many solutions it has arises, and then how this number varies with λ. Of particular interest is the process of bifurcation whereby a given solution of (1) splits into two or more solutions as λ passes through a critical value λ_o, called a bifurcation point. The main problem is to determine the properties of the solutions and how they depend upon λ.

To illustrate bifurcation, let us consider the linear eigenvalue problem

$$Lu = \lambda u. \tag{2}$$

Here L is a linear operator acting on vectors u in some normed linear space and λ is a real number. For every value of λ, a solution of (2) is

$$u = 0. \tag{3}$$

Let us suppose that there is a sequence of eigenvalues $\lambda_1 < \lambda_2 < \lambda_3 < \ldots$ and corresponding normalized eigenfunctions $u_1, u_2, u_3, \ldots$ such that

$$Lu_j = \lambda_j u_j, \quad \|u_j\| = 1, \quad j = 1,2,3,\ldots \,. \tag{4}$$

Then if c is any real number, other solutions of (2) are given by

$$u = cu_j, \qquad j = 1,2,3,\ldots \,. \tag{5}$$

The norm of the solution (3) is $\|u\| = 0$ while the norm of the solution (5) is $\|u\| = c$. A graph of the norms of these solutions is shown in Figure 1. As the figure shows, the solution $u = 0$ splits into two branches at each of the eigenvalues λ_j. Therefore the points $u = 0$, $\lambda = \lambda_j$ are bifurcation points of the problem (1).

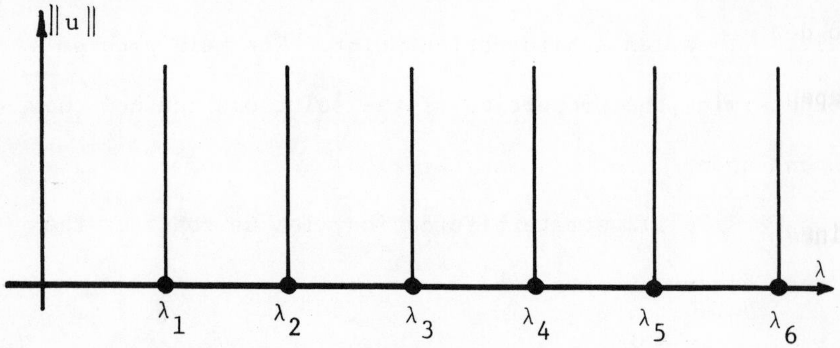

Figure 1.

We now consider the nonlinear eigenvalue problem (1) which has (2) as its linearization. An illustrative plot of $\|u\|$ versus λ, called the response diagram, is shown in Figure 2. It manifests the following behavior:

(i) The branches emanating from the eigenvalues of the linear problem are curved.

(ii) There may be no branch emanating from an eigenvalue of the linearized problem. This occurs at λ_2 in Figure 2.

(iii) There may be several branches emanating from an eigenvalue of the linearized problem as from λ_3 in Figure 2.

(iv) There may be a secondary bifurcation as on the branch from λ_4.

(v) The branches from distinct eigenvalues of the linearized problem may be connected. This happens with the branch through λ_5 and λ_6.

(vi) There may be branches that do not emanate from the eigenvalues of the linearized problem, such as the branch C.

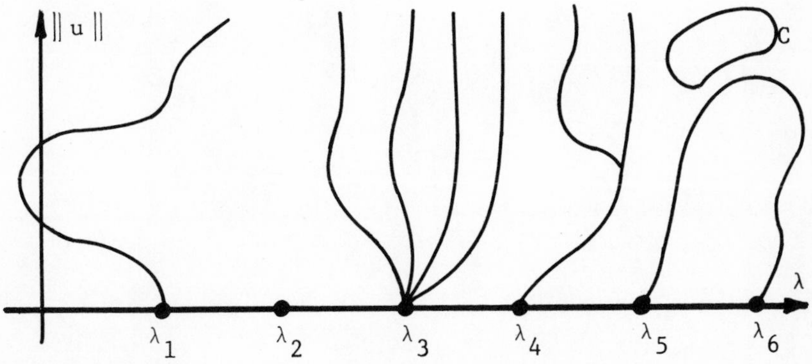

Figure 2.

Concrete examples of such response diagrams occur throughout these notes. In each case some but not necessarily all, of these phenomena occur. In the diagrams a quantity which can be either positive or negative is often plotted in place of $||u||$.

I. Column Buckling--An Elementary Example of Bifurcation

Edward L. Reiss

1. Introduction.

The buckling of a slender elastic rod or column due to a compressive axial thrust is perhaps the simplest example of a bifurcation phenomenon. It was analyzed by Euler, Bernoulli and Lagrange.

It is observed experimentally that as the thrust T increases gradually from zero, the rod first deforms by shortening and thickening. Its center line remains straight. At a critical value of the thrust the rod buckles out of the straight state into a bent state. As T increases beyond this critical value, the rod bends further. Since the straight rod is an equilibrium state for all T, the observations show that there are at least two possible equilibrium states for T greater than the critical thrust---the bent state and the straight state.

The classical linear theory of elasticity predicts a unique solution to any problem. It is therefore inadequate for the description of buckling. Consequently in the next section we employ a nonlinear theory to describe the buckling of a column due to an axial displacement of the ends. In Section 3 we use the nonlinear elastica theory to study the buckling of a column due to an applied axial thrust.

2. The boundary value problem for prescribed end displacements.

We consider a thin rod with pinned ends lying in the x,z plane. The x-displacements of its endpoints are prescribed. The shape of the rod is described by two functions u(x) and w(x) which are the dimensionless displacements in the x and z directions. These functions satisfy the following differential equations and boundary conditions:

$$w_{xx}(x) + \lambda w(x) = 0, \qquad 0 \le x \le 1, \tag{2.1}$$

$$u_x(x) + \frac{1}{2}[w_x(x)]^2 = -\beta\lambda, \qquad 0 \le x \le 1, \tag{2.2}$$

$$w(0) = w(1) = 0, \tag{2.3}$$

$$u(0) = -u(1) = c > 0. \tag{2.4}$$

The constant λ in (2.1) and (2.2) is to be determined. It is proportional to the axial stress in the rod. The positive constant c in (2.4) is proportional to the prescribed end displacement. We refer to c as the end-shortening. $\beta > 0$ is a given physical constant.

The problem (2.1)-(2.4) is nonlinear because $(w_x)^2$ appears in (2.2). We first consider the linear problem obtained by omitting this term. Thus (2.2) is replaced by,

$$u_x(x) = -\beta\lambda, \qquad 0 \leq x \leq 1. \tag{2.2'}$$

The solution of (2.2') is $u(x) = \text{const.} -\beta\lambda x$. The constant is determined by (2.4) as

$$c = \beta\lambda/2, \tag{2.5}$$

and hence

$$u(x) = c(1-2x). \tag{2.6}$$

The solution of (2.1) and (2.3) is $w(x) \equiv 0$ unless λ is an eigenvalue λ_n given by

$$\lambda = \lambda_n \equiv (n\pi)^2, \qquad n = 1,2,\ldots\,. \tag{2.7}$$

In this case w is a multiple of the eigenfunction w_n defined by

$$w(x) = A_n w_n(x) \equiv A_n \sin n\pi x, \quad n = 1,2,\ldots\,. \tag{2.8}$$

Here A_n is a constant which is so far undetermined. From

(2.5) and (2.7) we conclude that if $c = c_n \equiv \beta\lambda_n/2$ then the rod buckles into a shape given by (2.6) and (2.8) with an undetermined amplitude A_n. The quantities c_n, $n = 1,2,\ldots$, are called the critical end-shortenings. For $c \neq c_n$ the rod remains straight, since the solution of (2.1) and (2.3) is

$$w(x) \equiv 0. \tag{2.9}$$

We now consider the nonlinear problem (2.1)-(2.4). The solution of (2.1) and (2.3) for $w(x)$ is still given by (2.8) when $\lambda = \lambda_n$ and by (2.9) when $\lambda \neq \lambda_n$. To obtain $u(x)$ when $\lambda = \lambda_n$ we substitute (2.8) into (2.2) and integrate using (2.4) at $x = 0$. This yields

$$u(x) = u_n(x) \equiv c - \beta\lambda_n\left(1 + \frac{A_n^2}{4\beta}\right)x + \frac{n\pi A_n^2}{8} \sin 2n\pi x. \tag{2.10}$$

Applying (2.4) at $x = 1$ we obtain

$$c = c_n\left(1 + \frac{A_n^2}{4\beta}\right). \tag{2.11}$$

Equation (2.11) is a relation between the end-shortening and the amplitude. It gives the "response" of the rod. A graphical representation of (2.11) is sketched in Figure 1.

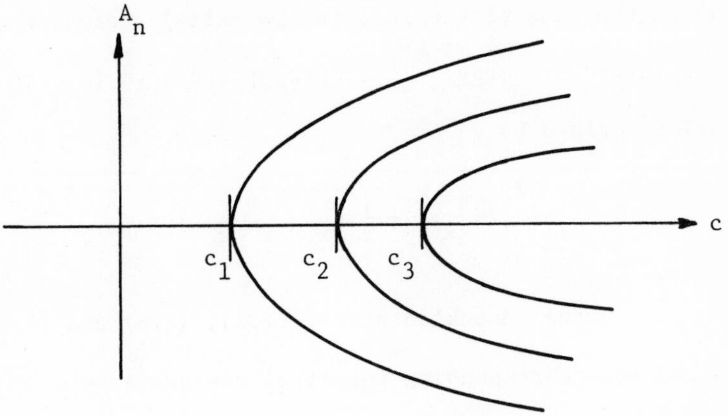

Figure 1

For each n, real solutions of (2.11) for A_n are possible if and only if $c \geq c_n$. The solutions branch or bifurcate from the unbuckled state $A_n = 0$ at c_n. Thus the solution of the linear problem determines the bifurcation points of the solution of the nonlinear problem. For any c in the interval $c_n < c < c_{n+1}$, there are 2n+1 solutions. For $c < c_1$, no buckling is possible. We observe from (2.11) that $dc/dA_n = c_n A_n/2\beta$. Thus for a fixed amplitude A, the parabola in Figure 1 branching from c_n has a steeper slope than that branching from c_m, if $m < n$. The parabolas therefore do not intersect.

For any fixed value of c, we can classify the solution branches by the values of the potential energy corresponding to them. Since the displacements are prescribed by

(2.4) at the ends of the rod, the potential energy is equal to the internal energy. It is proportional to the functional V defined by

$$V = \frac{1}{2}\int_0^1 [(w_{xx})^2 + \frac{1}{\beta}(u_x + \frac{1}{2} w_x^2)^2]dx. \tag{2.12}$$

In the unbuckled state, (2.5), (2.6) and (2.9) hold and the corresponding potential energy is

$$V_\infty = \frac{\beta}{2} (\frac{2c}{\beta})^2 . \tag{2.13}$$

The energy V_n of the buckled state $w = A_n w_n(x)$, obtained by substituting (2.7), (2.8), (2.10) into (2.12), is

$$V_n = \lambda_n(2c - c_n). \tag{2.14}$$

Thus

$$V_n - V_\infty = -\frac{2}{\beta} (c - c_n)^2 \leq 0, \quad c \geq c_n, \tag{2.15}$$

$$(V_n - V_m) = \frac{2}{\beta} (c_n - c_m)[(c-c_n) + (c-c_m)] \geq 0, \quad c \geq c_n > c_m. \tag{2.16}$$

We conclude from (2.15) and (2.16) that for fixed $c > c_1$, the straight state has the largest energy and the branch emanating from c_1 has the smallest energy. For fixed c in the interval $c_n < c < c_{n+1}$ the energies of the branches are ordered:

$$V_\infty > V_n > V_{n-1} > \cdots > V_1. \tag{2.17}$$

If we assume that the rod prefers the state of least energy, then the preferred state is

$$w = A_1 w_1 = \underline{+}2\beta^{1/2}(\frac{c}{c_1} - 1) \sin \pi x, \tag{2.18}$$

for all $c > c_1$.

3. The elastica with prescribed end thrust.

We shall now treat the boundary value problem for a pinned inextensible rod subject to prescribed axial thrust. Experimentally this condition can be attained by loading a vertical rod with weights at its upper end. The shape of the rod is determined by $\psi(x)$, the angle between the centerline of the deformed rod and the x-axis, and the displacements $u(x)$ and $w(x)$ parallel and perpendicular to the x-axis. It is a solution of the boundary value problem for the inextensible elastica, given by,

$$\psi_{xx} + \lambda \sin \psi = 0, \qquad 0 \leq x \leq 1 \tag{3.1a}$$

$$\psi_x(0) = \psi_x(1) = 0. \tag{3.1b}$$

$$u_x = \cos \psi - 1, \qquad w_x = \sin \psi, \qquad 0 \leq x \leq 1. \tag{3.2a}$$

$$u(0) = w(0) = w(1) = 0. \tag{3.2b}$$

The constant λ in (3.1a) is proportional to the applied thrust.

The conditions (3.1b) imply that the ends of the rod are free to rotate. The conditions (3.2b) imply that the end $x = 0$ is fixed and the end $x = 1$ is constrained to lie on the x-axis. When a solution of (3.1) is obtained, u and w are determined by solving (3.2).

The linearization of (3.1) and (3.2) about the solution $\psi = 0$ leads to the eigenvalue problem

$$\psi_{xx} + \lambda\psi = 0, \qquad 0 \le x \le 1, \qquad \psi_x(0) = \psi_x(1) = 0$$
$$u_x = 0,\ w_x = \psi,\ \ u(0) = w(0) = w(1) = 0. \tag{3.3a}$$

It has the solutions

$$\psi = A_n \cos n\pi x, \qquad u = 0, \qquad n = 0,1,\ldots,$$
$$w = A_o = 0, \qquad n = 0, \qquad w = \frac{A_n}{n\pi}\sin n\pi x, \quad n = 1,2,\ldots, \tag{3.3b}$$

when

$$\lambda = \lambda_n \equiv (n\pi)^2, \qquad n = 0,1,\ldots\ . \tag{3.3c}$$

The value $\lambda_o = 0$ has only $\psi = A_o = 0$ as a solution so λ_o is not an eigenvalue.

For the nonlinear problem it is clear that whenever $\psi(x)$, $u(x)$, $w(x)$ is a solution for some value of λ then so is $\pm\psi(x) + 2n\pi$, $u(x)$, $\pm w(x)$ for any integer n and the same value of λ. In addition $\pm\psi(x) + (2n+1)\pi$, $-u(x)-2x, w(x)$ is a solution for $-\lambda$. Thus without loss of generality we can assume that $\lambda \ge 0$ and that

$$\psi(0) = \alpha, \qquad 0 \le \alpha \le \pi. \tag{3.4}$$

A first integral of (3.1a) can be obtained by multiplying (3.1a) by ψ_x, integrating the result and using (3.1b) and (3.4). This gives

$$\psi_x^2 = 2\lambda(\cos\psi - \cos\alpha). \tag{3.5}$$

Since ψ is continuous and satisfies (3.4), and the right side of (3.5) must be non-negative, we conclude from (3.5) that ψ satisfies the inequality,

$$|\psi| \leq \alpha. \tag{3.6}$$

Clearly $\psi(x) \equiv 0$ and $\psi(x) \equiv \pi$ are solutions of (3.1) and (3.2) for all λ.

Theorem: If $0 < \lambda < \lambda_1$, then $\psi(x) \equiv 0$ and $\psi(x) \equiv \pi$ are the only solutions of (3.1) which satisfy (3.4).

Proof: Let ψ be another solution of (3.1) for $\lambda < \lambda_1$. Then using integration by parts and the boundary conditions (3.1b), we have

$$0 = -\int_0^1 (\psi_{xx} + \lambda \sin\psi)\psi dx = \int_0^1 (\psi_x^2 - \lambda \psi\sin\psi)dx. \tag{3.7}$$

Since $\psi \sin\psi \leq |\psi| |\sin \psi| \leq \psi^2$, (3.7) implies that

$$0 \geq \int_0^1 [\psi_x^2 - \lambda \psi^2]dx. \tag{3.8}$$

This is impossible since the minimum characterization of λ_1 implies that the integral in (3.8) is positive for all $0 < \lambda < \lambda_1$ and for all admissible functions $\psi(x) \not\equiv$ constant ($\lambda = 0$ is not an eigenvalue of (3.3a)).

To study the solutions of (3.1) for $\lambda \geq \lambda_1$, we introduce a new dependent variable $\phi(x)$ defined by

$$k\sin\phi = \sin\frac{\psi}{2}, \quad k \equiv \sin\frac{\alpha}{2}. \tag{3.9}$$

Differentiating (3.9) to express ϕ_x as a function of ψ_x and using the half-angle trigonometric formula, we reduce (3.5) to

$$\phi_x = \mu\sqrt{1-k^2\sin^2\phi}, \qquad \mu \equiv \sqrt{\lambda} \tag{3.10a}$$

We have dropped the "$\pm$" in front of the right hand side of (3.10a) because the resulting solutions differ only in sign. We write (3.10a) in the form

$$\mu\frac{dx}{d\phi} = (1 - k^2\sin^2\phi)^{-1/2}. \tag{3.10b}$$

The range of ϕ is required in order to integrate this equation. From (3.9), we obtain $\sin\phi(0) = 1$; hence

$$\phi(0) = \underline{\phi}_p \equiv (\frac{4p+1}{2})\pi, \qquad p = 0,\pm1,\pm2,\ldots . \tag{3.11}$$

Equations (3.5), (3.1b) and (3.9) imply that $\sin^2\phi(1) = 1$. Therefore

$$\phi(1) = \bar{\phi}_q \equiv \frac{2q+1}{2}\pi, \qquad q = 0,\pm1,\ldots . \tag{3.12}$$

Integrating (3.10b) subject to (3.11) gives

$$\mu x = \int_{\underline{\phi}_p}^{\phi(x)} (1-k^2\sin^2\phi)^{-1/2}d\phi, \quad p = 0,\pm1,\ldots, \tag{3.13}$$

which for each p is a Jacobian elliptic integral of the first kind. The integrand is a periodic function of period

π. It has maxima of $(1-k^2)^{-1/2}$ at $\phi = \bar{\phi}_q$ and minima of 1 at $\phi = n\pi$, $n = 0, \pm 1, \ldots$. Setting $x = 1$ in (3.13), we obtain

$$\mu = \int_{\underline{\phi}_p}^{\bar{\phi}_q} (1-k^2\sin^2\phi)^{-1/2} d\phi, \quad p,q = 0,\pm 1,\ldots \; . \tag{3.14}$$

We introduce the complete elliptic integral of the first kind

$$K(k) \equiv \int_0^{\frac{\pi}{2}} (1-k^2\sin^2\phi)^{-1/2} d\phi. \tag{3.15}$$

The integrals (3.14) taken over one period are equal to 2K. Since the integrals in (3.14) are taken from any $\underline{\phi}_p$ to any $\bar{\phi}_q$, all the integrals in (3.14) are given by

$$\mu = \mu_m \equiv 2mK(k), \qquad m = 1,2,\ldots \; . \tag{3.16}$$

Thus for each m we obtain the response of the rod, i.e., a relation between the load parameter μ and the measure of deformation $k = \sin \frac{\alpha}{2}$. (See Figure **2**). Since $K(0) = \pi/2$, each curve branches from $k = 0$, $\mu = \mu_m(0) = m\pi$, which are just the square roots of the eigenvalues of the linear problem (3.3). Thus the linear eigenvalue problem yields the points of bifurcation for the nonlinear problem.

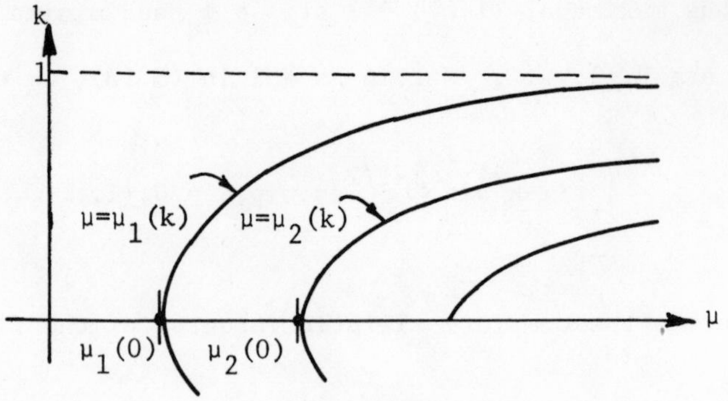

Figure 2.

From (3.16) we find that $\frac{d\mu_m}{dk} > 0$ for $k > 0$, and hence the curves in Figure 2 are monotonically increasing. They do not intersect. As $\mu_m \to \infty$, $K \to \infty$, $k \to 1$, and $\alpha \to (4m+1)\pi$, $m = 0,1,\dots$. The curves $\mu_m(k)$ are therefore asymptotic to $k = 1$ as $\mu_m \to \infty$.

To interpret the result that $\alpha \to (4m+1)\pi$ as $k \to 1$, we determine the axial component u of the displacement. Inserting (3.9) into (3.2) we obtain

$$u(x) = -2k^2 \int_0^x \sin^2\phi(\xi)d\xi, \tag{3.17}$$

where we have used $u(0) = 0$. The substitution of (3.10b) into (3.17) yields

$$u(1) = \frac{-2k^2}{\mu} \int_{\underline{\phi}_p}^{\overline{\phi}_q} (1-k^2\sin^2\phi)^{-1/2}\sin^2\phi \, d\phi, \quad p,q = 0,\pm 1,\dots \; . \tag{3.18}$$

Since the integrand in (3.18) is of period π, all the integrals in (3.18) are given by

$$u(1) = u_m(1) = \frac{-2k^2}{\mu_m} 2mJ(k), \quad m = 1,2,\ldots, \tag{3.19a}$$

where

$$J(k) \equiv \int_0^{\frac{\pi}{2}} (1-k^2\sin\phi)^{-1/2}\sin^2\phi \, d\phi. \tag{3.19b}$$

$J(k)$ can be expressed in terms of complete elliptic integrals. The substitution of (3.16) into (3.19a) gives

$$u_m(1) = 2k^2 J(k)/K(k). \tag{3.20}$$

As $\mu_m \to \infty$, $k \to 1$. Equation (3.20) implies that

$$\lim_{\mu_m \to \infty} u_m(1) = \lim_{k \to 1} u_m(1) = -2. \tag{3.21}$$

Thus, in the limit, the right end of the rod moves to the left a distance equal to twice the length of the rod. As $k \to 1$ the rod is straight except for "kinks", the number of which depend on the branch.

The number of internal nodes of a buckled shape is determined by the zeros of $w(x)$. From (3.2) and (3.9) we have

$$w' = \sin\psi = 2\sin\frac{\psi}{2}\cos\frac{\psi}{2} = \pm 2k\sin\phi\sqrt{1-k^2\sin^2\phi} \; . \tag{3.22}$$

Since $dw/d\phi = w'(dx/d\phi)$, (3.22), (3.10b) and (3.2b) imply that

$$w = \pm\frac{2k}{\mu}\cos\phi. \tag{3.23}$$

Thus the internal nodes occur at those x_j in (0,1) for which $\cos\phi(x_j) = 0$. From (3.12)-(3.15) we have on the branch corresponding to μ_m that

$$x_j = \frac{j2K(k)}{2mK(k)} = \frac{j}{m}, \qquad j = 0,1,\ldots,m. \tag{3.24}$$

Hence there are m-1 internal nodes. Illustrations of possible equilibrium configurations for the inextensible elastica can be found in Love, Mathematical Theory of Elasticity, Dover, New York, 1944 §263.

To decide whether the rod will buckle at λ_m and which branch is preferred for any $\lambda > \lambda_1$, we examine the potential energy. The energy of the unbuckled state $\psi \equiv 0$ is zero. The energy of a buckled state is proportional to

$$V \equiv \int_0^1 [\psi_x^2+2\lambda u_x]dx = \int_0^1 [\psi_x^2+2\lambda(\cos\psi-1)]dx. \tag{3.25}$$

Using (3.5), (3.9) and (3.13) we find after some calculation that

$$V = \lambda F(k) \equiv \lambda[k^2-2+2\frac{E(k)}{K(k)}] = \frac{\lambda}{K(k)}[2(E(k)-K(k)) + k^2K(k)]. \tag{3.26a}$$

Here E(k) is the elliptic integral of the second kind defined by

$$E(k) = \int_0^{\frac{\pi}{2}} \sqrt{1-k^2\sin^2\phi}\, d\phi. \tag{3.26b}$$

In (3.26a) we have used the relation $k^2J(k) = K(k) - E(k)$.

The functions K(k) and E(k) have the following power series expansions which converge for $k^2 < 1$:

$$K(k) = \frac{\pi}{2} \sum_{j=0}^{\infty} a_j k^{2j}, \qquad E(k) = \frac{\pi}{2} \sum_{j=0}^{\infty} \frac{a_j}{1-2j} k^{2j}, \tag{3.27}$$

$$a_o = 1,\ a_j \equiv \left[\frac{\frac{1}{2}(\frac{1}{2}+1)\ldots(\frac{1}{2}+j-1)}{j!}\right]^2 > 0,\ j = 1,2,\ldots .$$

Substituting (3.27) and (3.16) into (3.26) and denoting the energy of the buckled state which branches from λ_m by V_m, we find that

$$V_m = -2\pi m^2 k^2 K(k) \sum_{j=1}^{\infty} \frac{j}{1+j} a_j k^{2j} \leq 0,\ 0 \leq k^2 < 1,\ m = 1,2,\ldots, \tag{3.28}$$

where the equality holds only for k = 0. Thus every buckled solution has less energy than the unbuckled solution.

We consider a fixed value of λ in the interval $\lambda_n < \lambda < \lambda_{n+1}$. We shall show* that the energies are ordered by,

$$V_n > V_{n-1} > \cdots > V_1. \tag{3.29}$$

Let $k_m(\lambda)$, m = 1,2,...,n denote the value of **k** corresponding to the state which branches from $\lambda_m = \mu_m^2(0)$; See Figure **2** . That is, k_m is the unique root of (3.16) for $\mu_m = \lambda^{1/2}$. Since K(k) is monotone increasing we conclude from (3.16)

---

*The proof is due to A. J. Callegari

that $k_m < k_\ell$ if $m > \ell$. From (3.26a) we obtain,

$$\frac{V_m - V_\ell}{\lambda} = F(k_m) - F(k_\ell), \tag{3.30}$$

for any two branches $m > \ell$ in the interval $1 \leq m, \ell \leq n$. We differentiate the expression (3.26a) for F(k) and obtain

$$F' = \frac{-2}{kK^2}[E-(1-k^2)K]^2 \leq 0, \tag{3.31}$$

where we have used the differentiation formulae*,

$$E' = (E-K)/k, \quad K' = (E-(1-k^2)K)/k(1-k^2). \tag{3.32}$$

The equality in (3.31) holds only when $k = 0$ since, as it is easily shown using (3.32), $E-(1-k^2)K$ is monotone increasing for $k > 0$. Therefore F(k) is strictly monotone decreasing for $k > 0$. We conclude from (3.30) that

$$V_m > V_\ell, \quad m > \ell, \tag{3.33}$$

and (3.29) is established. If we assume that the rod prefers the state of least energy then for λ increasing above λ_1, the rod will deform in either of the buckled states branching from λ_1 and it will remain in this state for all $\lambda > \lambda_1$.

---

* See Byrd and Friedman, Handbook of Elliptic Integrals for Engineers and Physicists, Springer 1954.

II. Bifurcation Theory for Ordinary Differential Equations

Joseph B. Keller

1. Introduction

Bifurcation theory concerns the solution $u(\lambda)$ of a problem which depends upon a scalar or vector parameter λ. The solution is said to bifurcate from the solution u_o at the parameter value $\lambda = \lambda_o$ if there are two or more distinct solutions which approach u_o as λ tends to λ_o. The first problem of bifurcation theory is to determine the solutions u_o and parameter values λ_o at which bifurcation occurs. The second problem is to find the number of solutions which bifurcate from u_o. A third problem is to determine the behavior of these solutions for λ near λ_o.

The behavior of the solutions for λ outside a small neighborhood of λ_o is also important, but is not considered in bifurcation theory. In the previous lecture we considered two special boundary value problems for ordinary differential equations which were solved explicitly. Therefore all of the problems described above were resolved for them. Now we shall consider the general theory of bifurcation for problems involving ordinary differential equations.

Let $u(t)$ denote an n-component vector function of t and let $f(u,t,\lambda)$ denote an n-component vector function of u, t and the m-component parameter λ. In terms of u and f we form the following system of n ordinary differential equations in the interval $t_1 \leq t \leq t_2$,

$$u_t = f(u,t,\lambda) \qquad t_1 \leq t \leq t_2. \tag{1.1}$$

To characterize a particular solution of this equation, we may impose n additional conditions such as initial, boundary or periodicity conditions. To include all these possibilities, as well as many others, we shall introduce n functionals of $u(t)$ which may depend upon the values of $u(t)$ at any or all points of the interval $t_1 \leq t \leq t_2$ and upon λ. We form an n component vector of these functionals and denote it by $B[u(t),\lambda]$. Then we can write the n additional conditions as

$$B[u(t),\lambda] = 0. \tag{1.2}$$

The problem we consider is that of finding solutions $u(t,\lambda)$ of (1.1) and (1.2). We shall call it problem B for short.

2. Derivation of the bifurcation equation

Suppose that $u_o(t)$ is a solution of problem B for $\lambda = \lambda_o$. We wish to determine whether solutions bifurcate from u_o. To investigate this we consider the initial value problem for (1.1) with the initial value a prescribed t_1,

$$u(t_1,\lambda) = a. \tag{2.1}$$

We must be sure that the initial value problem (1.1) and (2.1) has a solution defined in the whole interval $t_1 \leq t \leq t_2$. To do so we shall utilize the fact that for $\lambda = \lambda_o$, $u_o(t)$ is such a solution with the initial value

$$u_o(t_1) = a_o . \tag{2.2}$$

Then we can rely upon the following theorem which we shall not prove.

<u>Theorem</u> 1. <u>Let</u> $f(u,t,\lambda)$ <u>and</u> $f_u(u,t,\lambda)$ <u>be defined and continuous in</u> (u,t,λ) <u>for u in a closed convex region</u> R, $t_1 \leq t \leq t_2$, <u>and</u> *$||\lambda-\lambda_o|| \leq c$ <u>where</u> $c > 0$. <u>Let</u> $u_o(t)$ <u>be a solution of</u> (1.1) <u>for</u> $t_1 \leq t \leq t_2$ <u>with</u> $\lambda = \lambda_o$, <u>lying in R</u>

*The norm $||\lambda||$ of a vector λ is defined to be the maximum of the absolute value of its components.

and satisfying (2.2). Then there exist positive constants α and β with $\beta \leq c$ such that for every a and λ satisfying $||a-a_o|| \leq \alpha$ and $||\lambda - \lambda_o|| \leq \beta$ there exists a unique solution $u(t,\lambda,a)$ of (1) defined for $t_1 \leq t \leq t_2$, lying in R, continuous in (t,λ,a) and satisfying the initial condition

$$u(t_1,\lambda,a) = a. \tag{2.3}$$

In order that the solution $u(t,\lambda,a)$ of the initial value problem (1.1) and (2.3) be a solution of problem B, it must satisfy (1.2). The value of the functional $B[u(t,\lambda,a),\lambda]$is a function of λ and the initial value a, which we shall write as an n component vector $b(a,\lambda)$,

$$B[u(t,\lambda,a),\lambda] \equiv b(a,\lambda). \tag{2.4}$$

Then (1.2) becomes

$$b(a,\lambda) = 0. \tag{2.5}$$

If $u(t,\lambda,a)$ satisfies (1.2), then a and λ satisfy (2.5). Conversely, if a and λ satisfy (2.5) then $u(t,\lambda,a)$ satisfies (1.2). We shall state this conclusion as a corollary of Theorem 1.

Corollary 1. The solution $u(t,\lambda,a)$ of the initial value problem (1.1) and (2.3), the existence and uniqueness of which are assured by Theorem 1, is a solution of the problem (1.1) and (1.2) if and only if a and λ satisfiy (2.5).

As a consequence of Theorem 1 and Corollary 1, the solution of problem B for a near a_o and λ near λ_o is reduced to the problem of solving (2.5). In particular, bifurcation from $u_o(t)$ at $\lambda = \lambda_o$ occurs if and only if (2.5) has two or more distinct solutions $a(\lambda)$ which approach a_o as λ tends to λ_o. Each such solution yields a solution $u(t,\lambda)$ of problem B, given by

$$u(t,\lambda) = u[t,\lambda,a(\lambda)]. \tag{2.6}$$

The number of solutions of problem B which split off from $u_o(t)$ at $\lambda = \lambda_o$ is clearly equal to the number of distinct solutions $a(\lambda)$ of (2.5) for which $a(\lambda_o) = a_o$. This number is equal to one if (2.5) has a unique solution $a(\lambda)$ satisfying $a(\lambda_o) = a_o$. In view of these facts, we shall call (2.5) the bifurcation equation.

Let us suppose that $b(a,\lambda)$is continuous and has a derivative $b_a(a,\lambda)$ which is also continuous for (a,λ) in a neighborhood of (a_o,λ_o). This will be the case if the functional $B[u(t,\lambda,a),\lambda]$ is continuous and has a continuous derivative B_u for (u,λ) in a neighborhood of (u_o,λ_o). Then we can attempt to find a solution $a(\lambda)$ of (2.5) for λ near λ_o and a near a_o by using the implicit function theorem. This theorem asserts that if the Jacobian does not vanish, i.e. if $\det b_a(a_o,\lambda_o) \neq 0$, then there exists a positive constant $\beta' \leq \beta$ such that for every λ satisfying $||\lambda-\lambda_o|| \leq \beta'$ there exists a solution $a(\lambda)$ of (2.5) which depends continuously upon λ and for which $a(\lambda_o) = \lambda_o$. Furthermore this solution is unique. (The constant β is defined in Theorem 1 and enters here because $b(a,\lambda)$ is defined only for $||\lambda-\lambda_o|| \leq \beta$.) Upon using this solution in (2.6) we obtain a solution of problem B which is continuous in t and λ, since $u(t,\lambda,a)$ is continuous in t,λ,a, and for which $u(t,\lambda_o) = u_o(t)$. In addition this solution is unique. We shall state this result as a theorem.

Theorem 2. Suppose the hypotheses of Theorem 1 are satisfied, that also $b(a,\lambda)$ and $b_a(a,\lambda)$ are defined and continuous in a neighborhood of a_o,λ_o and that

$$\det b_a(a_o,\lambda_o) \neq 0. \tag{2.7}$$

Then there exists a positive constant β' such that for every λ satisfying $||\lambda-\lambda_o|| \leq \beta'$, problem B has a solution $u(t,\lambda)$ continuous in t and λ with $u(t,\lambda_o) = u_o(t)$. This solution is unique.

The significance of Theorem 2 is that it gives a condition which guarantees that a particular solution $u_o(t)$ for $\lambda = \lambda_o$ can be uniquely embedded in a family of solutions $u(t,\lambda)$ for λ near λ_o. Thus when (2.7) holds, it shows that problem B can be solved for λ near λ_o if it can be solved for $\lambda = \lambda_o$. We may say that it shows when the solution $u_o(t)$ can be uniquely continued to neighboring solutions. From the point of view of bifurcation theory it shows that bifurcation cannot occur when (2.7) is satisfied. Therefore bifurcation can occur only if (2.7) is not satisfied, i.e. only if

$$\det b_a(a_o, \lambda_o) = 0. \tag{2.8}$$

This criterion can be given a useful interpretation in terms of the variational problem, which we shall now consider.

Before doing so we observe that the preceding analysis applies not only to ordinary differential equations, but to any equations whose solutions can be characterized by a finite dimensional vector a. If, for such equations, there is an analogue of Theorem 1, then the other results of this section are valid.

3. The variational problem

The variational problem associated with problem B can be formulated by considering a family of solutions depending differentiably on a scalar parameter. If we differentiate (1.1) and (1.2) with respect to this parameter, and denote the derivative of u by $\dot{u}$, we obtain the variational problem

$$\dot{u}_t = f_u[u(t,\lambda),t,\lambda]\dot{u}, \qquad t_1 \leq t \leq t_2 \tag{3.1}$$

$$B_u[u(t,\lambda),\lambda]\dot{u} = 0. \tag{3.2}$$

In (3.1) f_u denotes the matrix of derivatives of the components of f with respect to the components of u. In (3.2) $B_u\dot{u}$ denotes n linear functionals of $\dot{u}$. In order that (3.2) be defined, we must assume that the functionals $B[u(t,\lambda),\lambda]$ are differentiable with respect to u.

The variational problem is a linear homogeneous problem for $\dot{u}(t,\lambda)$. To analyze it we introduce $U(t,\lambda)$, the fundamental matrix solution of (3.1), defined by

$$U_t = f_u[u(t,\lambda),t,\lambda]U \ , \quad t_1 \leq t \leq t_2 \tag{3.3}$$

$$U(t_1,\lambda) = I \ . \tag{3.4}$$

In (3.4) I denotes the unit matrix. The existence, uniqueness and continuity of $U(t,\lambda)$ with respect to t and λ follow from a standard theorem for linear equations, together with the continuity of f_u, provided that $u(t,\lambda)$ is continuous in t and λ. With the aid of U, we can solve the initial value problem for (3.1) with initial condition

$$\dot{u}(t_1,\lambda) = \dot{a} \ . \tag{3.5}$$

The solution of (3.1) and (3.5), which we denote by $\dot{u}(t,\lambda,\dot{a})$, is

$$\dot{u}(t,\lambda,\dot{a}) = U(t,\lambda)\dot{a}. \tag{3.6}$$

In order to solve the variational problem (3.1) and (3.2), we insert (3.6) into (3.2) and obtain

$$B_u[u(t,\lambda),\lambda]U(t,\lambda)\dot{a} = 0. \tag{3.7}$$

This equation can be written in simpler form by considering $u(t,\lambda,a+\varepsilon\dot{a})$, the solution of (1.1) with initial condition $a+\varepsilon\dot{a}$. Here ε is a parameter and $a = u(t_1,\lambda)$ where $u(t,\lambda)$ is the solution about which the variational problem is constructed. Differentiation of $u(t,\lambda,a+\varepsilon\dot{a})$with respect to ε at $\varepsilon = 0$ yields

$$\frac{d}{d\varepsilon} u(t,\lambda,a+\varepsilon\dot{a})\Big|_{\varepsilon=0} = u_a(t,\lambda,a)\dot{a} = U(t,\lambda)\dot{a} . \tag{3.8}$$

The last equality in (3.8) is based on the relation $u_a = U$. This is true because u_a satisfies (3.1), as we see by differentiating (1.1) with respect to a, and it satisfies $u_a(t_1,\lambda,a) = I$ as we see by differentiating (2.3) with respect to a. Therefore u_a satisfies the same equation as U does, so by the uniqueness of the solution of the initial value problem , $u_a = U$ and (3.8) is justified. Now we have from the definition (2.4) of $b(a,\lambda)$

$$B[u(t,\lambda,a + \varepsilon\dot{a}),\lambda] = b(a + \varepsilon\dot{a},\lambda). \quad (3.9)$$

Differentiating (3.9) with respect to ε at $\varepsilon = 0$ and then using (3.8) yields

$$B_u[u(t,\lambda,a),\lambda]u_a(t,\lambda,a)\dot{a} = B_u[u(t,\lambda,a),\lambda]U(t,\lambda)\dot{a} = b_a(a,\lambda)\dot{a} \quad (3.10)$$

Thus (3.7) can be rewritten as

$$b_a(a,\lambda)\dot{a} = 0 \quad (3.11)$$

From (3.11) we see that when $b_a(a,\lambda)$ is nonsingular then $\dot{a} = 0$. In this case the only solution of the variational problem (3.1) and (3.2) is $\dot{u} \equiv 0$, as we see by setting $\dot{a} = 0$ in (3.6). Conversely if the variational problem has a solution $\dot{u}$ which is not identically zero then $\dot{a} = \dot{u}(t_1,\lambda)$ is not zero and $\dot{a}$ is a solution of (3.11). Therefore $b_a(a,\lambda)$ must be a singular matrix and its determinant is zero. Thus the variational problem has only the trivial solution if and only if det $b_a(a,\lambda) = 0$. More generally, suppose the nullity of $b_a(a,\lambda)$ is ν. [The nullity is the order n of b_a minus its rank.] Then $b_a(a,\lambda)$ has exactly ν linearly independent null vectors $\dot{a}_1,\ldots,\dot{a}_\nu$. To each of them corresponds a solution of the variational problem, which is given by (3.6). Thus the variational problem has ν linearly independent solutions in this case. Conversely if the variational problem has exactly ν linearly independent solutions then their initial values at $t = t_1$ are ν linearly independent solutions of (3.11). Therefore the nullity of $b_a(a,\lambda)$ is ν. We shall summarize these results as a theorem.

Theorem 3. *Let* $f_u[u(t,\lambda,a),t,\lambda]$ *be defined and continuous in t for* $t_1 \leq t \leq t_2$ *and* let $B_u[u(t,\lambda,a),\lambda]$ *be defined. Then the number of linearly independent solutions of the variational problem (3.1), (3.2) is equal to the nullity* ν *of* $b_a(a,\lambda)$. *In particular the trivial solution* $\dot{u}(t) \equiv 0$ *is the only solution of the variational problem if and only if* det $b_a(a,\lambda) = 0$.

We can now combine the last conclusion of Theorem 3 with Theorem 2 to obtain the following result.

Theorem 4. *Suppose that the hypotheses of Theorem 1 are satisfied, that* $b(a,\lambda)$ *and* $b_a(a,\lambda)$ *are defined and continuous for* a,λ *in a neighborhood of* a_o,λ_o *and that* $B_u[u_o(t),\lambda_o]$ *is defined. Let the variational problem (3.1), (3.2) with* $\lambda = \lambda_o$ *and* $u(t,\lambda)$ *replaced by* $u_o(t)$, *have only the trivial solution* $\dot{u}(t) \equiv 0$. *Then there exists a positive constant* β' *such that for every* λ *satisfying* $||\lambda-\lambda_o|| \leq \beta'$, *problem B has a solution* $u(t,\lambda)$ *continuous in* t *and* λ *with* $u(t,\lambda_o) = u_o(t)$. *This solution is unique.*

From Theorem 4 we see that bifurcation from $u_o(t)$ is possible at $\lambda = \lambda_o$ only if the variational problem at $u_o(t), \lambda_o$ has a non-trivial solution. In this case we shall call problem B degenerate of degree ν at $u = u_o$, $\lambda = \lambda_o$ if the variational problem at $u = u_o$, $\lambda = \lambda_o$ has ν linearly independent solutions.

Whether or not bifurcation does occur must still be considered. One way of considering it is to examine the matrix of order n by n+m defined by

$$[b_a(a_o,\lambda_o) b_\lambda(a_o,\lambda_o)] \quad . \tag{3.12}$$

If the rank of this matrix is n then some minor of order n is nonsingular. Consequently we can employ the implicit function theorem to solve (2.5) for the components of a and λ corresponding to this minor, in terms of the remaining components. This solution will yield, in the neighborhood of (a_o,λ_o), a unique continuous manifold of dimension m in the n+m dimensional a,λ space, passing through (a_o,λ_o). It may yield several values of a for some values of λ, in which case bifurcation does occur at (a_o,λ_o). It may also yield no values of a for other values of λ.

If the rank of the matrix(3.12)is less than n, the bifurcation equation may still have solutions near

a_o, λ_o. One method of finding them is to expand the function $b(a,\lambda)$ in a finite Taylor series around a_o, λ_o. This can be done if b has some derivatives at a_o, λ_o, which it will have if $f(u,t,\lambda)$ and $B[u(t,\lambda,a),\lambda]$ have some derivatives with respect to u and λ at u_o, λ_o. Then the solutions of (2.5) with b given by a finite Taylor series plus a remainder must be examined. An example of this procedure will be given in lecture XV.

4. Bifurcation for a second order equation

We shall now consider a boundary value problem for a particular type of nonlinear second order equation. We shall assume that the problem has a solution $u_o(t,\lambda)$ and that the problem is degenerate at this solution for $\lambda = \lambda_o$. Nevertheless we shall show that the bifurcation equation can be solved near λ_o and thus prove that bifurcation does occur.

The problem for the scalar function u(t) is

$$[I(t)u_t]_t + f(u,t,\lambda) = 0, \qquad t_1 \leq t \leq t_2 \tag{4.1}$$

$$\alpha_1 u_t(t_1) + \beta_1 u(t_1) = 0 \tag{4.2}$$

$$\alpha_2 u_t(t_2) + \beta_2 u(t_2) = 0 \tag{4.3}$$

Here I(t) is positive and continuously differentiable while f, f_u and f_{uu} exist and are continuous in u,t and λ for some interval $u_1 \leq u \leq u_2$, $\lambda_1 \leq \lambda \leq \lambda_2$ and $t_1 \leq t \leq t_2$. Of the constants α_1, α_2, β_1 and β_2, we require that $\alpha_1 \neq 0$ and $\alpha_2^2 + \beta_2^2 \neq 0$. We assume that for $\lambda_1 \leq \lambda \leq \lambda_2$ this problem has a solution $u_o(t,\lambda)$ such that $u_1 \leq u_o(t,\lambda) \leq u_2$.

The variational problem at u_o,λ is

$$(I\dot{u}_t)_t + f_u[u_o(t,\lambda),t,\lambda]\dot{u} = 0, \quad t_1 \leq t \leq t_2 \qquad (4.4)$$

$$\alpha_1\dot{u}_t(t_1) + \beta_1\dot{u}(t_1) = 0 \qquad (4.5)$$

$$\alpha_2\dot{u}_t(t_2) + \beta_2\dot{u}(t_2) = 0 . \qquad (4.6)$$

We assume that this problem has a nontrivial solution for $\lambda = \lambda_o$, where $\lambda_1 < \lambda_o < \lambda_2$, and we denote it by

$$\dot{u}(t) = \phi(t) . \qquad (4.7)$$

The function $\phi(t)$ is normalized by the condition

$$\phi(t_1) = 1. \qquad (4.8)$$

This is always a possible normalization, since if $\phi(t_1) = 0$ then (4.5) would yield $\phi_t(t_1) = 0$ because $\alpha_1 \neq 0$, and then the uniqueness theorem would imply $\phi(t) \equiv 0$. To see that $\phi(t)$ is unique we note that the initial value problem (4.4), (4.5) and (4.8) has a unique solution.

We wish to prove that the bifurcation equation can be solved despite the fact that the problem is degenerate at u_o, λ_o. To this end we express $u(t,\lambda)$ in terms of a new function $v(t)$ and a constant a by the equation

$$u(t,\lambda) = u_o(t,\lambda) + av(t,\lambda,a). \tag{4.9}$$

The constant a has been introduced so that we can impose the condition

$$v(t_1) = 1. \tag{4.10}$$

Upon using (4.9) in (4.1)-(4.3) we find that v and a satisfy the equations

$$(Iv_t)_t + a^{-1}[f(u_o+av,t,\lambda)-f(u_o,t,\lambda)]=0, t_1 \le t \le t_2 \tag{4.11}$$

$$\alpha_1 v_t(t_1) + \beta_1 v(t_1) = 0 \tag{4.12}$$

$$\alpha_2 v_t(t_2) + \beta_2 v(t_2) = 0. \tag{4.13}$$

In writing (4.11) we used the fact that u_o satisfies (4.9) in order to replace $(Iu_{ot})_t$ by $-f(u_o,t,\lambda)$.

We shall now show that the problem (4.10)-(4.13) has a solution when $\lambda = \lambda_o$ and $a = 0$. First we define $a^{-1}[f(u_o+av,t,\lambda)-f(u_o,t,\lambda)]$ at $a = 0$ so that it be continuous in a. Then we set $\lambda = \lambda_o$ and $a = 0$ in (4.10)-(4.13) and find that (4.11) becomes

$$(Iv_t)_t + f_u[u_o(t,\lambda_o),t,\lambda_o]v = 0, \quad t_1 \le t \le t_2 . \tag{4.14}$$

This is the same as (4.4) at $\lambda = \lambda_o$ and the conditions

(4.12) and (4.13) are the same as (4.5) and (4.6). Thus for $a = 0$ and $\lambda = \lambda_o$, $v(t)$ is a multiple of $\dot{u}$. From (4.10) and (4.8) it follows that

$$v(t) = \phi(t) \quad \text{for } a = 0,\ \lambda = \lambda_o . \tag{4.15}$$

When this solution is used in (4.9), it merely yields $u(t) = u_o(t,\lambda_o)$ because $a = 0$.

We next consider the initial value problem (4.10)-(4.12). This problem has a solution for (a,λ) near $(0,\lambda_o)$ and we shall denote it by $v(t,\lambda,a)$. It will solve the boundary value problem (4.10)-(4.13) if and only if it satisfies (4.13). Thus (4.13) becomes the bifurcation equation

$$b(a,\lambda) \equiv \alpha_2 v_t(t_2,\lambda,a) + \beta_2 v(t_2,\lambda,a) = 0. \tag{4.16}$$

We have just seen that for $a = 0$, $\lambda = \lambda_o$ the boundary value problem (4.10)-(4.13) has a solution $v = \phi(t)$. Therefore $(0,\lambda_o)$ is a solution of (4.16). To show that (4.16) can be solved for a near 0 when λ is near λ_o we consider $b_a(0,\lambda_o)$ which is given by

$$b_a(0,\lambda_o) = \alpha_2 v_{at}(t_2,\lambda_o,0) + \beta_2 v_a(t_2,\lambda_o,0). \tag{4.17}$$

We shall evaluate (4.17) by differentiating (4.10)-(4.12) with respect to a at $a = 0$, $\lambda = \lambda_o$. This yields the following problem for $v_a(t,\lambda_o,0)$:

$$(Iv_{at})_t + f_u[u_o(t,\lambda_o),t,\lambda_o]v_a = -\frac{3}{2}f_{uu}[u_o(t,\lambda_o),t,\lambda_o]\phi^2(t) \tag{4.18}$$

$$v_a(t_1) = 0 \tag{4.19}$$

$$\alpha_1 v_{at}(t_1) + \beta_1 v_a(t_1) = 0\ . \tag{4.20}$$

This problem has a unique solution $v_a(t,\lambda_o,0)$ and with it we can evaluate $b_a(0,\lambda_o)$ given by (4.17). If $b_a(0,\lambda_o) = 0$ then v_a satisfies the same boundary conditions (4.5) and (4.6) as $\dot{u} = \phi(t)$ does, as we see from (4.17) and (4.20). In addition (4.18) is the inhomogeneous form of (4.4) satisfied by $\dot{u} = \phi$. Then the right side of (4.18) must be orthogonal to $\phi(t)$, since that is the condition for solvability of the inhomogeneous boundary value problem when the homogeneous one has a solution $\phi(t)$. This yields the condition

$$\int_{t_1}^{t_2} f_{uu}[u_o(t,\lambda_o),t,\lambda_o]\phi^3(t)dt = 0. \tag{4.21}$$

If (4.21) is satisfied then $b_a(0,\lambda_o) = 0$. However if (4.21) is not satisfied it follows that $b_a(0,\lambda_o) \neq 0$. Then the implicit function theorem shows that (4.16) can be solved uniquely for $a(\lambda)$ when λ is near λ_o and a near zero, and that $a(\lambda)$ is continuous in λ with $a(\lambda_o) = 0$. The corresponding function $v[t,\lambda,a(\lambda)]$ is a solution of the boundary value problem (4.10)-(4.13). Then (4.9) becomes

$$u(t,\lambda) = u_0(t,\lambda) + a(\lambda)v[t,\lambda,a(\lambda)]. \tag{4.22}$$

This function is a solution of the original problem (4.1)-(4.3) for λ near λ_0. It is continuous in λ and $u(t,\lambda_0) = u_0(t,\lambda_0)$. If $a(\lambda) \neq 0$ for $\lambda \neq \lambda_0$ then $u(t,\lambda) \neq u_0(t,\lambda)$ for $\lambda \neq \lambda_0$ since v is not identically zero for λ near λ_0. Thus if (4.21) is not satisfied and if $a(\lambda) \neq 0$ for $\lambda \neq \lambda_0$, the distinct functions $u(t,\lambda)$ given by (4.22) and $u_0(t,\lambda)$ are solutions of (4.1)-(4.3) which become identical at $\lambda = \lambda_0$. Thus in this case bifurcation does occur at u_0, λ_0.

We can decide whether $a(\lambda) \neq 0$ for λ near λ_0 by evaluating $b_\lambda(0,\lambda_0)$ since (4.16) can be solved for $a(\lambda)$ in the form

$$a(\lambda) = -\frac{b_\lambda(0,\lambda_0)}{b_a(0,\lambda_o)}(\lambda-\lambda_o) + o(\lambda-\lambda_o). \tag{4.23}$$

If $b_\lambda(0,\lambda_0) \neq 0$ then $a(\lambda) \neq 0$ for λ near λ_0. In order to see if $b_\lambda(0,\lambda_0)$ is zero or not, we set $a = 0$ and differentiate (4.10)-(4.12) with respect to λ at λ_0, assuming that $f_{u\lambda}$ and $u_{0\lambda}$ exist.

$$(Iv_{\lambda t})_t + f_u[u_0(t,\lambda_0),t,\lambda_0)]v$$
$$= - f_{uu}[u_0(t,\lambda_0),t,\lambda_0]u_{0\lambda}(t,\lambda_0)\phi - f_{u\lambda}[u_0(t,\lambda_0),t,\lambda_0]\phi \ ,$$
$$t_1 \le t \le t_2 \tag{4.24}$$

$$v_\lambda(t_1) = 0 \tag{4.25}$$

$$\alpha_1 v_{\lambda t}(t_1) + \beta_1 v_\lambda(t_1) = 0 \ . \tag{4.26}$$

Just as in the discussion of v_a, we conclude from (4.24)-(4.26) that $b_\lambda(0,\lambda_o) \neq 0$ provided that the right side of (4.24) is not orthogonal to $\phi(t)$. This condition is

$$\int_{t_1}^{t_2} \{ f_{uu}[u_o(t,\lambda_o),t,\lambda_o]u_{o\lambda}(t,\lambda_o)+f_{u\lambda}[u_o(t,\lambda_o),t,\lambda_o]\}\phi^2(t)dt \neq 0. \tag{4.27}$$

When (4.27) is satisfied, $b_\lambda(0,\lambda_o)$ is not zero and therefore $a(\lambda)$ is not zero for λ near λ_o but not equal to λ_o. Consequently $u(t,\lambda)$ given by (4.22) is distinct from $u_o(t,\lambda)$ for λ near λ_o except at $\lambda = \lambda_o$. We shall now summarize the results of this section in the following theorem.

Theorem 5. *Let* $I(t)$ *be positive and continuously differentiable for* $t_1 \leq t \leq t_2$. *Let* f, f_u, f_{uu} *and* $f_{u\lambda}$ *exist and be continuous in* u,t,λ *for* $u_1 \leq u \leq u_2$, $\lambda_1 \leq \lambda \leq \lambda_2$, $t_1 \leq t \leq t_2$. *Let* $\alpha_1 \neq 0$ *and* $\alpha_2^2 + \beta_2^2 \neq 0$. *Suppose* $u_o(t,\lambda)$ *is a solution of the following problem for* $\lambda_1 \leq \lambda \leq \lambda_2$

$$[I(t)u_t]_t + f(u,t,\lambda) = 0, \quad t_1 \leq t \leq t_2 \tag{4.28}$$

$$\alpha_1 u_t(t_1) + \beta_1 u(t_1) = 0 \tag{4.29}$$

$$\alpha_2 u_t(t_2) + \beta_2 u(t_2) = 0. \tag{4.30}$$

In addition let $u_{o\lambda}(t,\lambda)$ exist and be continuous and $u_1 \le u_o(t,\lambda) \le u_2$ for $t_1 \le t \le t_2$, $\lambda_1 \le \lambda \le \lambda_2$. Suppose the variational problem at $u_o(t,\lambda_o),\lambda_o$ has a nontrivial solution $\phi(t)$ such that

$$\int_{t_1}^{t_2} f_{uu}[u_o(t,\lambda_o),t,\lambda_o]\phi^3(t)dt \neq 0 \tag{4.31}$$

$$\int_{t_1}^{t_2} \{f_{uu}[u_o(t,\lambda_o),t,\lambda_o]u_{o\lambda}(t,\lambda_o)-f_{u\lambda}[u_o(t,\lambda_o),t,\lambda_o]\}\phi^2(t)dt\neq 0. \tag{4.32}$$

Then there exists a positive constant γ such that for every λ satisfying $|\lambda-\lambda_o| \le \gamma$ the problem (4.28)-(4.30) has a solution $u(t,\lambda)$ continuous in λ which is distinct from $u_o(t,\lambda)$ for $\lambda \neq \lambda_o$ but which is identical with it at $\lambda = \lambda_o$. This solution is unique.

If (4.31) is not satisfied but (4.32) is, the bifurcation equation (4.16) can be solved uniquely for $\lambda(a)$ when (a,λ) is near $(0,\lambda_o)$. Let us suppose that this is the case and that $b_{aa}(0,\lambda_o)$ exists. Then we can write the solution of (4.16) in the form

$$\lambda(a) = \lambda_o - \frac{b_{aa}(0,\lambda_o)}{b_\lambda(0,\lambda_o)} \frac{a^2}{2} + o(a^2) . \tag{4.33}$$

If $b_{aa}(0,\lambda_o) \neq 0$ we can solve (4.33) for a, obtaining two solutions $a_\pm(\lambda)$ given by

$$a_{\pm}(\lambda) = \pm\left[\frac{2b_{\lambda}(0,\lambda_o)}{b_{aa}(0,\lambda_o)}(\lambda_o-\lambda)\right]^{1/2} + o([\lambda_o-\lambda]^{1/2}). \qquad (4.34)$$

We see that $a_{\pm}(\lambda)$ is real only if $\lambda_o-\lambda$ has the same sign as $b_{\lambda}(0,\lambda_o)/b_{aa}(0,\lambda_o)$. In this case the problem (4.28)-(4.30) has two (real) solutions distinct from $u_o(t,\lambda)$ and from each other when $\lambda_o-\lambda$ is small and of the same sign as $b_{\lambda}(0,\lambda_o)/b_{aa}(0,\lambda_o)$. These two solutions are continuous in λ and at $\lambda = \lambda_o$ they are identical with $u_o(t,\lambda_o)$. There is no solution distinct from $u_o(t,\lambda)$, when $\lambda_o - \lambda$ is small and of the opposite sign from $b_{\lambda}(0,\lambda_o)/b_{aa}(0,\lambda_o)$, which approaches $u_o(t,\lambda_o)$ as λ tends to λ_o. The value of $b_{aa}(0,\lambda_o)$ can be found by differentiating the problem for v twice with respect to a to get a problem for $v_{aa}(t,\lambda_o,0)$, and solving this problem.

We shall state these results as a theorem.

Theorem 6. *Suppose the hypotheses of Theorem 5 are satisfied with equality in (4.31) and that* $b_{aa}(0,\lambda_o)$ *exists and is not zero. Then there exists a positive constant* γ *such that for every* λ *satisfying* $0 \leq \lambda-\lambda_o \leq \gamma$ *if* $b_{aa}(0,\lambda_o)/b(0,\lambda_o) < 0$, *or* $0 \leq \lambda_o-\lambda \leq \gamma$ *if* $b_{aa}(0,\lambda_o)/b_{\lambda}(0,\lambda_o) > 0$, *the problem (4.28)-(4.30) has two real solutions which are distinct from each other and from* $u_o(t,\lambda)$ *for* $\lambda \neq \lambda_o$, *continuous in* λ *and both identical with*

$u_o(t,\lambda_o)$ *at* $\lambda = \lambda_o$. *These solutions are unique. There is no solution distinct from* $u_o(t,\lambda)$ *which approaches it as* λ *tends to* λ_o *when* $0 < \lambda_o - \lambda \leq \gamma$ *if* $b_{aa}(0,\lambda_o)/b_\lambda(0,\lambda_o) < 0$ *or when* $0 < \lambda - \lambda_o \leq \gamma$ *if* $b_{aa}(0,\lambda_o)/b_\lambda(0,\lambda_o) > 0$.

5. Example

Let us apply the results of section 4 to the case in which $f(u,t,\lambda)$ has the special form

$$f(u,t,\lambda) = \lambda g(u,t) \quad . \tag{5.1}$$

We assume that g, g_u and g_{uu} exist and are continuous and in addition that

$$g(0,t) \equiv 0. \tag{5.2}$$

Then for all λ the problem (4.1)-(4.3) has the solution

$$u_o(t,\lambda) \equiv 0. \tag{5.3}$$

For this solution the variational equation (4.4) becomes

$$(I\dot{u}_t)_t + g_u(0,t)\dot{u} = 0 \quad , \quad t_1 \leq t \leq t_2 \quad . \tag{5.4}$$

The variational problem (5.4), (4.5) and (4.6) is self-adjoint so it has a countable set of distinct eigenvalues λ_n, $n = 0,1,\ldots$ with corresponding eigenfunctions $\phi_n(t)$. They can be normalized by the condition $\phi_n(t_1) = 1$ and are then unique. The λ_n can be indexed so that $\lambda_{n+1} > \lambda_n$ and then $\phi_n(t)$ has n simple zeros in the open interval $t_1 < t < t_2$. Thus bifurcation from u_o can occur only if $\lambda = \lambda_n$ for some n.

Conditions (4.31) and (4.32) become for $\lambda = \lambda_n$,

$$\lambda_n \int_{t_1}^{t_2} g_{uu}(0,t)\phi^3_n(t)dt \neq 0. \tag{5.5}$$

$$\lambda_n \int_{t_1}^{t_2} g_u(0,t)\phi^2_n(t)dt \neq 0. \tag{5.6}$$

If (5.5) and (5.6) are both satisfied for some integer n, then the conclusion of Theorem 5 holds with λ_o replaced by λ_n. Furthermore the solution $u(t,\lambda)$ given by (4.22) is $u(t,\lambda) = a(\lambda)v[t,\lambda,a(\lambda)]$ since $u_o(t,\lambda) \equiv 0$. At $\lambda = \lambda_n$ we have $v = v(t,\lambda_n,0) = \phi_n(t)$ which has n simple zeros. Therefore by continuity, $u(t,\lambda)$ has n simple zeros for λ near λ_n.

A simple condition which guarantees that (5.6) holds for all n with $\lambda_n \neq 0$ is

$$g_u(0,t) > 0, \quad t_1 \leq t \leq t_2 . \tag{5.7}$$

On the other hand, a condition which shows that (5.5) is violated for all n is

$$g_{uu}(0,t) \equiv 0, \ t_1 \leq t \leq t_2 . \tag{5.8}$$

When (5.8) holds we cannot tell if the bifurcation equation can be solved for $a(\lambda)$. However if (5.7) holds it can be solved for λ and the solution can be written in the form (4.33) with λ_o replaced by λ_n and $\lambda(a)$ replaced by $\lambda_n(a)$. Upon setting $\lambda = \lambda_n(a)$ in $v(t,\lambda,a)$ we obtain a solution $v(t,a) = v[t,\lambda_n(a),a]$ of (4.10)-(4.13). Upon using it in (4.9), we obtain a solution $u_n(t,a)$ of (4.1)-(4.3).

Once we know that $\lambda(a)$ can be written in the form (4.33) there is a simpler way of obtaining the coefficient of a^2 than finding $b_{aa}(0,\lambda_n)/b_\lambda(0,\lambda_n)$. It is to assume that $v(t,a)$ and $\lambda(a)$ both have two derivatives with respect to a at $a = 0$ and that the derivatives v_a and v_{aa} are twice continuously differentiable with respect to t. These assumptions are justified by the conditions we have imposed on $g(u,t)$ and the added requirement that $g_{uuu}(0,t)$ exist and be continuous in t. Then differentiation of (4.10)-(4.13) with respect to a at $a = 0$ yields a sequence of problems for the derivatives of $v(t,a)$ and $\lambda(a)$ at $a = 0$. We have already found that $v(t,0) = \phi_n(t)$ and $\lambda(0) = \lambda_n$. The problem for v_a is given by (4.18)-(4.20) provided $\lambda_a(0) = 0$, which is the case from (4.33). If $g_{uu}(0,t) = 0$ then the unique solution of this problem is $v_a(t,0) \equiv 0$.

The problem for $v_{aa}(t,0)$ is

$$(Iv_{aat})_t+\lambda_n g_u(0,t)v_{aa} = -\frac{\lambda_n}{3}g_{uuu}(0,t)\phi^3_n(t)-\lambda_{aa}(0)g_u(0,t)\phi_n(t) \tag{5.9}$$

$$\alpha_1 v_{aat}(t_1) + \beta_1 v_{aa}(t_1) = 0 \tag{5.10}$$

$$\alpha_2 v_{aat}(t_2) + \beta_2 v_{aa}(t_2) = 0 \tag{5.11}$$

$$v_{aa}(t_1) = 0 \quad . \tag{5.12}$$

In order that (5.9)-(5.11) be solvable, the right side of (5.9) must be orthogonal to ϕ_n, the solution of the corresponding homogeneous problem. This orthogonality condition, when solved for $\lambda_{aa}(0)$, yields

$$\lambda_{aa}(0) = \frac{-\lambda_n \int_{t_1}^{t_2} g_{uuu}(0,t)\phi_n^4(t)dt}{3 \int_{t_1}^{t_2} g_u(0,t)\phi^2(t)dt} \ . \tag{5.13}$$

Since $\lambda_{aa}(0)$ is the coefficient of $a^2/2$ in the finite Taylor expansion of $\lambda(a)$ around $a = 0$, it is just $-b_{aa}(0,\lambda_n)/b_\lambda(0,\lambda_n)$, which appears in (4.33).

The condition $\lambda_{aa}(0) \neq 0$ is, from (5.13),

$$\lambda_n \int_{t_1}^{t_2} g_{uuu}(0,t)\phi_n^4(t)dt \neq 0. \tag{5.14}$$

When (5.14) holds, (4.33) can be solved for a with the two results

$$a_\pm(\lambda) = \pm\left[\frac{2(\lambda-\lambda_n)}{\lambda_{aa}(0)}\right]^{1/2} + o\,[(\lambda-\lambda_n)^{1/2}]. \tag{5.15}$$

In this case Theorem 6 applies and shows the nature of the bifurcation at $\lambda = \lambda_n$. We shall summarize the results of this section in two theorems.

Theorem 7. *Let* $I(t)$ *be positive and continuously differentiable for* $t_1 \leq t \leq t_2$. *Let* $g(u,t)$, g_u, g_{uu} *exist and be continuous for* $t_1 \leq t \leq t_2$ *and* $|u| \leq B$, $B > 0$ *and let* $g(0,t) \equiv 0$, $g_u(0,t) > 0$. *Furthermore let* $\alpha_1 \neq 0$ *and* $\alpha_2^2 + \beta_2^2 \neq 0$. *Consider the problem*

$$[I(t)u_t]_t + \lambda g(u,t) = 0, \qquad t_1 \leq t \leq t_2 \tag{5.16}$$

$$\alpha_1 u_t(t_1) + \beta_1 u(t_1) = 0 \tag{5.17}$$

$$\alpha_2 u_t(t_2) + \beta_2 u(t_2) = 0 \quad . \tag{5.18}$$

Let $\lambda_n \neq 0$ *be the* $(n+1)$st *smallest eigenvalue of the variational problem at* $u \equiv 0$ *with corresponding eigenfunction* $\phi_n(t)$ *normalized by* $\phi_n(t_1) = 1$. *Suppose that*

$$\int_{t_1}^{t_2} g_{uu}(0,t)\phi_n^3(t)dt \neq 0. \tag{5.19}$$

Then there exists a positive constant γ_n *such that for every* λ *satisfying* $|\lambda-\lambda_n| \leq \gamma_n$, *the problem (5.16)-(5.18) has a unique solution* $u(t,\lambda)$ *continuous in* λ *with* n *simple zeros in the open interval* $t_1 < t < t_2$ *for* $\lambda \neq \lambda_n$ *and* $u(t,\lambda_n) \equiv 0$. *For all* λ, $u_o(t,\lambda) \equiv 0$ *is also a solution.*

Theorem 8. *Suppose the hypotheses of Theorem 7 hold with (5.19) replaced by*

$$g_{uu}(0,t) = 0, \quad t_1 \leq t \leq t_2 \quad . \tag{5.20}$$

In addition suppose that $g_{uuu}(0,t)$ exists and satisfies

$$\int_{t_1}^{t_2} g_{uuu}(0,t)\phi_n^4(t)dt \neq 0 \ . \tag{5.21}$$

Then there exists a positive constant γ_n such that for every λ satisfying $0 \leq \lambda_n - \lambda \leq \gamma_n$ or $0 \leq \lambda - \lambda_n \leq \gamma_n$, according as the integral in (5.21) is positive or negative, the problem (5.16)-(5.18) has two real solutions distinct from each other and from zero for $\lambda \neq \lambda_n$. They are continuous in λ, vanish identically for $\lambda = \lambda_n$ and each has n simple zeros in the open interval $t_1 < t < t_2$ for $\lambda \neq \lambda_n$. These solutions are unique. There is no solution other than $u_o(t,\lambda) \equiv 0$ for $0 < \lambda - \lambda_n \leq \gamma_n$, when the integral (5.21) is negative, or for $0 < \lambda_n - \lambda \leq \gamma_n$, when the integral (5.21) is positive, which approaches $u_o \equiv 0$ as λ tends to λ_o.

6. Buckling of a nonuniform column

We shall now apply the preceding theory to the buckling of a nonuniform column pinned at its ends and subjected to a given compressive load. The slope angle $\psi(x)$ of the column satisfies the following equilibrium equation and boundary conditions

$$[I(x)\psi_x]_x + \lambda \sin \psi = 0, \quad 0 \leq x \leq 1 \tag{6.1}$$

$$\psi_x(0) = \psi_x(1) = 0 \ . \tag{6.2}$$

In (6.1) the constant λ is proportional to the applied thrust and $I(x)$ is proportional to the product of the moment of inertia of the cross-section of the column at x and the Young's modulus of the column material at x. We assume that $I(x)$ is positive and continuously differentiable. The problem is to solve (6.1) and (6.2) for $\psi(x)$, given $I(x)$ and λ.

This problem is of the form (5.16)-(5.18) with u replaced by ψ, t by x and $g(\psi,x) = \sin\psi$. Therefore $g(0,x) = \sin 0 = 0$, $g_\psi(0,x) = \cos 0 = 1 > 0$, $g_{\psi\psi}(0,x) = -\sin 0 = 0$ and $g_{\psi\psi\psi}(0,x) = -\cos 0 = -1$. The function $\psi_0(x) \equiv 0$ is a solution of (6.1) and (6.2) for all values of λ and the variational problem at ψ_0 is

$$[I(x)\dot{\psi}_x]_x + \lambda\dot{\psi} = 0, \qquad 0 \le x \le 1 \tag{6.3}$$

$$\dot{\psi}_x(0) = \dot{\psi}_x(1) = 0 \ . \tag{6.4}$$

The lowest eigenvalue of this problem is $\lambda_0 = 0$ and the corresponding normalized eigenfunction is $\psi_0(x) = 1$. All other λ_n are positive.

The preceding discussion shows that the hypotheses of Theorem 8 are satisfied by the problem (6.1),(6.2) for all the eigenvalues λ_n, $n = 1,2,\ldots$ but not for λ_o. Consequently Theorem 8 applies for each $n \geq 1$. For each n the integral (5.21) is negative since $g_{\psi\psi\psi}(0,x) = -1$, so the theorem holds for $\lambda_n \leq \lambda \leq \lambda_n + \gamma_n$ in each case. In addition, whenever $\psi(x)$ is a solution of (6.1) and (6.2) for some λ so is $\pm\psi(x) + 2k\pi$, where k is an integer, while $\pm\psi(x) + (2k+1)\pi$ is a solution for $-\lambda$. In particular $-\psi(x)$ is a solution for the same λ. We can now state our results as follows.

Theorem 9. Let $I(x)$ be positive and continuously differentiable for $0 \leq x \leq 1$. Then for each positive integer n there exists a positive constant γ_n such that the problem (6.1), (6.2) has two solutions $\psi_n(x,\lambda)$ and $-\psi_n(x,\lambda)$ provided $\lambda_n \leq \lambda \leq \lambda_n + \gamma_n$. The function $\psi_n(x,\lambda)$ is continuous in λ, has n simple zeros in $0 < x < 1$ for $\lambda \neq \lambda_n$ and $\psi_n(x,\lambda_n) \equiv 0$. There is no solution other than $\pm\psi_n(x,\lambda)$ and $\psi_o(x,\lambda) \equiv 0$ which tends to zero as λ tends to λ_n. For $\lambda = 0$, $\psi(x) = c$ is a solution where c is any constant.

This theorem shows that the column buckles in the nth mode at the load λ_n predicted by the linear theory (6.3), (6.4) and the buckled state exists for all loads slightly larger than λ_n. Whether it persits for very much larger loads is not decided by this theorem. The values of $\pm\psi_n(x,\lambda)$ at $x = 0$ are given by (5.15) and shown in Figure II.1. Some of the other solutions $\pm\psi + 2k\pi$ and $\pm\psi + (2k+1)\pi$ are also shown. The probable extrapolation of each solution for λ much larger than λ_n is shown as a broken line.

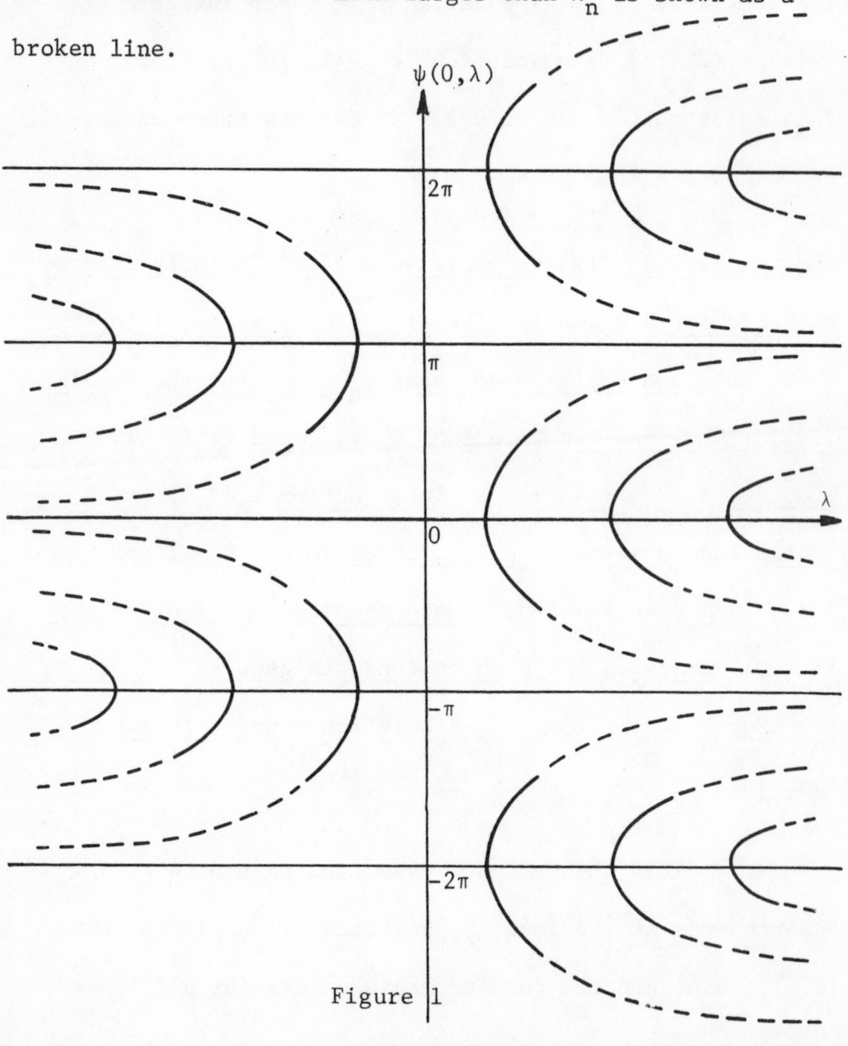

Figure 1

7. References

The bifurcation theory for ordinary differential equations was originally devised by Poincaré for the purpose of finding periodic solutions of the equations of celestial mechanics. The theory has been extended, developed and applied by various authors, but always for the case of periodic solutions. Accounts of that theory are given by E.A. Coddington and N. Levinson, Theory of Ordinary Differential Equations, McGraw-Hill, New York, 1955, and by K.O. Friedrichs, Advanced Ordinary Differential Equations, Courant Institute of Mathematical Sciences, New York University, 1956. We have followed the presentation of Friedrichs in developing the present extension of the theory to include boundary value problems and problems with more general subsidiary conditions. We first applied this theory to the problem of section 6 in section 6 of "The shape of the strongest column" by J. B. Keller, Archive for Rational Mechanics and Analysis, 5, 275-285(1960). It was later applied to a singular fourth order system in "Buckled states of circular plates" by J. B. Keller, H. B. Keller and E. L. Reiss, Quarterly of Applied Mathematics, 20, 55-65 (1962). H. B. Keller suggested that this bifurcation theory for boundary value problems could be extended by using side conditions involving linear functionals of the solution. We have found it no more difficult to develop the theory employing conditions involving nonlinear functionals.

The bifurcation theory for boundary value problems for ordinary differential equations has also been developed by O. Vejvoda, On perturbed nonlinear boundary value problem, Czech Math. J. 11 (86) 323-364 (1961).

III. Existence of Buckled States of Circular Plates Via the Schauder Fixed Point Theorem

Jay H. Wolkowisky

1. Introduction and formulation of the boundary value problem.

We consider the axisymmetric deformation of a thin circular elastic plate of constant thickness in equilibrium under a uniform compressive thrust applied around its edge. We describe the behavior of this plate by the nonlinear von Kármán equations [1] which for our problem can be reduced to the fourth order system:

$$GQ(r) + \lambda^2(1-P(r))Q(r) = 0, \quad 0 < r < 1, \tag{1.1}$$

$$GP(r) = -\frac{1}{2}Q(r)^2 \quad , \quad 0 < r < 1, \tag{1.2}$$

where the ordinary differential operator G is defined by

$$G = \frac{1}{r^3}\frac{d}{dr}\left(r^3\frac{d}{dr}\right).$$

Here r is the dimensionless radial distance, λ^2 is the dimensionless load parameter, Q is the dimensionless radial derivative of the transverse displacement, and P-1 is the dimensionless radial stress. Symmetry and smoothness require that

$$Q'(0) = 0 \ , \quad P'(0) = 0 \ , \tag{1.3a}$$

where a prime denotes differentiation with respect to r. If the edge r = 1 of the plate is clamped, the additional boundary conditions

$$Q(1) = 0 \ , \quad P(1) = 0 \tag{1.3b}$$

must be satisfied. The first condition of (1.3b) requires that the slope at the edge be zero and the second, that the radial membrane stress at the edge equal the prescribed thrust.

For all λ the boundary value problem (1.1)-(1.3) admits the trivial solution, $Q(r) \equiv 0$, $P(r) \equiv 0$, corresponding to a state of pure radial compression. This solution is called the unbuckled state. Other real solutions are called buckled states. If (Q(r), P(r)), is a nontrivial solution of (1.1)-(1.3) for a fixed value of λ, then (-Q(r), P(r)) is also a solution for the same value of λ. Thus the buckled states occur in pairs which differ only in the sign of Q.

Problem (1.1)-(1.3) may be linearized about the unbuckled state to yield the second order linear boundary value problem

$$G\bar{Q} + \lambda^2\bar{Q} = 0 ,$$
$$\bar{Q}'(0) = \bar{Q}(1) = 0 , \qquad (1.4)$$
$$\bar{P} \equiv 0$$

which possesses nontrivial solutions

$$Q_n = \frac{\text{const}}{r} J_1(\lambda_n r) , \quad J_1(\lambda_n) = 0 , \; n = 1,2,\ldots,$$

when $\lambda = \lambda_n$ where the eigenvalue λ_n is the nth zero of the Bessel function J_1.

The rotationally symmetric buckling of a simply supported plate was previously investigated by K. O. Friedrichs and J. J. Stoker [2] and by H. B. Keller, J. B. Keller, and E. L. Reiss [3]. In the first paper it was shown that there is one pair of buckled states with no internal node for all values of λ greater than λ_1 and that no other buckled states exist when λ is less than or equal to λ_2. In the second paper it was shown that for every positive integer n, a pair of rotationally symmetric buckled states with n-1 internal nodes exists when the thrust λ is slightly larger than λ_n. In this lecture it is shown that these pairs of buckled states continue to exist for all $\lambda > \lambda_n$. More precisely, we shall prove the

Existence Theorem: For all $\lambda > \lambda_n$, there exist n pairs $\{(+Q_j,P_j),(-Q_j,P_j)\}$, $j = 1,\ldots,n$, of nontrivial real solutions of (1.1)-(1.3), the members of each pair differing only in the signs of Q_j. Each Q_j has j-1 internal nodes.

This theorem will be proved by reducing the boundary value problem (1.1)-(1.3), to a form to which we can apply the Schauder Fixed Point Theorem. A novel feature of our work is that we use this theorem to show the existence of more than one solution. However, we do not prove the conjecture that these are the only axisymmetric buckled states.

In the appendix we shall show how the proof of the existence theorem can be modified to yield an analogous theorem for a plate with a simply supported edge.

2. Formulation of the boundary value problem as a mapping.

Let C_1 denote the Banach space of continuously differentiable functions ϕ on the closed interval [0,1] with the norm

$$||\phi|| = \max_{[0,1]} |\phi| + \max_{[0,1]} |\phi'| .$$

For fixed λ, let S denote the subset of C_1 consisting of those functions ϕ which have the following properties:

$$\phi(0) = 1 \ , \tag{2.1a}$$

$$\phi(1) = 0 \ , \tag{2.1b}$$

$$-\frac{r}{2}\lambda^2 \le \phi'(r) \le 0 \quad , \quad r \in [0,1] \ . \tag{2.1c}$$

These three properties imply

$$\phi'(0) = 0 \ , \tag{2.1d}$$

$$0 \le \phi(r) \le 1 \ , \tag{2.1e}$$

$$||\phi|| \le 1 + \frac{\lambda^2}{2} \tag{2.1f}$$

We observe that (2.1b) and (2.1d) are the boundary conditions on P given in (1.3).

Let

$$S_\varepsilon = \{\phi | \phi \varepsilon S, \ \phi \ge m_\varepsilon(r) \quad ,$$

where

$$m_\varepsilon(r) = \begin{cases} \varepsilon \ , & 0 \le r \le 1 - \frac{1}{\lambda^2} \\ 0 \ , & 1 - \frac{1}{\lambda^2} < r \le 1 \end{cases}$$

and $0 < \varepsilon \le \frac{1}{2}$. (Since ϕ is monotonic, S_ε consists of just those elements ϕ of S for which $\phi(1-1/\lambda^2) > \varepsilon$.)

<u>Remark 1</u>. It is clear that the sets S and S_ε are closed convex subsets of C_1.

For λ and ε fixed and for $\phi \in S_\varepsilon$ we consider the following system of equations:

$$(r^3 q_j')' + \lambda^2 r^3 [1 - c_j^2 \phi(r)] q_j = 0 \tag{2.2}$$

$$q_j'(0) = q_j(1) = 0 \tag{2.3}$$

$$\int_0^1 \frac{1}{s^3} \int_0^s t^3 q_j^2(t) dt ds = 2 \tag{2.4}$$

$$\psi_j = \frac{1}{2} \int_r^1 \frac{1}{s^3} \int_0^s t^3 q_j^2(t) dt ds \quad . \tag{2.5}$$

Here the c_j^2 are the eigenvalues and the q_j the corresponding eigenfunctions of the linear eigenvalue problem (2.2) and (2.3). Equation (2.2) is just equation (1.1) with P replaced by $c_j^2 \phi$ and with Q replaced by $c_j q_j$. Equation (2.4) is a normalizing condition on the eigenfunction q_j and (2.5) is the integral form of (1.2) subject to the conditions $P(0) = 0$ and $P(1) = 0$, with Q replaced by $c_j q_j$ and P replaced by $c_j^2 \psi_j^2$. Since the eigenvalues c_j^2 of (2.2) and (2.3) are simple, (2.2)-(2.5) defines for a given c_j^2, a <u>unique</u> mapping of ϕ into ψ_j which we represent by

$$T_j(\phi) = \psi_j \tag{2.6}$$

In view of the relationship between the mapping (2.6) and our original boundary value problem (1.1)-(1.3) it is clear that the existence of nontrivial, real solutions of (1.1)-(1.3) can be demonstrated by showing that for c_j^2 positive the mapping T_j has a fixed point. Toward this end we shall employ the following form [5] of the Schauder Fixed Point Theorem: A compact mapping of a closed convex subset of a Banach space into itself has a fixed point. In the next section we shall prove our existence theorem by showing that T_j on S_ε fulfills the hypotheses of this theorem and that the corresponding solutions (Q_j, P_j) with $Q_j = c_j q_j$ and $P_j = c_j^2 \psi_j$ have the requisite qualitative behavior.

3. Proof of the existence theorem.

Remark 2. The Sturm-Liouville theory tells us that (2.2) and (2.3) have an infinite number of simple eigenvalues, c_j^2, whose only accumulation point is at $-\infty$. Later we shall see that these eigenvalues have a finite upper bound, so that we may order them with c_1^2 the largest:

$$c_1^2 > c_2^2 > \cdots > c_{k-1}^2 > c_k^2 > \cdots \quad . \tag{3.1}$$

Theorem 1. *If $\lambda > \lambda_1$ and $\phi \in S_\varepsilon$, then the largest eigenvalue, c_1^2 of (2.2) and (2.3) satisfies the inequality*

$$c_1^2 \leq \frac{1}{\varepsilon} \quad . \tag{3.2}$$

Moreover, the eigenfunction $q_j (j = 1,2,\ldots)$ *corresponding to*

c_j^2 <u>has only</u> j-1 <u>internal zeros</u>.

Proof: Consider the following eigenvalue problem

$$(r^3 z_j')' + \lambda^2 r^3 [1 - \beta_j^2 m_\varepsilon(r)] z_j = 0 \tag{3.3}$$

$$z_j'(0) = z_j(1) = 0 \text{ and } \lambda > \lambda_1 , \tag{3.4}$$

where the β_j^2 are the eigenvalues. Without loss of generality we assume that $z_j(0) > 0$. From the explicit representation for the solutions of (3.3) and (3.4) in terms of Bessel functions, it is readily shown that $z_1'(r) < 0$ for $1-1/\lambda^2 \leq r \leq 1$. In order that the boundary conditions (3.4) not be violated, it is further necessary that

$$1 - \beta_1^2 \varepsilon \geq 0 \quad , \text{ i.e., } \beta_1^2 \leq \frac{1}{\varepsilon} \quad .$$

Since $\phi \geq m_\varepsilon(r)$, the Sturm Comparison Theorem implies that

$$c_j^2 \leq \beta_j^2 \quad .$$

Consequently

$$c_1^2 \leq \frac{1}{\varepsilon} \quad .$$

The explicit solution of eigenvalue problem (3.3) and (3.4) shows that $z_j(r)$ has j-1 internal zeros. From the Sturm Comparison Theorem we therefore conclude that $q_j(r)$ also has j-1 internal zeros.

We note that the hypothesis that $\phi \in S_\varepsilon$ is essential for the conclusion that q_j has j-1 zeros since there do exist functions ϕ in the set S for which this result is not true. For example, any function ϕ in S which vanishes identically on a large enough interval, say $[\frac{1}{2},1]$, will generate a set of eigenfunctions, the first of which, q_1, will have many internal zeros for sufficiently large λ.

We are interested only in the positive eigenvalues c_j^2 since these correspond to real solutions. The following theorem gives the conditions for positive eigenvalues to exist.

Theorem 2. If $\lambda > \lambda_n$ and $\phi \in S_\varepsilon$, then there exist n positive eigenvalues c_j^2, j = 1,2,...,n. Moreover

$$c_j^2 \geq \left(1 - \frac{\lambda_j^2}{\lambda^2}\right) \quad . \tag{3.5}$$

Proof: Consider the following eigenvalue problem,

$$(r^3y')' + \lambda^2 r^3[1-a^2]y = 0$$

$$y'(0) = y(1) = 0$$

where λ is fixed and a^2 is a constant. By comparing this problem with the linearized problem (1.4), we see that

$$\lambda_j^2 = \lambda^2(1-a_j^2) \; ;$$

$$a_j^2 = 1 - \frac{\lambda_j^2}{\lambda^2} .$$

The use of (2.1e) ($\phi(r) \leq 1$) and the Sturm Comparison Theorem yields the result that $c_j^2 \geq a_j^2$. Q.E.D.

We need the following lemma.

<u>Lemma</u> 1. <u>If</u> $\lambda > \lambda_n$, <u>and</u> $\phi \in S_\varepsilon$, <u>then</u>

$$q_j^2 \leq 4\lambda^2\psi_j \leq 4\lambda^2 \qquad \text{for} \quad j = 1,2,\ldots,n, \tag{3.6}$$

and

$$|r^3(q_j^2)'| \leq 2\lambda^4 \qquad \text{for} \quad j = 1,2,\ldots,n. \tag{3.7}$$

Proof: Multiplying (2.2) by q_j we have

$$\tfrac{1}{2}[r^3(q_j^2)']' - r^3(q_j')^2 + \lambda^2 r^3 q_j^2 - \lambda^2 r^3 c_j^2 \phi q_j^2 = 0 .$$

By Theorem 2, $c_j^2 > 0$ for $j \leq n$. Since $\phi \geq 0$ we have

$$[r^3(q_j^2)'] + 2\lambda^2 r^3 q_j^2 \geq 0 . \tag{3.8}$$

The integration of (3.8) from 0 to r yields

$$(q_j^2)' + 2\lambda^2 \frac{1}{r^3}\int_0^r t^3 q_j^2(t)dt \geq 0 .$$

Rewriting this as

$$[q_j^2 + 2\lambda^2 \int_0^r \frac{1}{s^3}\int_0^s t^3 q_j^2(t)dt\, ds]' \geq 0 ,$$

we see that the function

$$q_j^2(r) + 2\lambda^2 \int_o^r \frac{1}{s^3} \int_o^s t^3 q_j^2(t)dt\, ds$$

is a monotonic increasing function of r and therefore, using (2.3), we have

$$q_j^2(r) + 2\lambda^2 \int_o^r \frac{1}{s^3} \int_o^s t^3 q_j^2(t)dt\, ds \leq 2\lambda^2 \int_o^1 \frac{1}{s^3} \int_o^s t^3 q_j^2 dt\, ds$$

or

$$q_j^2 \leq 2\lambda^2 \int_r^1 \frac{1}{s^3} \int_o^s t^3 q_j^2(t)dt\, ds \ .$$

Using (2.5) and (2.4) we obtain

$$q_j^2(r) \leq 4\lambda^2 \psi_j(r) \leq 4\lambda^2 \psi_j(0) = 4\lambda^2 \ , \qquad (3.9)$$

which proves (3.6).

To prove (3.7) we rewrite (3.8) as

$$[r^3 (q_j^2)' + 2\lambda^2 \int_o^r t^3 q_j^2(t)dt]' \geq 0 \ .$$

Thus the function

$$r^3 (q_j^2)' + 2\lambda^2 \int_o^r t^3 q_j^2(t)dt$$

is a monotonic increasing function of r and from (2.3) we therefore obtain

$$0 \leq r^3 (q_j^2)' + 2\lambda^2 \int_o^r t^3 q_j^2(t)dt \leq 2\lambda^2 \int_o^1 t^3 q_j^2(t)dt$$

or

$$-2\lambda^2\int_0^r t^3 q_j^2(t)dt \leq r^3(q_j^2(r))' \leq 2\lambda^2\int_r^1 t^3 q_j^2(t)dt \;.$$

From (3.9) we get

$$|r^3(q_j^2(r))'| \leq 2\lambda^4. \qquad \text{Q.E.D.}$$

We now prove

Theorem 3. For $\lambda > \lambda_n$, T_j is compact* (completely continuous) on S_ε, $j = 1,2,\ldots,n$.

Proof: We first show that T_j is continuous for $\lambda > \lambda_n$. Consider a sequence of functions $\{\phi_\nu\}\varepsilon\ S_\varepsilon$ ($\varepsilon > 0$, fixed) which converge in the norm of C_1 to a function ϕ (which of course is in S_ε). Let $\psi_{j\nu}$ be the images of this sequence under the mapping T_j, i.e. $T_j(\phi_\nu) = \psi_{j\nu}$. For each ϕ_ν, let $C_{j\nu}^2$ be the eigenvalues of (2.2) and (2.3). For fixed $j \leq n$, the corresponding eigenfunction $q_{j\nu}$ satisfying the normalizing condition (2.4) and the nonrestrictive assumption $q_{j\nu}(0) > 0$ is unique. Lemma 1 implies that the $q_{j\nu}$ are uniformly bounded. The eigenfunction $q_{j\nu}$ satisfies the following integral equation corresponding to (2.2) and (2.3):

---

*The mapping T_j is compact if it is continuous and if $T_j(S_\varepsilon)$ is (sequentially) compact.

$$q_{j\nu} = -\lambda^2 \int_r^1 \frac{1}{s^3} \int_0^s t^3 (1-c_{j\nu}^2 \phi_\nu) q_{j\nu} dt\, ds . \qquad (3.10)$$

Since $c_{j\nu}^2 \leq \varepsilon - 1$, it is easily shown from (10) that $\{q_{j\nu}\}$ are equicontinuous. Therefore from Arzela's Theorem we may select a subsequence $\{q_{j\nu_\sigma}\}$ which converges uniformly to a function q_j. Since the eigenvalues of a Sturm-Liouville problem depend continuously upon the coefficients [4], the sequence of eigenvalues $\{c_{j\nu}^2\}$ and consequently the subsequence $\{c_{j\nu_\sigma}^2\}$ both converge to c_j^2, the jth eigenvalue of the problem

$$(r^3 y')' + \lambda^2 r^3 [1-c_j^2 \phi] y = 0 \quad , \qquad y'(0) = y(1) = 0 . \quad (3.11)$$

From (3.10) we note that the derivatives $q'_{j\nu_\sigma}$ converge uniformly to q'_j and therefore from the differential equation itself it follows that the second derivatives $q''_{j\nu_\sigma}$ converge uniformly to q''_j. We now show that the limit function q_j satisfies (3.11). We have

$$|(r^3 q'_j)' + \lambda^2 r^3 (1-c_j^2 \phi) q_j| \leq |[r^3 (q_j - q_{j\nu_\sigma})]'| + \lambda^2 r^3 |(1-c_j^2 \phi) q_j$$
$$- (1-c_{j\nu_\sigma}^2 \phi_{\nu_\sigma}) q_{j\nu_\sigma}| + |(r^3 q'_{j\nu_\sigma})' + \lambda^2 r^3 (1-c_{j\nu_\sigma}^2 \phi_{\nu_\sigma}) q_{j\nu_\sigma}| \quad .$$

The last term on the right hand side of this inequality vanishes identically. Letting $\nu_\sigma \to \infty$ we see that q_j satisfies

(3.11) and is the eigenfunction corresponding to c_j^2. The imposition of the normalizing condition (2.4) and the restriction that $q_j(0) > 0$ renders q_j unique. We therefore conclude a posteriori that the selection of the subsequence was unnecessary. Hence

$$q_{j\nu} \to q_j$$

uniformly. Therefore from (2.5) we have

$$||\psi_{j\nu} - \psi_j|| \to 0$$

and

$$T_j(\phi) = \psi_j.$$

Thus T_j is continuous on S_ε.

We now show that for $\lambda > \lambda_n$, $T_j(S_\varepsilon)$ is sequentially compact. (Since $T_j(S_\varepsilon)$ is a metric space, sequential compactness is equivalent to compactness.) Thus we must prove that any sequence $\{\psi_{j\nu}\}$ of elements of $T_j(S_\varepsilon)$ possesses a convergent subsequence.

From (2.4), (2.5), and (3.6) we find that if $\phi \in S_\varepsilon$, then $\psi_j = T_j(\phi)$ satisfies the inequalities:

$$|\psi_j| \leq 1, |\psi_j'| \leq \lambda^2/2, \quad |\psi_j''| \leq 2\lambda^2 \quad .$$

Since any sequence of functions whose derivatives are uniformly bounded is equicontinuous, it follows that $\{\psi_{j\nu}\}$ and

$\{\psi_{j\nu}\}$ are uniformly bounded and equicontinuous. It follows from Arzela's theorem that $T_j(S_{\varepsilon^*})$ is a compact set. Q.E.D.

<u>Theorem</u> 4. <u>For</u> $\lambda > \lambda_n$ <u>there exists an</u> $\varepsilon^* > 0$ <u>such that</u> T_j <u>maps</u> S_{ε^*} <u>into</u> S_{ε^*} <u>for</u> $j = 1,2,\ldots,n$.

<u>Proof</u>: We first verify that $\psi_j \in S$. That ψ_j is continuously differentiable is obvious from (2.5). Conditions (2.1a) and (2.1b) follow immediately from (2.4) and (2.5). We now show that (2.1c) is satisfied. From (2.5) we have

$$\psi_j'(r) = -\frac{1}{2r^3}\int_o^r t^3 q_j^2(t)\,dt \leq 0.$$

Equation (3.6) then implies

$$\psi_j \geq -\frac{r\lambda^2}{2}.$$

Thus $\psi_j \in S$ and T_j maps S_{ε^*} into S.

We now prove by contradiction that there is an $\varepsilon = \varepsilon^*$ for which T_j maps S into itself for $j = 1,\ldots,n$. Assume that for $\lambda > \lambda_n$ there exists <u>no</u> $\varepsilon^* > 0$, such that T_j maps S_{ε^*} into S_{ε^*} for $j = 1,\ldots,n$. This implies that there exists a convergent sequence of functions $\{\phi_\nu\} \in \bigcup_{\varepsilon > 0} S_{\varepsilon^*}$ such

$$\lim_{\nu \to \infty} \psi_{j\nu} = \psi_j \in S - \bigcup_{\varepsilon > 0} S_{\varepsilon^*}$$

where $\psi_j = T_j(\phi_\nu)$. This implies that $\psi_j(r)$ must vanish identically at $1-1/\lambda^2$. Hence

$$\lim_{\nu \to \infty} \int_{1-1/\lambda^2}^{1} s^{-3}\int_o^s t^3 q_{j\nu}^2(t)dt\, ds = 0 .$$

Let $\theta_\nu = s^{-3}\int_o^s t^3 q_{j\nu}^2(t)dt$. From (3.6) we see that θ_ν and $d\theta_\nu/ds$ are uniformly bounded for $1-1/\lambda^2 \leq s \leq 1$. Since $d\theta_\nu/ds$ is uniformly bounded, $\{\theta_\nu\}$ is an equicontinuous sequence of functions. By Arzela's theorem it possesses a uniformly convergent subsequence $\{\theta_{\nu_\sigma}\}$. Therefore

$$\int_{1-1/\lambda^2}^{1} \lim_{\nu\to\infty} \theta_{\nu_\sigma}\, ds = 0$$

and since θ_ν is nonnegative, $\lim_{\nu \to \infty} \theta_{\nu_\sigma} = 0$. In particular, for s = 1, this implies

$$\lim_{\nu \to \infty} \int_o^1 t^3 q_{j\nu_\sigma}^2 (t)dt = 0 .$$

From (3.6) and (3.7) we see that $t^3 q_{j\nu_\sigma}^2$ and its derivative are uniformly bounded. Reproducing the last argument, we find that there exists a further subsequence $\{q_{j\nu_{\sigma_{\sigma'}}}\}$ such that

$$\lim_{\nu \to \infty} q_{j\nu_{\sigma_{\sigma'}}}^2 (t) = 0 \quad \text{for } t\ [0,1] .$$

Since the original sequence $\{\phi_\nu\}$ could have been taken to be its subsequence $\{\phi_{\nu_{\sigma_{\sigma'}}}\}$, this last result violates the normalizing condition (2.4) and this contradiction implies that there does exist an $\varepsilon^* > 0$ such that T_j maps S_{ε^*} into itself for $j = 1,\ldots,n$. Q.E.D.

By Remark 1, Theorem 3, and Theorem 4, we have proved that the conditions of the Schauder fixed point theorem are satisfied. Thus there is a $\psi_j^* \in S_{\varepsilon^*}$ such that

$$\psi_j^* = T_j(\psi_j^*).$$

This proves the first part of the Existence Theorem. That $Q_j = c_j q_j$ has $j - 1$ zeros was proved in Theorem 1.

4. Discussion.

The boundary value problem (1.1)-(1.3) was formulated as the mapping (2.2)-(2.5). It may also be posed in the following alternate form: For a fixed value of λ, for what values of c^2 does the following boundary value problem have non-trivial solutions?

$$G_q + \lambda^2(1-c^2p)q = 0$$

$$G_p = -\frac{1}{2}q^2$$

$$q'(0) = p'(0) = q(1) = p(1) = 0, \quad p(0) = 1.$$

We call the set $\{c_j^2\}$ of these eigenvalues the spectrum of this nonlinear problem. Our previous results indicate that this spectrum consists of a negative part and a positive part. As λ increases, the spectrum shifts to the right and more positive eigenvalues appear. This corresponds to the emergence of real solutions from imaginary ones.

The results of this lecture are based on [6]. The general technique used here to show existence of solutions can be applied to more general nonlinear boundary value problems for ordinary differential equations.

5. Appendix: The Simply Supported Plate.

If the edge of the plate is simply supported then the boundary value problem is given by equation (1.1), (1.2), (1.3a), and

$$Q'(1) + (1+\nu)Q(1) = 0 \quad , \quad p(1) = 0. \tag{5.1}$$

Here ν is Poisson's ratio, a prescribed physical constant. Equation (5.1) replaces (1.3b). The linearized form of this problem is

$$G\bar{Q} + \lambda^2\bar{Q} = 0$$

$$\bar{Q}'(0) = 0 \quad , \quad \bar{Q}'(1) + (1+\nu)\bar{Q}(1) = 0 \quad .$$

The nontrivial solutions of these equations are given by

$$\bar{Q}_j = \frac{\text{const}}{r} J_1(\lambda_j r)$$

when $\lambda = \lambda_j$ where λ_j is the jth root of $\lambda J_1'(\lambda) + \nu J_1(\lambda) = 0$.

An existence theorem for this problem completely analogous to that for the clamped plate can be obtained in precisely the same way if we replace (2.1a) in the definition of the set S by

$$\phi(0) \leq 1$$

and if we replace the normalizing condition (2.4) by

$$q_j^2(1) + 2\lambda^2 \int_0^1 s^{-3} \int_0^s t^3 q_j^2(t)\,dt\,ds = 4\lambda^2 \quad .$$

BIBLIOGRAPHY

[1] von Kármán, T., Festigheitsprobleme im Maschinenbau, Encyklopädie der mathematischen Wissenschaften, Vol. 4, Leipzig, 1910, pp. 348-352.

[2] Friedrichs, K. O., and Stoker, J. J., The non-linear boundary value problem of the buckled plate, Amer. J. Math., Vol. 63, 1941, pp. 839-888.

[3] Keller, H. B., Keller, J. B., and Reiss, E. L., Buckled states of circular plates, Q. Appl. Math., Vol. 20, 1962, pp. 55-65.

[4] Courant, R., and Hilbert, D., Methods of Mathematical Physics, Vol. 1, Interscience Publishers, New York, 1953, p. 418.

[5] Cronin, J., Fixed Points and Topological Degree in Non-linear Analysis, A.M.S., Providence, 1964, pp. 130ff.

[6] Wolkowisky, J., Existence of Buckled States of Circular Plates, Comm. on Pure and Appl. Math., Vol. 20,1967, pp. 549-560.

IV. Buckled States of Elastic Rings*

I. Tadjbakhsh*

1. Introduction

In this lecture we examine the existence of nontrivial solutions (buckled states) of the nonlinear equilibrium equations for inextensible elastic rings under hydrostatic pressure. We formulate the governing equations by requiring the potential energy of the ring to be stationary. The method of Lecture II is used to treat the bifurcation of solutions from the unbuckled state. We

---

*This lecture is based on the work of Tadjbakhsh and Odeh [7].

prove the existence of at least one buckled state for all values of the pressure exceeding the critical pressure by showing that there is a nontrivial smooth solution that minimizes the potential energy. (This is the "preferred" solution. Cf. Lecture I.) We then exploit the fact that the boundary value problem admits an alternative variational formulation to prove the existence of at least one solution for an arbitrary value of the norm. Finally we exhibit numerical results.

2. Formulation of the boundary value problem

We consider the equilibrium configurations of an inextensible elastic ring subject to a (dimensionless) hydrostatic pressure p. The undeformed shape of the ring is a circle of radius 1. The geometry of the ring is given in Figure 1. Here s denotes the arc length coordinate of the ring and $\theta(s)$, the angle between the tangent to the ring and the x-axis. The curvature k(s) is defined by

$$k = \theta_s. \tag{2.1}$$

x(s) and y(s) are cartesian coordinates of the particle s of the ring; they satisfy the relations:

$$x_s = \cos\theta(s),\ y_s = \sin\theta(s). \tag{2.2}$$

The coordinates are fixed by the requirement that

$$\theta(0) = 0, \quad x(0) = 0, \quad y(0) = 0. \tag{2.3}$$

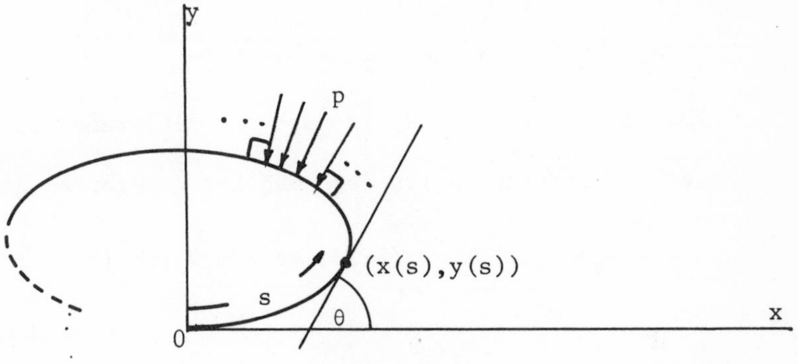

Figure 1

The deformed ring must satisfy the following conditions:

$$\theta(s + 2\pi) = \theta(s) + 2\pi \tag{2.4}$$

$$x(s+2\pi) = x(s) \quad , \quad y(s+2\pi) = y(s) . \tag{2.5}$$

These equations imply that

$$\int_0^{2\pi} k(\xi)d\xi = 2\pi , \tag{2.6}$$

$$\int_0^{2\pi} \cos\theta(\xi)d\xi = 0, \qquad \int_0^{2\pi} \sin\theta(\xi)d\xi = 0 . \tag{2.7}$$

The dimensionless potential energy of the ring is

$$V = \frac{1}{2}\int_0^{2\pi}(k-1)^2 ds - W \tag{2.8}$$

where the integral expression on the right hand side of (2.8) is the strain energy of the ring (corresponding to the Euler-Bernoulli theory) and W is the work done on the body by the external (hydrostatic) forces. W is given by

$$W = -p\,\frac{1}{2}\int_0^{2\pi}(xy_s - yx_s)ds - \pi \quad . \qquad (2.9)$$

The bracketed term in (2.9) is just the difference in area enclosed by the ring in its deformed and undeformed states.

Using (2.1) and (2.2), we can write (2.8) in the form

$$V[\theta] = \text{const} + \frac{1}{2}\int_0^{2\pi}\{\theta_s^2 + p\int_0^s \sin[\theta(s)-\theta(\xi)]d\xi\}ds. \qquad (2.10)$$

We denote the variation of θ by $\dot{\theta}$ which must satisfy

$$\dot{\theta}(0) = \dot{\theta}(2\pi) = \int_0^{2\pi}\dot{\theta}(s)\sin\theta(s)ds = \int_0^{2\pi}\dot{\theta}(s)\cos\theta(s)ds=0. \qquad (2.11)$$

The first variation of V in an arbitrary admissible "direction" $\dot{\theta}$ is

$$\dot{V}[\theta] = \frac{1}{2}\int_0^{2\pi}\{2\theta_s(s)\dot{\theta}_s(s) + p\dot{\theta}(s)\int_0^s \cos[\theta(s)-\theta(\xi)]d\xi$$
$$- p\int_0^s \dot{\theta}(\xi)\cos[\theta(s)-\theta(\xi)]d\xi\}ds. \qquad (2.12a)$$

When we change the order of integration, the third expression in the sum on the right hand side of (2.12a) becomes

$$-\frac{p}{2}\int_0^{2\pi}\dot{\theta}(\xi)d\xi\int_\xi^{2\pi}\cos[\theta(s)-\theta(\xi)]ds = -\frac{p}{2}\int_0^{2\pi}\dot{\theta}(s)ds\int_s^{2\pi}\cos[\theta(s)-\theta(\xi)]d\xi$$

In virtue of (2.7) this becomes

$$\frac{p}{2}\int_{0}^{2\pi}\dot{\theta}(s)\int_{0}^{s}\cos[\theta(s)-\theta(\xi)]d\xi ds\ .$$

Hence (2.12a) can be written as

$$\dot{V}[0] = \int_{0}^{2}\{\theta_s(s)\dot{\theta}_s(s) + p\dot{\theta}(s)\int_{0}^{s}\cos[\theta(s)-\theta(\xi)]d\xi\}ds. \qquad (2.12b)$$

The vanishing of $\dot{V}[\theta]$ subject to (2.11) yields the following Euler equation for $\theta(s)$:

$$\theta_{ss} - p\int_{0}^{s}\cos[\theta(s)-\theta(\xi)]d\xi = \mu_1 \cos\theta(s)+\mu_2\sin\theta(s),$$
$$0 \le s \le 2\pi\ . \qquad (2.13)$$

Here μ_1 and μ_2 are constant multipliers. By successive differentiations we can eliminate μ_1 and μ_2 from the integro-differential equation (2.13) to obtain the following ordinary differential equation for $k = \theta_s$:

$$\left(\frac{kss}{k}\right)_s + k\,k_s - p\left(\frac{1}{k}\right)_s = 0 \qquad (2.14)$$

This can be integrated to yield

$$k_{ss} + \frac{1}{2}k^3 - ck - p = 0\ . \qquad (2.15)$$

Here c is an arbitary integration constant.

Equation (2.14) can also be obtained by treating V as a functional of θ,x,y and introducing the differential constraint equations (2.2) by means of variable multipliers.

Equations (2.15), (2.6), (2.7) possess

the trivial solution $k = 1$, $c = \frac{1}{2} - p$ for all p. It is convenient to introduce the new variables:

$$v(s) = k(s) - 1,\ \mu = \frac{3}{2} - c,\ \beta = c+p - \frac{1}{2} = p+1-\mu, \tag{2.16}$$

in terms of which (15) becomes

$$v_{ss} + \mu v = \beta - \frac{1}{2} v^2 (v+3). \tag{2.17}$$

The pressure is given by

$$p = \mu + \beta - 1. \tag{2.18}$$

The trivial solution for the boundary value problem (2.17), (2.6), (2.7) is now given by $v(s) \equiv 0$, $\beta = 0$, $\mu = p+1$, for all p.

The differential equation (2.17) can be integrated by quadratures (1) and (2) and the resulting solution v(s) can be expressed in terms of elliptic functions. The boundary conditions (2.6) and (2.7) are then reduced to transcendental equations for the arbitrary constants of integration. We do not pursue this approach.

From (2.4) it follows that v(s) must be periodic with period $2\pi/n$, $n = 1,2,\ldots$. In the appendix it is shown that $n = 1$ is inconsistent with the boundary conditions. We shall therefore assume in the sequel that $n \geq 2$.

Since (17) is invariant under the change of independent variable $s^* = \pm s + \text{const}$, it is sufficient to consider the solution of (2.17) in the half period interval $(0, \pi/n)$ with the boundary conditions

$$v_s(o) = v_s(\pi/n) = 0. \qquad (2.19)$$

The periodicity of v implies that (2.6) can be reduced to

$$\int_o^{\pi/n} v(s)ds = 0 \ . \qquad (2.20)$$

Once v is determined in the interval $0 \leq s \leq \pi/n$, it can be extended continuously and periodically from the relations $v(-s) = v(s)$ and $v(s-2\pi/n) = v(s)$.

We now show that the solution v of (2.17) which satisfies (2.19) and (2.20) for $n \geq 2$, automatically satisfies the condition (2.7) which we write as

$$\int_o^{2\pi} e^{i\theta(s)}ds = 0 \ .$$

From (2.1), (2.3) and (2.16), we have

$$\theta(s) = s + \psi(s) \qquad (2.22)$$

where

$$\psi(s) = \int_o^s v(\xi)d\xi \ . \qquad (2.23)$$

Since v is even, is periodic with period $2\pi/n$, and has zero average over its period (from (2.20)) it follows that ψ

is odd and periodic with the same period. Hence $q = e^{i\psi}$ is also periodic in $2\pi/n$ and therefore has the representation

$$q(s) = \sum_{m=-\infty}^{\infty} q_m e^{imns} \quad . \tag{2.24}$$

Thus

$$\int_0^{2\pi} e^{i\theta(s)} ds = \int_0^{2\pi} \sum_{m=-\infty}^{\infty} e^{i(1+mn)s} ds \quad . \tag{2.25}$$

For $n \geq 2$, $1 + mn \neq 0$, so (2.21) is satisfied.

Thus our boundary value problem (2.17), (2.6), (2.7) admits the alternate formulation of (2.17), (2.19), (2.20).

3. Bifurcation

We follow the development of Lecture II, Section 4, to show the existence of solutions bifurcating from the trivial solution $v \equiv 0$. Our boundary value problems is

$$v_{ss} + \mu v = \beta - \frac{1}{2} v^2 (v + 3), \; 0 < s < \pi/n, \tag{3.1a}$$

$$v_s(0) = 0 \quad , \tag{3.1b}$$

$$v_s(\pi/n) = 0, \tag{3.1c}$$

$$\int_0^{\pi/n} v(s) ds = 0. \tag{3.1d}$$

We let $a = v(0)$ and introduce a new dependent variable w by relation

$$v = aw. \tag{3.2}$$

We set aside (3.1c) and (3.1d) and consider the resulting initial value problem for w:

$$w_{ss} + \mu w = \gamma - \frac{3}{2}aw^2 - \frac{1}{2}a^2w^3, \quad s > 0, \tag{3.3a}$$

$$w_s(0) = 0, \tag{3.3b}$$

$$w(0) = 1, \tag{3.3c}$$

where $\gamma = \beta/a$. For $a = 0$,(3.3) has the solution

$$w = \phi(s,\mu,\gamma) = (1 - \frac{\gamma}{\mu})\cos\sqrt{\mu}s + \frac{\gamma}{\mu}. \tag{3.4}$$

By Theorem 1 of Lecture II, (3.3) possesses a unique solution $w(x,\mu,\gamma,a)$ for a sufficiently small. Among all such solutions we seek those which satisfy

$$w_s(\frac{\pi}{n},\mu,\gamma,a) \equiv b_1(\mu,\gamma,a) = 0, \tag{3.5}$$

$$\int_0^{\pi/n} w(s,\mu,\gamma,a)ds \equiv b_2(\mu,\gamma,a) = 0. \tag{3.6}$$

To show the existence of bifurcating solutions, we must show that for $a \neq 0$, μ and γ can be chosen so that (3.5) and (3.6) are satisfied.

For $a = 0$, (3.4) satisfies (3.5) and (3.6) if

$$\mu = n^2, \gamma = 0. \tag{3.7}$$

By the implicit function theorem (3.5) and (3.6) have solutions $\mu = \mu(a)$, $\gamma = \gamma(a)$ in a neighborhood of $a = 0$ if the Jacobian

$$J = \frac{\partial(b_1, b_2)}{\partial(\mu, \gamma)} \neq 0 \text{ for } a = 0.$$

We verify this:

$$J = [\phi_{s\mu}(\pi/n, \mu, \gamma) \int_0^{\pi/n} \phi_\gamma(s, \mu, \gamma) ds - \phi_{s\gamma}(\pi/n, \mu, \gamma) \int_0^{\pi/n} \phi_\mu(s, \mu, \gamma) ds] \Big|_{\substack{\gamma = 0 \\ \mu = n^2}} = \frac{\pi^2}{2n^2} \neq 0. \quad (3.8)$$

Thus bifurcations do occur for

$$p = n^2 - 1. \quad (3.9)$$

By a regular perturbation we find that

$$v = a \cos ns + \frac{a^2}{4n^2} (\cos 2ns - \cos ns) + o(a^2) \quad (3.10)$$

$$p = (n^2 - 1) + \frac{3a^2}{8}(1 - 1/n^2) + 0(a^2). \quad (3.11)$$

Hence the response curve of p vs. a for small a has the form shown in Figure 2.

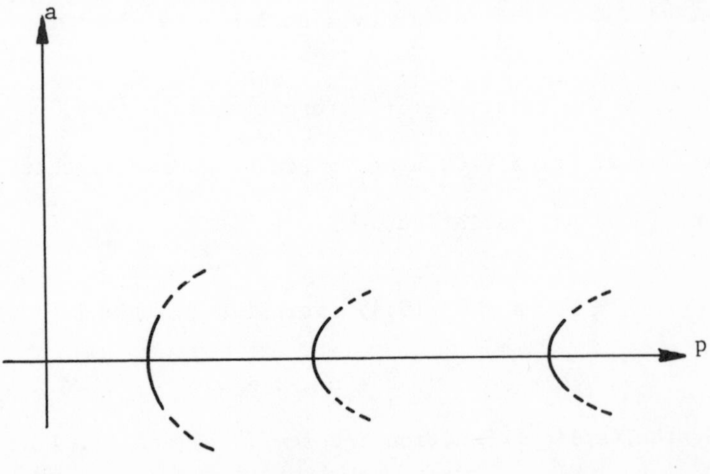

Figure 2

4. Functional analytic preliminaries

In the last section we have demonstrated the existence of solutions with small norms for p near the critical values n^2-1, $n = 2,3,\ldots$. To prove the existence of nontrivial solutions for $p > 3$ and the existence of solutions with arbitrary norm, we use the methods of functional analysis. In this section we discuss those concepts which are needed in our ensuing work. Proofs of the theorems stated here can be found in [3] and [4].

We introduce the Sobolev space

$$W_2^{(1)}(a,b) = \{x:\ x, x_s \varepsilon\ L_2(a,b)\} \tag{4.1}$$

(where derivatives are taken in the distributional sense), which is a Hilbert space with inner product

$$(x,y) = \int_a^b (xy + x_s y_s)ds \tag{4.2}$$

and norm

$$||x|| = [\int_a^b (x^2 + x_s^2)ds]^{1/2} . \tag{4.3}$$

$W_2^{(1)}(a,b)$ is the completion in the norm (4.3) of differentiable functions whose derivatives belong to $L_2(a,b)$. The norm $||x||$ is equivalent to the norm $[\int_b^a x_s^2 ds]^{1/2}$, i.e. there exist positive constants m, M such that

$$m||x||^2 \le \int_a^b x_s^2 \, ds \le M \, ||x||^2 \quad . \tag{4.4}$$

Definition: A sequence $\{x_n\}$ of elements of a Hilbert space H is said to <u>converge weakly</u> to a limit x in H if

$$(x_n, y) \to (x, y)$$

for all y in H. We denote this weak convergence by

$$x_n \overset{w}{\to} x.$$

Definition: A set E in a Hilbert space H is called <u>weakly closed</u> if it contains all its weak limit points; i.e., if $x_n \varepsilon$ E and $x_n \overset{w}{\to} x$, then $x \varepsilon$ E.

Definition: A functional U defined on a Hilbert space H is called <u>weakly lower semi-continuous</u> at the point $x \varepsilon H$ if for any sequence $\{x_n\}$ that converges weakly to x,

$$U[x] \le \underline{\lim}_{n\to\infty} U[x_n] \quad .$$

Theorem A: If the functional U is weakly lower semi-continuous on a bounded weakly closed set E in a Hilbert space, then U assumes its minimum on E.

Theorem B: In $W_2^{(1)}(a,b)$, $\int_a^b x_s^2 ds$ is a weakly lower semi-continuous functional.

Definition: Let X and Y be two Banach spaces. Then X is said to be <u>imbedded</u> in Y if

i) every element $x \in X$ is also an element of Y

ii) every strongly convergent sequence in X is also strongly convergent in Y.

The imbedding of X in Y is <u>compact</u> if the imbedding operator $i: X \to Y$ defined by $i(x) = x$ is compact.

Theorem C (a special case of the Sobolev imbedding theorem): The Hilbert space $W_2^{(1)}(a,b)$ can be compactly imbedded in the Banach space $C([a,b])$ of continuous functions (having the maximum norm). Moreover,

$$\max_{[a,b]} |x| \leq \text{const}||x|| \text{ for all } x \in W_2^{(1)}(a,b). \tag{4.5}$$

Theorem D: If $x_n \overset{W}{\to} x$ in a Hilbert space H and H is compactly imbedded in a Banach space B, then $x_n \to x$ in B.

5. Existence of buckled states for $p > 3$.

In this section we show that for $p > 3$, the lowest buckling load, there exists a nontrivial smooth function $\theta(s)$ that furnishes the potential energy functional $V[\theta]$ with an absolute minimum.

We introduce the dependent variable

$$\psi(s) = \theta(s) - s \tag{5.1}$$

in terms of which V is given by

$$V = V_1 + V_2 \tag{5.2}$$

where

$$V_1[\psi] = \frac{1}{2}\int_0^{2\pi} \psi_s^2 \, ds \tag{5.3}$$

$$V_2[\psi] = \frac{1}{2}\, p \int_0^{2\pi}\int_0^{s} \sin[\psi(s) - \psi(\xi) + s-\xi]\, d\xi\, ds\ . \tag{5.4}$$

The function ψ satisfies boundary conditions

$$\psi(0) = \psi(2\pi) = 0\ , \tag{5.5}$$

and the constraints

$$\int_0^{2\pi} \cos[\psi(s)+s]ds = \int_0^{2\pi} \sin[\psi(s) + s]\, ds = 0\ .$$

We now prove the existence of a minimizing function ψ^* for the potential energy functional V by showing that the hypotheses of Theorem A are met. We shall do this in a series of lemmas.

Let S be the Hilbert space consisting of those elements of $W_2^{(1)}(0,2\pi)$ that satisfy the boundary conditions (5.5).

<u>Lemma</u> 1: $V[\psi] \to \infty$ <u>as</u> $||\psi|| \to \infty$.

Proof: This is an immediate consequence of (5.3) and (4.4).

Thus it is sufficient to consider V defined on bounded subsets of S.

Let E denote the set of elements of S that satisfy (5.6). (It is easy to show that E contains many elements. Cf (2.21).)

Lemma 2: E is weakly closed.

Proof: Let $\theta_n = \psi_n + s$ satisfy (5.6) and let $\theta_n \overset{w}{\to} \theta$. We must show that θ satisfies (5.6).

$$\left|\int_0^{2\pi}[\cos\theta - \cos\theta_n]ds\right| = 2\left|\int_0^{2\pi}\sin\tfrac{1}{2}(\theta+\theta_n)\sin\tfrac{1}{2}(\theta-\theta_n)ds\right|$$

$$\leq 2\int_0^{2\pi}\left|\sin\tfrac{1}{2}(\theta-\theta_n)\right|ds \leq \int_0^{2\pi}|\theta-\theta_n|ds \to 0 \qquad (5.7)$$

because of Theorem D. Hence

$$\int_0^{2}\cos\theta\, ds = 0\ . \qquad (5.8)$$

The proof that θ satisfies the second condition of (5.6) is identical.

Lemma 3: V is weakly lower semi-continuous on S.

Proof: By Theorem B, V_1 is weakly lower semi-continuous. We show that V_2 is weakly continuous. Let $\psi_n \overset{w}{\to} \psi$. Then

$$|V_2(\psi_n)-V_2(\psi)| \leq |p|\left|\int_0^{2\pi}\int_0^{s}\right|[\psi_n(s)-\psi(s) + \psi_n(\xi)-\psi(\xi)]\,|d\xi ds$$

$$\leq |p|\int_0^{2\pi}\{|\psi_n(s)-\psi(s)| + \int_0^{2\pi}|\psi_n(\xi)-\psi(\xi)|d\xi\}ds$$

$$= (2\pi+1)|p|\int_o^2 |\psi_n(s)-\psi(s)|ds \to 0 \tag{5.9}$$

by Theorem D. Q.E.D.

Lemmas 1-3 ensure that the conditions of Theorem A are satisfied. We have therefore proved:

Theorem 1: Let E denote the subset of $W_2^{(1)}(0,2\pi)$ satisfying (5.5) and (5.6). Then there exists an element ψ^* in E that furnished V with an absolute minimum on E.

Having established the existence of ψ^*, we turn to the regularity question. An immediate consequence of Theorems C and D is the following result:

Theorem 2: The minimizing function ψ^* of Theorem 4 is continuous on $[0,2\pi]$.

The smoothness of ψ^* is a consequence of the following regularity theorem.

Theorem 3: $\psi^* \varepsilon\ C^2(\ 0,2\pi\ )$ and is a classical solution of the Euler equation (2.13) with its subsidiary conditions (2.6) and (2.7).

The proof of this theorem depends strongly on Theorem 2 and on the fact that the second derivative of the integrand of $V[\psi]$with respect to ψ_s is positive (i.e., V satisfies a strong Legendre condition). The details of the proof are analogous to those in [5, pp.139 ff] and are omitted here.

From (2.13) it then follows that $\psi^* \varepsilon\ C([0,2])$ and is a classical solution of (2.15), (2.6) and (2.7).

Theorem 4: For p > 3 (the lowest buckling load), the "preferred" solution ψ^* is nontrivial.

Proof: We show that for $p > 3$ the solution $\psi \equiv 0$ does not furnish even a local minimum to V and consequently cannot equal ψ^*. To do this we examine the second variation of V. From (2.12) we get

$$\ddot{V}\Big|_{\psi\equiv 0} = \int_0^{2\pi} [-\dot{\theta}(s)\dot{\theta}_{ss}(s) - p\dot{\theta}^2(s)(1-\cos s) + p\dot{\theta}(s)\int_0^s \sin(s-\xi)\dot{\theta}(\xi)d\xi]\, ds. \tag{5.10}$$

The variation $\dot{\theta}(s)$ must satisfy (2.11) and

$$\int_0^{2\pi} \dot{\theta}^2(s) \sin s\, ds = \int_0^{2\pi} \dot{\theta}^2(s) \cos s\, ds = 0. \tag{5.11}$$

We write (10) as

$$\ddot{V}\Big|_{\psi\equiv 0} = (\dot{\theta}, [A-p + pG]\dot{\theta}) \tag{5.12}$$

where

$$A \equiv -\frac{d^2}{ds^2}, \quad G\dot{\theta} = \int_0^s \sin(s-\xi)\dot{\theta}(\xi)d\xi = (I-A)^{-1}\dot{\theta}\ . \tag{5.13}$$

The choice of $\dot{\theta}$ as the second eigenfunction of A satisfies

(2.11)and (5.11) and is therefore an admissible variation. Then

$$\ddot{V}\Big|_{\psi\equiv 0} = (\dot{\theta},[4-p-\tfrac{p}{3}]\dot{\theta}) \tag{5.14}$$

which is negative for all $p > 3$ and the theorem is proved.

An alternate method of proving this theorem would be to exhibit a function ψ satisfying (5.5) and (5.6) that rendered V negative.

To exploit the full power of this weak convergence method, we should show that there exist solutions for arbitrary values of the norm. Such a result will be obtained for the formulation given in the next section.

6. Existence of solutions with an arbitrary norm.

It is readily seen that the boundary value problem (2.17), (2.19), (2.20) is the Euler equation for the functional

$$U[v] = U_1[v] + U_2[v] \tag{6.1a}$$

where

$$U_1[v] = \frac{1}{2}\int_0^{\pi/n} {v_s}^2 ds \tag{6.1b}$$

$$U_2[v] = -\frac{1}{2}\int_0^{\pi/n} [v^3 + \frac{1}{4}v^4] ds \tag{6.1c}$$

subject to the constraints

$$\int_0^{\pi/n} v\,ds = 0, \tag{6.2}$$

$$\int_0^{\pi/n} v^2 ds = R(\text{const}), \tag{6.3}$$

$$v_s(0) = v_s(\pi/n). \tag{6.4}$$

Let H denote the Hilbert space consisting of those elements v of $W_2^{(1)}(0,\pi/n)$ that satisfy (6.2) and (6.4).

We shall prove the existence of a solution to the boundary value problem (2.17), (2.19), (2.20) by showing that the functional U has a smooth minimizer v* that satisfies (6.2), (6.3),(6.4). To this end we shall again use Theorem A. The existence theorem will be obtained in a series of lemmas.

Let E_R denote the set of elements of H satisfying (6.3).

<u>Lemma</u> 5: $U[v] \to \infty$ <u>as</u> $||v|| \to \infty$.

Proof. We first estimate U_2.

$$\int_0^{\pi/n} v^4 ds \le \max v^2 \int_0^{\pi/n} v^2 ds = R \max v^2 .$$

Since v is orthogonal to constants, there exists a point ξ in $(0,\pi/n)$ such that $v(\xi) = 0$. Hence using the Cauchy-Schwarz inequality, we have

$$v^2(s) = 2\int_\xi^s v\, v_s ds \le 2R^{1/2}\left(\int_0^{\pi/n} v_s{}^2 ds\right)^{1/2}.$$

Thus

$$\int_0^{\pi/n} v^4 ds \le 2R^{3/2}\left(\int_0^{\pi/n} v_s{}^2 ds\right)^{1/2}. \qquad (6.5)$$

Similarly,

$$\int_0^{\pi/n} v^3 ds = \int_0^{\pi/n} v v^2 ds \le \left(\int_0^{\pi/n} v^2 ds\right)^{1/2}\left(\int_0^{\pi/n} v^4\right)^{1/2} \le \sqrt{2}R^{5/4}\left(\int_0^{\pi/n} v_s^2 ds\right)^{1/2}. \qquad (6.6)$$

Now for v in E_R, $||v|| \to \infty$ only if $U_1[v] \to \infty$. By (6.5) and (6.6), $U_1[v]$ dominates $U_2[v]$ for $||v||$ sufficiently large and therefore the lemma is proved.

It is therefore sufficient to consider U defined on bounded subsets of E_R.

<u>Lemma</u> 6: <u>A bounded subset of</u> E_R <u>is weakly closed</u>.

Proof. Let $v_n \to v$, v_n E_R. We show that (6.3) is satisfied by v.

$$\left|\int_0^{\pi/n}(v^2 - v_n{}^2)ds\right| \le \max_{[0,\pi/n]}|(v+v_n)|\int_0^{\pi/n}|(v-v_n)|ds \qquad (6.8)$$

By Theorem C, (6.8) is less than

$$\text{const } ||v+v_n|| \int_0^{\pi/n} |(v-v_n)|ds . \tag{6.9}$$

Since $v + v_n$ is bounded, Theorem D implies that the expression in (6.9) approaches zero. Similarly condition (6.2) is met by the weak limit v. This completes the proof.

Lemma 7: U is weakly lower semi-continuous on bounded sets of E_R.

Proof: By Theorem B, U_1 is weakly lower semi-continuous. We now show that U_2 is weakly continuous. Let $v_n \overset{W}{\to} v$. Then using the same arguments as in Lemma 6, we obtain

$$|U_2(v)-U_2(v_n)| \le \frac{1}{2}\int_0^{\pi/n} |v^3-v_n^3|ds + \frac{1}{8}\int_0^{\pi/n} |v^4-v_n^4|ds \le \frac{1}{2}\max_{[0,\pi/n]}|v^2+v_n+v_n^2| \cdot \int_0^{\pi/n} |v-v_n|ds + \frac{1}{8}\max_{[0,\pi/n]} |v^2+v_n{}^2| \int_0^{\pi/n} |v^2-v_n^2|ds \to 0 \text{ as } n \to \infty .$$

This completes the proof.

Lemmas 5-7 and Theorem A now yield the following existence theorem.

Theorem 5: Let E_R denote the subset of $W_2^{(1)}(0,\pi/n)$ satisfying (6.2)-(6.4). Then there exists an element v* in E_R that furnishes U with an absolute minimum.

The regularity theory for v^* is somewhat simpler than that in Section 5 because the functional U is in a standard form for the calculus of variations. In direct analogy to Theorem 3 we have:

Theorem 6: $v^* \varepsilon C^2(0,\pi/n)$ and is a classical solution of (2.17), (2.19), (2.20).

Because R is an arbitrary positive number, no theorem corresponding to Theorem 4 is needed.

7. Numerical results

The Newton-Raphson method in function space (cf.[6]) proved more expeditious than the ordinary Newton-Raphson (shooting) method for obtaining the shapes of the deformed ring. The results of our numerical calculations are given in Fig. 3. For the range of p considered ($p \leq 70$) numerical computations indicated that the mode $n = 2$ gave the potential energy a minimum for fixed value of p.

8. Conclusion

Some of the proofs given in [7], upon which this lecture is based, have been modified for this presentation.

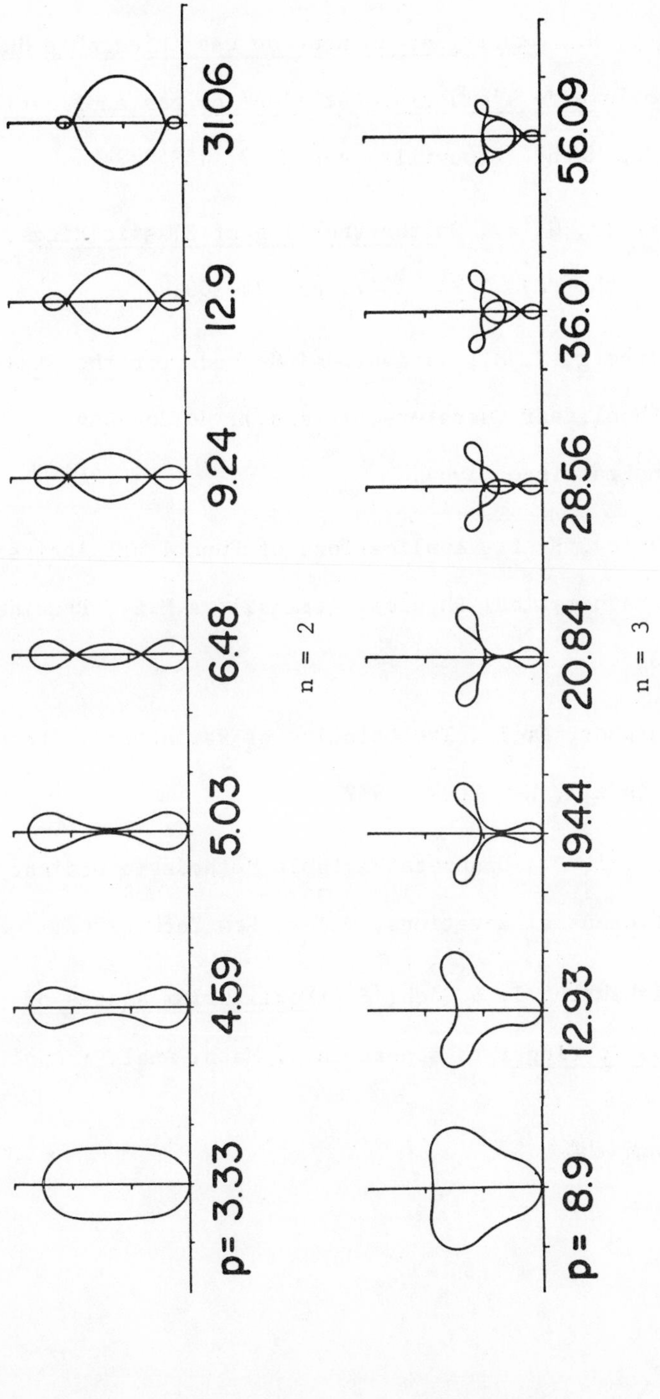
p= 3.33
4.59
5.03
6.48
9.24
12.9
31.06
n = 2
p= 8.9
12.93
19.44
20.84
28.56
36.01
56.09
n = 3

Figure 3

[1] Levy, M., Memoir sur un nouveau cas intégrable du probleme de l'elastique et l'une de ces applications, J. de Math. (Liouville) sec 3, 7, 1884

[2] Carrier, G. F., On the Buckling of Elastic Rings, J. Math. Phys., 26, 1947, pp. 94-103.

[3] Vainberg, M. M., Variational Methods for the Study of Nonlinear Operators, (trans.), Holden-Day, San Francisco, 1964.

[4] Sobolev, S. L., Applications of Functional Analysis in Mathematical Physics, (trans.), A.M.S., Providence, 1963.

[5] Akhiezer, N. I., The Calculus of Variations, (trans.), Blaisdell, New York, 1962.

[6] Henrici, P., Discrete Variable Methods in Ordinary Differential Equations, Wiley, New York, 1962.

[7] Tadjbakhsh, I. & Odeh, F., Equilibrium states of elastic rings, to appear in J. Math. Anal. & Appl.

9. Appendix: The case $n = 1$.

Stuart Antman

In this appendix we show by means of some elementary results of global differential geometry that there can be no deformed ring satisfying the boundary condition (2.4) and having but one axis of symmetry, i.e. the curvature k which must be periodic with period $2\pi/n$ cannot have least period 2π.

By examining (2.17) for arbitrary values of the parameters μ and β, we can show (by phase-plane methods, e.g.) that the periodic solutions of (2.17) have the form shown in Fig. 4, i.e., v is bounded in the strip $v_1 \leq v \leq v_2$, v is symmetric about its points of tangency to the lines $v = v_1$ and $v = v_2$, and v_s vanishes only on these lines.

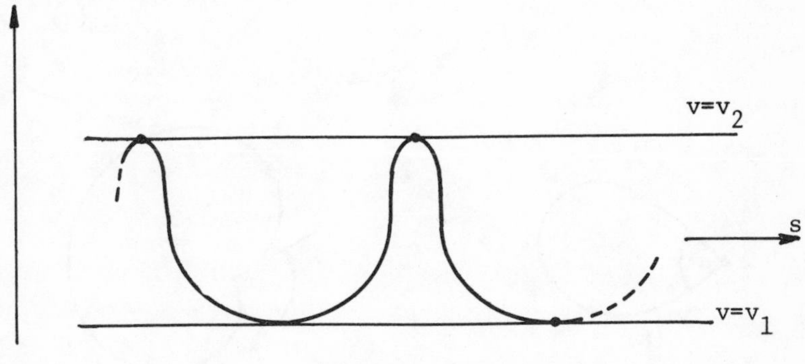

Figure 4

Thus we see that the least period of v is $2\pi(\frac{2}{N})$ where N is the number of extrema v has in an interval of length 2π. N must be at least 2 for any closed curve.

We now invoke the following theorem due to S. B. Jackson [8]:

Theorem E (Two Vertex Theorem): A smooth closed curve whose curvature has exactly two extrema consists of exactly two simple loops, one containing each extremum of the curvature. (Thus such a curve cannot be simple.)

Example of curves whose curvature has exactly two extrema are given in Fig. 5.

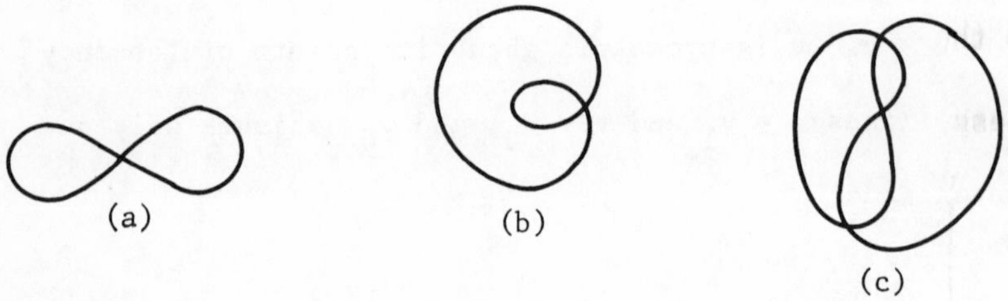

Figure 5

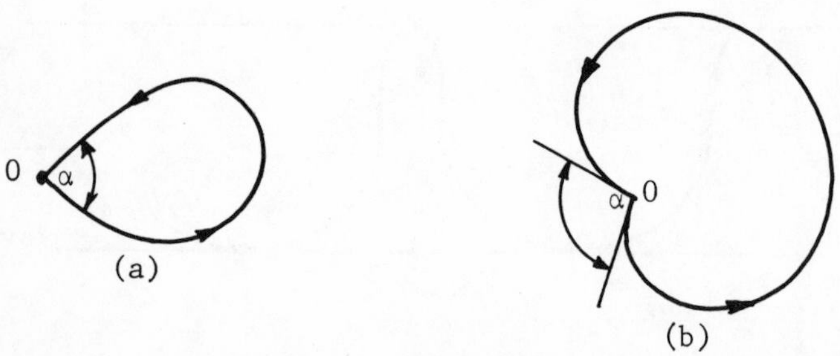

Figure 6

The change in the tangent angle in the loop of Fig. 6a is $\pi+\alpha$, that for the loops of Fig. 6b is $3\pi-\alpha$. An examination of the double point (Fig. 7) shows

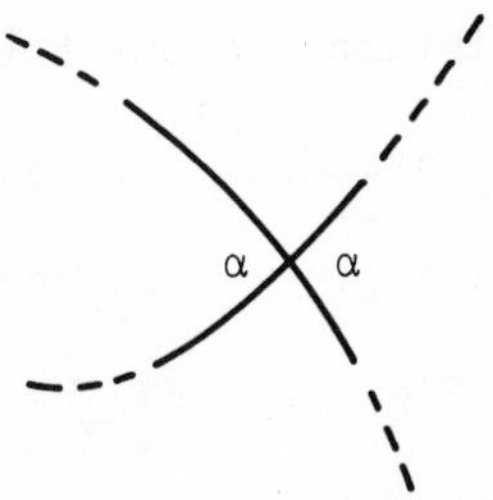

Figure 7

that the simple loops emanating from the double point must have the character of the loops of Fig. 9.3a or Fig. 9.3b. Thus the total angle change for a curve whose curvature has but two extrema consists of sums and differences of the numbers $\pm(\pi+\alpha)$ and $\pm(3\pi-\alpha)$. Since the total angle change is independent of α, it follows that the total angle change cannot equal $\pm 2\pi$ and hence the boundary condition (2.4) cannot be satisfied for $n = 1$.

This result is easier to prove if we consider only smooth simple closed curves, for then we can appeal to the Four Vertex Theorem (8): Any such curve has at least four points at which the curvature is an extremum. For the problem of a buckled ring, this is a physically reasonable restriction.

It is clear that if (2.4) is relaxed to the following restriction

$$\theta(s+2\pi) = \theta(s) + 2m\pi \quad , \qquad (9.1)$$

then the manifold of solutions to our boundary value problem is considerably extended. In particular, Fig. 5a corresponds to m = 0 and Fig. 5b correspond to m = 2. A physical realization of Fig. 5a can be obtained by twisting one end of a thin strip of paper through an angle of 2π and pasting it to the other end. (This is not a Möbius strip.) The resulting shape is shown in Fig. 8a.

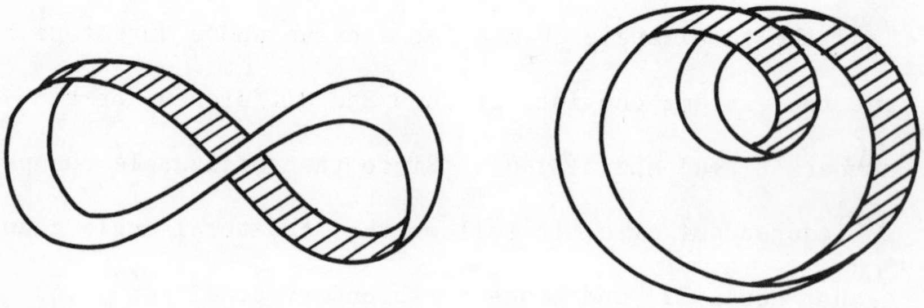

(a) (b)

Figure 8

It is interesting to observe that the strip of Fig. 8a can be twisted into that of Fig. 8b which may be regarded as the physical analog of Fig. 5b.

Other possible solutions to the boundary value problem (2.15), (9.1),(2.7) are

$$\theta = ms . \tag{9.2}$$

These are trivial solutions corresponding to an unloaded configuration consisting on m loops (just as Fig. 8b) has two loops). If we admit such solutions, the response diagram of p vs. some norm of k will not only contain the branches emanating from k = 1, but also branches emanating from k = 1/m. Moreover, the solutions (9.2) might be twisted into other shapes just as Fig. 8a could be twisted into Fig. 8b. The response diagram would have to account for such phenomena also. These considerations indicate the variety of solutions a nonlinear equation may give rise to.

Reference [9] was based upon this appendix.

[8] Jackson, S. B., Vertices of plane curves, Bull. A.M.S., 50, 1944, pp. 564-578.

[9] Antman, S., A note on a paper of Tadjbakhsh and Odeh, J. Math. Anal. & Appl., 21, 1968, 132-135.

V. A Bifurcation Problem in Superconductivity

by F. Odeh

1. Introduction and formulation of the boundary value problem.

The Ginzburg-Landau theory of superconductivity [1], [2] describes the behavior of a superconducting material in an external magnetic field in terms of a complex valued function $\phi(x,y,z)$, called the order parameter, and the vector potential $\underset{\sim}{a}(x,y,z)$ for the magnetic flux $\underset{\sim}{B} = \nabla x \underset{\sim}{a}$. The quantity $|\phi|^2$ measures the amount of superconductivity. In appropriate units the Ginzburg-Landau equations are

$$(ik^{-1}\nabla+\underset{\sim}{a}) \cdot (ik^{-1}\nabla+\underset{\sim}{a}) = \phi(1-|\phi|^2) \qquad (1.1)$$

$$-\nabla x\nabla x\underset{\sim}{a}=\mathrm{Re}[\phi^*(ik^{-1}\nabla+\underset{\sim}{a})\phi]=(i/2k)(\phi^*\nabla\phi-\phi\nabla\phi^*)+\underset{\sim}{a}|\phi|^2 \quad . \qquad (1.2)$$

Here k is a prescribed physical constant and the asterisk denotes the complex conjugate.

We assume that the conducting medium occupies the whole space and we seek solutions of (1.1) and (1.2) for which

$$\phi = \phi(x,y) \qquad (1.3a)$$

$$\underset{\sim}{B} = (0,0,B(x,y)) \qquad (1.3b)$$

$$|\phi(x+\xi_\nu,y+\eta_\nu)|^2 = |\phi(x,y)|^2 \quad , \quad \nu = 1,2 \qquad (1.3c)$$

$$B(x+\xi_\nu,y+\eta_\nu) = B(x,y) \quad , \quad \nu = 1,2 \; . \qquad (1.3d)$$

Here (ξ_1,η_1) and (ξ_2,η_2) are independent lattice vectors which characterize a "vortex" structure in the x,y-plane. The boundary value problem (1.1)-(1.3) corresponds to the Abrikosov mixed state.

We let Ω denote a primitive cell, i.e. a period parallelogram with vertices (x,y), $(x+\xi_1,y+\eta_1)$, $(x+\xi_1+\xi_2,y+\eta_1+\eta_2)$, $(x+\xi_2,y+\eta_2)$. If we set $\phi = |\phi|\exp[i\theta]$, then because ϕ is single valued, the change in phase $\Delta\theta$ in traversing the circuit $\partial\Omega$ is a multiple of 2π:

$$\Delta\theta \equiv -(i/2)\oint_{\partial\Omega} [(\phi^*\nabla\phi-\phi\nabla\phi^*)/|\phi|^2]\cdot d\underset{\sim}{s} = 2n\pi. \qquad (1.4)$$

Now the periodicity condition (1.3d) implies that

$$\oint_{\partial\Omega} [(\nabla x \nabla x \underset{\sim}{a})/|\phi|^2] \cdot d\underset{\sim}{s} = 0. \tag{1.5}$$

Operating on (1.2) with $\oint_{\partial\Omega} |\phi|^{-2} d\underset{\sim}{s} \cdot$ and using (1.4) and (1.5), we get

$$2n\pi = k\oint_{\partial\Omega} \underset{\sim}{a} \cdot d\underset{\sim}{s} = k\int_{\Omega} B\, dxdy = k\bar{B}(\xi_1\eta_2 - \eta_1\xi_2). \tag{1.6}$$

This is the flux quantization condition. $\bar{B}$ is the average of B over Ω.

We introduce the new variables: $(x',y') = (k\bar{B}/2\pi)^{1/2}(x,y), (\xi'_\nu,\eta'_\nu) = (k\bar{B}/2\pi)^{1/2}(\xi_\nu,\eta_\nu), \phi' = (\bar{B}/2\pi k)^{-1/2}\phi, \underset{\sim}{a}' = (\bar{B}/2\pi k)^{-1/2}\underset{\sim}{a}, \lambda = 2\pi k(\bar{B})^{-1}$. We now drop the primes. The equations (1.1), (1.2) become

$$[(i\nabla + \underset{\sim}{a}) \cdot (i\nabla + \underset{\sim}{a}) - \lambda]\phi = -\phi|\phi|^2 \tag{1.7}$$

$$- \nabla x \nabla x \underset{\sim}{a} = \frac{1}{2} k^{-2} \mathrm{Re}[\phi^*(i\nabla + \underset{\sim}{a})\phi]. \tag{1.8}$$

We make the (gauge) transformation

$$\underset{\sim}{a} = \underset{\sim}{A} + \underset{\sim}{A}_o \ . \tag{1.9}$$

Since $\underset{\sim}{a}$ is a vector potential, we may, for the sake of convenience, impose suitable restrictions on $\underset{\sim}{A}_o$ and $\underset{\sim}{A}$. The following set of subsidiary conditions for (1.7) and (1.8) embody these restrictions and the periodicity conditions (1.3c), (1.3d) in a manner consistent with the flux quantization condition (1.6).

$$\underset{\sim}{A}_o = \pi(y,-x,0). \tag{1.10}$$

$$\nabla \cdot \underset{\sim}{A} = 0 \tag{1.11}$$

$$\iint_\Omega \underset{\sim}{A}\, dxdy = 0 \tag{1.12}$$

$$\iint_\Omega (\nabla x \underset{\sim}{A})\, dxdy = 0 \tag{1.13}$$

$$\underset{\sim}{A}(x+\xi_\nu, y+\eta_\nu) = \underset{\sim}{A}(x,y) \quad , \quad \nu = 1,2 \tag{1.14}$$

$$\phi(x+\xi_\nu, y+\eta_\nu) = \exp[i\pi(x\eta_\nu - y\xi_\nu)]\phi(x,y) \ , \ \nu = 1,2 \ . \tag{1.15}$$

Thus our boundary value problem consists of equations (1.7)-(1.15). It has the trivial solution $\underset{\sim}{\phi} \equiv 0, \underset{\sim}{A} \equiv 0$ for arbitrary values of the parameter λ. In the next two sections we shall investigate nontrivial solutions.

2. <u>The bifurcation problem</u>.

In this section we examine the existence of the solutions of our equations in a neighborhood of the trivial solution. To this end we introduce a small parameter ε such that the trivial solution is characterized by $\varepsilon = 0$. We then convert the boundary value problem into a form to which we may apply a general implicit function theorem that will ensure the existence of solutions for small, but non-zero ε.

Using (1.9), (1.10), (1.11), we write (1.7) and (1.8) in the form:

$$-[(i\nabla+\mathbf{A}_0)\cdot(i\nabla+\mathbf{A}_0)-\lambda]\phi=\phi|\phi|^2+2\mathbf{A}\cdot(i\nabla+A_0)\phi+\mathbf{A}\cdot\mathbf{A}\phi \tag{2.1}$$

$$-\nabla x\nabla x\mathbf{A} = k^{-2}\mathrm{Re}[\phi^*(i\nabla+\mathbf{A}+\mathbf{A}_0)\phi] \quad . \tag{2.2}$$

We introduce a small parameter ε and set

$$\phi = \varepsilon^{1/2}\psi \quad , \qquad \boldsymbol{\alpha} = \varepsilon\mathbf{A} \quad . \tag{2.3}$$

Equations (2.1) and (2.2) become

$$(L-\lambda)\psi \equiv \{(i\nabla+\mathbf{A}_0)\cdot(i\nabla+\mathbf{A}_0)-\lambda\}\psi = -\varepsilon f \ , \tag{2.4}$$

$$M\boldsymbol{\alpha} \equiv -\nabla x\nabla x\boldsymbol{\alpha} = \mathbf{g} \quad , \tag{2.5}$$

where

$$f(\psi,\mathbf{a}) = \psi|\psi|^2 + 2\boldsymbol{\alpha}\cdot(i\nabla+\mathbf{A}_0)\psi + \varepsilon\boldsymbol{\alpha}\cdot\boldsymbol{\alpha}\psi, \tag{2.6}$$

$$\mathbf{g}(\psi,\mathbf{a}) + k^{-2}\mathrm{Re}[\psi^*(i\nabla+\mathbf{A}_0)\psi] + \varepsilon k^{-2}\boldsymbol{\alpha}|\psi|^2 \quad . \tag{2.7}$$

The conditions (1.11)-(1.15) remain the same for $\boldsymbol{\alpha}$ and ψ.

For $\varepsilon = 0$, it can be shown (Cf.[3] section 4) that (2.4), (1.15) has solutions for a discrete set of positive values of λ. The smallest eigenvalue λ_0 (corresponding to the greatest $\bar{B}$) is

$$\lambda_0 = 2\pi \ .$$

Associated with this eigenvalue are one or more eigenfunctions ψ_0. The multiplicity depends on the lattice symmetry. For the important cases of square and equilateral triangular lattices, it can be shown that there exists only one eigenfunction ψ_o(Cf. [4], [5]). We restrict ourselves to such cases.

For $\psi = \psi_o$ and $\varepsilon = 0$, (2.5), (1.11)-(1.14) can be solved for a unique vector function $\underset{\sim}{\alpha}_o$. Thus the triple $(\lambda_o, \psi_o, \underset{\sim}{\alpha}_o)$ is a solution of (2.4)-(2.7),(1.11)-(1.15) for $\varepsilon = 0$ and by (2.3) is just a trivial solution. For ε sufficiently small we now seek solutions to this system in the form $(\lambda, \psi, \underset{\sim}{\alpha}) = (\lambda_o + \varepsilon\mu(\varepsilon),\ \psi_o + \theta(\varepsilon),\ \underset{\sim}{\alpha}_o + \underset{\sim}{\beta}(\varepsilon))$, where θ is orthogonal to ψ_o.

If we project (2.4) on the one-dimensional subspace E_o generated by ψ_o we obtain

$$\begin{aligned} 0 &= ([L-\lambda_o-\varepsilon\mu(\varepsilon)][\psi_o+\theta] + \varepsilon f,\ \psi_o) \\ &= ([L-\lambda_o]\theta, \psi_o) - \varepsilon\mu(\varepsilon)(\psi_o, \psi_o) + \varepsilon(f, \psi_o). \qquad (2.8) \end{aligned}$$

Since $([L-\lambda_o]\theta, \psi_o) = (\theta, [L-\lambda_o]\psi_o) = (\theta, 0) = 0$, (2.8) implies that

$$\mu(\varepsilon) = (f, \psi_o)/||\psi_o||^2 \ . \qquad (2.9)$$

Equation (2.9) determines $\mu(0)$. We decompose f into projections onto E_o and its orthogonal complement $E_o^{\perp}$:

$$f = (f, \psi_o)\psi_o/||\psi_o||^2 + f^{\perp},\ f^{\perp} \in E_o^{\perp}. \qquad (2.10a)$$

By (2.9) this equals

$$f = \mu(\varepsilon)\psi_o + f^{\perp} \ . \qquad (2.10b)$$

The substitution of (2.10b) into (2.4) yields

$$[L-\lambda_o]\theta = \varepsilon[\mu\theta+f^{\perp}]. \tag{2.11}$$

If we let R_o denote the inverse of the restriction of $L-\lambda_o$ to $E_o^{\perp}$ (which certainly exists) then (2.11) may be written as

$$\theta = \varepsilon R_o[\mu(\varepsilon)\theta+f^{\perp}]. \tag{2.12}$$

(R_o is called the pseudo-inverse of $L-\lambda_o$.) The inversion of (2.5) yields

$$\underset{\sim}{\alpha} = M^{-1}\underset{\sim}{g} \quad . \tag{2.13}$$

These inverses involve the conditions (1.11)-(1.15). They may be written explicitly in terms of eigenfunction expansions. Our boundary value problem has been reduced to the system (2.9), (2.12), (2.13).

To discuss the properties of the operators R_o and M^{-1}, we introduce the Sobolev space $W_2^{(n)}(\Omega)$ consisting of scalar or vector distributions whose derivatives up to the nth order belong to $L_2(\Omega)$. $W_2^{(n)}(\Omega)$ is a Hilbert space with the natural scalar product and norm. (The natural norm squared is the integral over Ω of the sum of the squares of the absolute values of all derivatives up to order n.) Let $||u||_n$ denote the norm of u in $W_2^{(n)}(\Omega)$. Then we have

Lemma 1: The operators R_o and M^{-1} are compact operators in $W_2^{(n)}(\Omega)$ that satisfy the inequalities

$$||R_o h||_{n+2} \leq \text{const}||h||_n \tag{2.14}$$

$$||M^{-1}\underset{\sim}{g}||_{n+2} \leq \text{const}||\underset{\sim}{g}||_n \quad . \tag{2.15}$$

The proof of this lemma follows from standard estimates for uniquely invertible, uniformly elliptic operators. The details are omitted here.

Theorem 1: *There exists an* $\varepsilon_o > 0$ *such that for* $\varepsilon \leq \varepsilon_o$ *the system* (2.9), (2.12), (2.13) *has a unique nontrivial solution.*

Proof: Let $\underset{\sim}{v}$ denote the triple $(\mu(\varepsilon),\theta(\varepsilon),\underset{\sim}{\alpha}(\varepsilon))$, $\underset{\sim}{v} \in S \equiv R \times W_2^{(3)}(\Omega) \times W_2^{(3)}(\Omega)$, where R denotes the real numbers. Define the nonlinear mapping

$$N[\underset{\sim}{v}(\varepsilon),\varepsilon] \equiv \begin{pmatrix} N^1 \\ N^2 \\ \underset{\sim}{N}^3 \end{pmatrix} = \begin{pmatrix} \mu(\varepsilon)-(f,\psi_o)/||\psi_o||^2 \\ \theta(\varepsilon)-\varepsilon R_o[\mu(\varepsilon)\theta+f\ ] \\ \underset{\sim}{\alpha} - M^{-1}\underset{\sim}{g} \end{pmatrix} \tag{2.16}$$

N maps the Hilbert space S x R into S. Using the fact that

$$N[\underset{\sim}{v}(0),0] = 0, \quad \underset{\sim}{v}(0) = (\mu(0),0,\underset{\sim}{\beta}(0)) \ , \tag{2.17}$$

we wish to show that there exists a $\underset{\sim}{v}(\varepsilon)$ such that

$$N[\underset{\sim}{v}(\varepsilon),\varepsilon] = 0 \tag{2.18}$$

for sufficiently small ε.

To accomplish this, we invoke the following

Implicit Function Theorem: Let X, Y, Z be Banach spaces and let F(x,y) be a map of X x Y into Z. If

i) $F(x_o,y_o) = 0 \quad ,$

ii) $F(x,y)$ has a continuous (Frechet) derivative $F_y(x,y)$ in a neighborhood of (x_o,y_o),

iii) $[F_y(x_o,y_o)]^{-1}$ exists and is bounded, then there exists a number ε_o such that for $||x-x_o||\leq\varepsilon_o$, the equation $F(x,y) = 0$ has a unique continuous solution $y = f(x)$ with $y_o = f(x_o)$. (The proof of this theorem can be found in standard works on functional analysis.)

We identify the mapping N with F and the points ε and $\underset{\sim}{v}$ with x and y. We must verify that conditions (i)-(iii) of the implicit function theorem are met by N. Condition (i) is equivalent to (2.17). To demonstrate (ii), we first note that by Sobolev's embedding Theorem [6], the norm $||\cdot||_3$ dominates the corresponding maximum norm. Then by Lemma 1 and the fact that f and $\underset{\sim}{g}$ are smooth functions of their arguments in the maximum norm, it follows that N is bounded and continuously differentiable.

To check (iii) we exhibit the linear operator

$$N_{\underset{\sim}{v}}[\underset{\sim}{v}(0),0] = \begin{pmatrix} 1 & [-(f,\psi_o)_\theta/\|\psi_o\|^2] & [-(f,\psi_o)_{\underset{\sim}{\alpha}}/\|\psi_o\|^2] \\ 0 & I & 0 \\ 0 & [-(M^{-1}\underset{\sim}{g})_\theta] & I \end{pmatrix} \tag{2.19}$$

where I is the identity operator. From the form of (2.19),

it can be shown that $N_{\underset{\sim}{v}}[\underset{\sim}{v}(0),0]$ is invertible. This completes the proof.

Remark: For $\varepsilon = 0$, (2.4) has solutions for a discrete set of eigenvalues $\{\lambda_n\}$, $\lambda_n \to \infty$. Using the same method as that leading to Theorem 1, we could prove the existence of nontrivial solutions for values of λ near and slightly higher than each of these eigenvalues.

3. Existence of nontrivial solutions for $\lambda > \lambda_o$.

In this section we employ the direct methods of the calculus of variations to prove the existence of at least one nontrivial solution to the Ginzburg-Landau equations for the Abrikosov mixed state, equations (1.7)-(1.15), for all $\lambda > \lambda_o = 2\pi$. (Thus the Abrikosov mixed state occurs for all values of the average flux below its critical value.)

Equations (1.7) and (1.8) are the Euler equations for the free energy functional

$$E[\phi,\underset{\sim}{a}]=\iint_\Omega \{(i\nabla+\underset{\sim}{a})\phi\cdot(-i\underset{\sim}{\nabla}+\underset{\sim}{a})\phi^*+\frac{1}{2}|\phi|^4-\lambda|\phi|^2+2k^2|\nabla x\underset{\sim}{a}|^2\}dxdy \tag{3.1}$$

Let $\underset{\sim}{u}$ represent the pair $(\phi,\underset{\sim}{A})$ where $\underset{\sim}{A}$ is defined by (1.9). Then the admissible functions are the elements of the Hilbert space H consisting of those elements $\underset{\sim}{u}$ of $W_2^{(1)}(\Omega)$ that satisfy (1.11)-(1.15). We denote the norm of these functions by $||\cdot||$. We shall show that there exists a nontrivial element $\underset{\sim}{u}_0$ of H that renders E a minimum for $\lambda > \lambda_0$. Our procedure is similar to that used in Lecture IV.

<u>Lemma</u> 2: $E[\underset{\sim}{u}] \to \infty$ <u>as</u> $||\underset{\sim}{u}|| \to \infty$ <u>for all</u> $\underset{\sim}{u} \in H$. (λ <u>is held fixed</u>).

<u>Proof</u>: If $||\underset{\sim}{u}|| \to \infty$ then at least one of the L_2 norms of ϕ, $\underset{\sim}{A}$, $\nabla\phi$, $\nabla\underset{\sim}{A}$ must $\to \infty$. We denote such a norm by $||\cdot||_{L_2}$. We check the behavior of E in each case.

<u>Case 1</u>: $||\phi||_{L_2} \to \infty$. By the Cauchy-Schwarz inequality

$$||\phi^2||^2_{L_2} = \iint_\Omega |\phi|^4 \cdot 1\, dxdy \leq ||\phi^4||_{L_2} \cdot ||1||_{L_2}.$$

Therefore $||\frac{1}{2}|\phi|^4-\lambda|\phi|^2||_{L_2} \to \infty$ when $||\phi||_{L_2} \to \infty$. Since all the other terms of (3.1) are positive, it follows that $E \to \infty$ when $||\phi||_{L_2} \to \infty$. We may henceforth assume that $||\phi||_{L_2}$ is bounded.

<u>Case 2</u>: $||\nabla\underset{\sim}{A}||_{L_2} \to \infty$. From (1.10) and (1.13) it follows that $||\nabla x\underset{\sim}{a}||^2_{L_2} = ||\nabla x\underset{\sim}{A}||^2_{L_2} + 8k^2\pi^2[\xi_1\eta_2-\xi_2\eta_1]$. The use of Green's theorem, (1.11), and (1.14) gives the result that $||\nabla\underset{\sim}{A}||_{L_2} = ||\nabla x\underset{\sim}{A}||_{L_2}$. Since the other terms of E are

bounded below, it follows that $E \to \infty$ when $||\nabla \underset{\sim}{A}||_{L_2} \to \infty$. We now assume that $||\nabla \underset{\sim}{A}||_{L_2}$ is also bounded.

<u>Case 3</u>: (1.12) and (1.14) imply $||\underset{\sim}{A}||_{L_2}$ is bounded.

<u>Case 4</u>: $||\nabla\phi||_{L_2} \to \infty$. We can expand the first term of (3.1) into the form

$$\iint_\Omega \{|\nabla\phi|^2 - 2\,\mathrm{Im}(\phi^* \underset{\sim}{a}\cdot\nabla\phi) + |\phi \underset{\sim}{a}|^2\}dxdy \ .$$

The use of the Cauchy-Schwarz inequality then implies that $E \to \infty$ when $||\nabla\phi||_{L_2} \to \infty$. This completes the proof. Thus it is sufficient to consider E defined on bounded sets of H. Let B_r denote the ball $||u|| \leq r$ in the Hilbert space H. For fixed r we have

<u>Lemma</u> 3: E <u>is weakly lower semi-continuous on</u> B_r.

<u>Proof</u>: The terms in (3.1) not involving derivatives can be shown to be weakly continuous by the same methods used in Lecture IV. The remaining terms in (3.1) are, for fixed ϕ and $\underset{\sim}{A}$, convex in the first derivatives of $\underset{\sim}{u} = (\phi, \underset{\sim}{A})$. We can therefore invoke a theorem of Morrey [7] to the effect that the integrals of these terms must be weakly lower semi-continuous.

<u>Theorem</u> 2: <u>There exists a vector</u> $\underset{\sim}{u}_0$ <u>that renders</u> E <u>a</u>

<u>minimum on H</u>.

<u>Proof</u>: Since any ball B_r is weakly closed in a Hilbert space, it follows from Lemmas 2 and 3 that E is weakly lower semi-continuous on the bounded weakly closed set B_r in the Hilbert space H, and thus by Theorem A of Lecture IV it follows that E assumes its minimum on B_r.

$\underset{\sim}{u}_0$ is a weak or variational solution of the boundary value problem (1.7)-(1.15). We now prove

<u>Theorem</u> 3: <u>For</u> $\lambda > \lambda_0$, $\underset{\sim}{u}_0 \not\equiv 0$.

<u>Proof</u>: We calculate the second variation of E at $\underset{\sim}{u} = 0$ in the 'direction' $\dot{u} = (\dot{\phi}, \dot{\underset{\sim}{A}})$. With $L \equiv (i\nabla + \underset{\sim}{A}_0) \cdot (-i + \underset{\sim}{A}_0)$, the second variation is

$$\ddot{E} = (\dot{\phi}, [L-\lambda]\dot{\phi}) + 2k^2(\dot{\underset{\sim}{A}}, -\Delta\dot{\underset{\sim}{A}}) \qquad (3.2)$$

Choosing $\dot{\underset{\sim}{A}} = 0$ and $\dot{\phi}$ to be the eigenfunction of L corresponding to the lowest eigenvalue $\lambda = \lambda_0$, we find $\ddot{E} = -(\lambda-\lambda_0)||\dot{\phi}||^2$, which is negative for $\lambda > \lambda_0$. Hence $\underset{\sim}{u} = 0$ does not even furnish a local minimum to E for $\lambda > \lambda_0$ and must therefore be distinct from $\underset{\sim}{u}_0$.

Theorems 2 and 3 immediately yield

<u>Theorem</u> 4: <u>There exists at least one nontrivial variational solution of</u> (1.7)-(1.15) <u>for all</u> $\lambda > \lambda_0$.

Techniques for the regularity theory for boundary

value problems such as this will be discussed in subsequent lectures.

This lecture is based on [8].

BIBLIOGRAPHY

[1] Ginzburg, V. L. & Landau, L. D., J. Exptl. Theoret. Phys. (U.S.S.R.) 20, 1064 (1950.

[2] Abrikosov, A. A., J. Exptl. Theoret. Phys. (U.S.S.R.) 32, 1442, 1957; English transl. JETP 5, 1174, 1957.

[3] Brown, E., Phys. Rev. 133, A1038, 1964.

[4] Eilenberger, G., Zeit. Physik 180, 32, 1964.

[5] Kleiner, W. Roth, L. & Autler, S., Phys. Rev. 133, A1226, 1964.

[6] Dunford, N. & Schwartz, J. T., Linear Operators, Part II, Interscience Publishers, New York, chap. XIV, 1686, 1963.

[7] Morrey, C. B., Pacific J. Math., 2, 25, 1952.

[8] Odeh, F., Existence and Bifurcation Theorems for the Ginzburg-Landau Equations, to appear in J. Math. Phys.

A Bifurcation Theory for Nonlinear Elliptic Partial Differential Equations and Related Systems*

Melvyn S. Berger

1. Introduction.

In this and the following lecture bifurcation theory is understood to mean the study of the multiplicity of real solutions of the nonlinear operator equation $Au = \lambda Bu$ and the dependence of these solutions on the real parameter λ. We assume that this operator equation possesses a nondegenerate "linearized" equation as an approximation to the full nonlinear problem.

---

*This lecture is based in part on the author's papers [1].

We shall treat a large class of such problems, which includes many difficult equations from physics, by the following procedure. We distinguish the nonlinear invariants of a given problem and calculate them by an appropriate linearization. The full nonlinear equation is then regarded as a perturbed linear one and we show that the invariants, calculated for the linear equation, are in some sense "stable" under the nonlinear perturbation. Next we show that these invariants measure qualitative features connected with the existence and multiplicity of solutions of the nonlinear equation. Finally we combine this approach with a more classical one (e.g. the bifurcation theory of E. Schmidt [2]), and the combined methods of study enable us to make more explicit statements about the bifurcation question at hand.

We say that the equation $Au = \lambda Bu$ has a bifurcation point at $\lambda = \lambda_0$ if the equation has at least two distinct solutions $u_1(\lambda)$ and $u_0(\lambda)$ such that as $\lambda \to \lambda_0$ both $u_1(\lambda)$ and $u_0(\lambda)$ tend to $u_0(\lambda_0)$. (We generally choose $u_0(\lambda) \equiv 0$). Following the outline given in Lecture II, we divide our study into 3 parts:

(i) Existence theory, in which we determine the values of λ, say λ', at which changes in multiplicity of

$Au = \lambda Bu$ occur.

(ii) Multiplicity theory, in which we determine the number of solutions in the neighborhood of λ'.

(iii) Spectral theory, in which we calculate the behavior of solutions " of small norm" in the neighborhood of λ'.

In formulating any such general bifurcation theory adapted for boundary value problems arising from quasilinear elliptic partial differential equations or systems of ordinary differential equations, we immediately encounter difficulties of existence, regularity, degeneracy, and non-integrability. We shall define these terms later and show how these difficulties can be overcome.

We employ the techniques of functional analysis in our study. Functional analysis provides the frame-work of the modern approach to nonlinear partial differential equations because it illuminates the structure of a given problem and enables us to isolate features common to broad classes of problems. On the other hand, each example has its own peculiarities that require special treatment.

Our work is organized in the following manner: Sections 1-3 give a short survey of some previous studies on bifurcation theory, counterexamples to well-known conjectures in the subject, and some relations of the theory to other branches of mathematics and mathematical physics. Sections 4-9 discuss the formulation of elliptic boundary value problems in terms of operator equations in Hilbert space, the general formulation of bifurcation problems, and a perturbation method modeled on that of E. Schmidt [2] applicable to any bifurcation problem as defined by our study. A spectral theory is then carried out by means of the perturbation method.

Sections 10-15 treat specific classes of nonlinear operator equations, for each of which, a specific nonlinear invariant can be established. The first class of operator equations are those arising from problems in the calculus of variations, which possess a "symmetry" property. The appropriate invariant to those problems is expressed in terms of the Lyusternik-Schnirelmann category of topological spaces together with the Courant minimax principle for eigenvalues of linear operators. This class is discussed in Sections 10 and 11, together with applications to the von Kármán equations for the buckling of plates and periodic solutions of autonomous systems of ordinary differential equations. In Sections 12 and 13, this procedure is then modified to treat bifurcation arising from problems in the calculus of variations without symmetry and is applied to problems in the buckling of thin curved elastic structures. Finally in Sections 14 and 15 we focus attention on operators for which an appropriate nonlinear invariant is the degree of a mapping introduced by Schauder and Leray in 1934. The relationship of this invariant to problems in hydrodynamic instability is then discussed.

2. Historical Remarks.

In 1908, the third part of the thesis of E. Schmidt [2] was published. This paper, based on Schmidt's earlier work on linear integral equations, gave a general formulation of bifurcation theory for nonlinear integral equations. (Specific problems had arisen earlier; cf. Poincaré [2'].) All solutions of small norms for a large class of equations could be studied by Schmidt's procedure.

This procedure used the idea of orthogonality to divide the equation into two parts, one part in a finite dimensional subspace of dimension p, and the other part in its infinite dimensional orthogonal complement. The problem is reduced to a system of p equations in p unknowns (the so-called "branching equation") by showing that for sufficiently "small" solutions the equation in the space with codimension p is uniquely solvable once the branching equation has been solved. Thus in case $p = 0$, or 1, a relatively complete bifurcation theory for real solutions can be achieved. If $p > 1$, the associated bifurcation problem is called "degenerate" and the existence of real solutions cannot be guaranteed.

In 1930, A. Hammerstein [3], combined Schmidt's method with a variational approach to obtain a new insight into bifurcation theory. Hammerstein was able to apply his studies to second order elliptic boundary value problems. More recent studies made by Bartle [4], Cronin [5], and others are well reported in the review article of Vainberg and Tregonin [6].

Another problem of long standing bearing a remarkable (and intrinsic) relation to the bifurcation theory presented here is the determination of periodic solutions of nonlinear autonomous systems of ordinary differential equations. These equations arise naturally in the study of celestial mechanics. (Such systems arising from a variational principle are called Hamiltonian systems.)

One stage of development was initiated by Poincaré [7], the mathematical content of which is discussed in Lecture II. However for many specific problems "transcendental" methods of solution are necessary. Such methods were used in G. D. Birkhoff's study [7] of the restricted 3-body problem. One of the difficulties with such problems is called nonintegrability, i.e., the impossibility of introducing new variables by a "canonical transformation" such that the resulting system is integrable by quadrature. A second difficulty with such problems is the determination of the period of solutions. An approximation to the period w can often be made by linearization. We shall show that the period w can be related to the bifurcation parameter λ. A third difficulty with such problems is degeneracy, which occurs when determinants, (whose non-vanishing is essential to the Poincaré bifurcation theory), are identically zero. This phenomenon is, in turn, related to the difficulties of the Schmidt bifurcation theory with $p > 1$.

Another field in which the calculus of variations and bifurcation theory are related was initiated by Euler in his study of the buckling of columns. (See Lecture I).

Indeed the buckling of elastic structures provides excellent concrete examples of systems of elliptic partial differential equations and bifurcation theory throughout these lectures. In [8] Friedrichs and Stoker make a complete study of one aspect of this problem from the viewpoint of the calculus of variations.

The variational approach to bifurcation theory was studied intensively by Vainberg and Krasnosel'skii in a series of papers written throughout the 1950's, culminating in their books [9], [10]. The results obtained in their work are applicable to nonlinear integral equations and represent a new advance in the general theory.

There are however many bifurcation problems for which the methods of the calculus of variations do not apply. Important among these are the problems connected with hydrodynamic instability and turbulence. Such problems are generally expressed in terms of the Navier-Stokes equations for incompressible fluid flow at large Reynolds numbers. In such problems the Reynolds numbers is generally the bifurcation parameter λ. Models for such equations have been constructed by E. Hopf and Burgers. Nonlinear invariants for the study of such problems were investigated by Leray and Schauder in the 1930's and applied to specific problems since that time. We call special attention to the work of O. Ladyzhenskaya [11]. Recent progress of specific problems has been achieved by Velte [12] and Yudovich [13] using the invariant introduced by Leray and Schauder.

We briefly mention finite dimensional bifurcation theory, one aspect of which is the study of algebraic geometry over the real numbers. For plane curves, results in this direction were obtained by Harnack [14] 1876 and Hilbert in 1891 [15].

3. Examples.

The following examples illustrate the theory to be presented in these lectures.

Example 1. (A boundary value problem with no bifurcation from any eigenvalue of the linearized problem).

We consider the following system of equations:

$$\ddot{u} + \lambda[u + v(u^2 + v^2)] = 0 \tag{3.1a}$$

$$\ddot{v} + \lambda[v - u(u^2 + v^2)] = 0 \tag{3.1b}$$

$$u(0) = u(a) = v(0) = v(a) = 0 \tag{3.1c}$$

The linearized problem has a countable set of double eigenvalues λ_n. On the other hand, for any real-valued solution (u,v) of (3.1), we must have

$$\lambda\int_0^a (u^2 + v^2)^2 = 0.$$

This identity is obtained by multiplying (3.1a) by v, (3.1b) by u, integrating the resulting equations by parts over $[0,a]$, using (3.1c), and then subtracting the second integral from the first. However the identity implies $u \equiv v \equiv 0$, so there is no bifurcation at all. We also note that the system (3.1) is not variational, i.e. the vector

$[u + v(u^2 + v^2), v - u(u^2 + v^2)]$ is not the gradiant of some function $F(u,v)$. We shall show later in this lecture that if this system had been variational, bifurcation would necessarily take place from each eigenvalue λ_n, in spite of the degeneracy caused by eigenvalues of multiplicity 2.

It is interesting to note the effect of changing the boundary conditions slightly, say to

$$u(0) = u(a) = v(0) = v(a + \varepsilon^2) = 0 \qquad (3.1c')$$

and considering periodic solutions of (3.1a,b). Then, in general, bifurcation will take place from each eigenvalue of the linearized problem. This result can be proved by the methods of Lecture VII and a theory for this case will be presented in that lecture.

Example 2. (A theorem of Liapunov and some counter examples of C. L. Siegel).

A Hamiltonian system of ordinary differential equations has the form:

$$\frac{dx_i}{dt} = \frac{\partial H}{\partial y_i}$$

$$\frac{dy_i}{dt} = -\frac{\partial H}{\partial x_i}$$

where $H = H(x_1,\ldots,x_n,y_1,\ldots,y_n)$ does not depend on t. Let H and all its first partial derivatives vanish at $x_1 = 0,\ldots,y_n = 0$. We assume that H is holomorphic in a neighborhood of the origin.

Theorem. (Liapunov). Suppose a Hamiltonian system can be written

$$\dot{x} = Ax + f(x) \tag{3.2}$$

where A is a constant matrix, $f(x)$ is a power series beginning with quadratic terms, and x denotes the vector $(x_1,\dots,x_n,y_1,\dots,y_n)$. Suppose the matrix A has k pairs of purely imaginary eigenvalues $\pm i\lambda_j$, and that no ratio λ_i/λ_j is an integer $(i,j = 1,\dots,k)$. Then the system (3.2) has k distinct real one-parameter families of periodic solutions. Furthermore, if the period of the jth family is denoted by $\tau_j(R)$, then $\lim_{R \to 0} \tau_j(R) = 2\pi/\lambda_j$, the period of the linearized equation $\dot{x} = Ax$.

(Remark: A slightly sharper result is possible, namely, if for some fixed j, $\lambda_i/\lambda_j \neq$ integer, then the jth one-parameter family always exists.)

Two possible extensions of this result would entail

(i) elimination of the Hamiltonian restriction on (3.2).

(ii) elimination of the integral condition $\lambda_i/\lambda_j \neq$ integer for A.

In this regard we present two counterexamples of C.L. Siegel.

Example 2(a). (Liapunov's Theorem is not true, in general, for non-Hamiltonian systems.) Consider the system

$$\dot{x} = y - \frac{x}{2}(x^2 + y^2) \tag{3.3a}$$

$$y = -x - \frac{y}{2}(x^2 + y^2) \tag{3.3b}$$

The linearized equation has the periodic solution $(x,y) = (c \cos t, c \sin t)$. However (3.3) has no nontrivial periodic solution. Indeed, multiplying (3.3a) by x and adding to it (3.3b) times y, we obtain after introducing polar coordinates (r,θ)

$$r\dot{r} = -\frac{1}{2} r^4.$$

Thus

$$r^{-2} = t + b$$

where b is a constant of integration which we may choose to be 0. There is no periodic solution of (3.3) since $r \to 0$ as $t \to \infty$ and $r \to \infty$ as $t \to -b$.

Furthermore this system is not Hamiltonian as there is no function $H(x,y)$ which yields the system (3.3).

Example 2(b). (Liapunov's Theorem is not true, in general, without the integral condition $\lambda_i/\lambda_k \neq$ integer).

Let

$$H = \frac{1}{2}(x_1^2 + y_1^2) - (x_2^2 + y_2^2) + x_1 y_1 x_2 + \frac{1}{2}(x_1^2 - y_1^2)y^2$$

then the Hamiltonian equations are:

$$\begin{aligned} \dot{x}_1 &= y_1 + x_1x_2 - y_1y_2 \\ \dot{y}_1 &= -x_1 - y_1x_2 - x_1y_2 \\ \dot{x}_2 &= -2y_2 + \frac{1}{2}(x_1^2 - y_1^2) \\ \dot{y}_2 &= 2x_2 - x_1y_1 \end{aligned} \tag{3.4}$$

The eigenvalues of the linear terms are $\pm i$, $\pm 2i$. If $\lambda_1 = 2i, \lambda_2 = i$, $\lambda_2/\lambda_1 = 1/2$, so by Liapunov's theorem there is a family of periodic solutions such that $\lim_{R \to 0} \tau_1(R) = 2\pi i/\lambda_1 = \pi$. On the other hand if $\lambda_1 = i$, $\lambda_2 = 2i$ the integral condition is not satisfied and Siegel [16] shows that there is no periodic solution with minimal period approximately 2π. In this example it is important to notice that the level surface H = constant is not homeomorphic to a sphere.

We shall show as a consequence of our work how both extensions of Liapunov's theorem considered above can be obtained by additional hypothesis on the matrix A and the function f(x). One such general result has already been achieved by Moser [17].

Example 3. (The von Kármán equations for the buckling of thin elastic structures).

(a) The von Kármán equations for the buckling of clamped plates of general shape are:

$$\Delta^2 f = -[u,u] \qquad \text{in } \Omega, \tag{3.5a}$$

$$\Delta^2 u = \lambda[F,u] + [f,u] = 0 \qquad \text{in } \Omega, \tag{3.5b}$$

$$u = u_x = u_y = f = f_x = f_y = 0 \text{ on } \partial\Omega, \tag{3.5c}$$

where $[f,g] = f_{xx}g_{yy} + f_{yy}g_{xx} - 2f_{xy}g_{xy}$, Δ^2 denotes the biharmonic operator, Ω is a bounded domain in R^2, $F(x,y)$ is a smooth function. The physical meaning of the functions f, u and F was mentioned in Lecture III.

We consider (3.5a) as determining $f(x,y)$ uniquely once $u(x,y)$ is known. Thus (3.5b) is written symbolically as the following equation for u:

$$Au + Cu = \lambda Lu. \tag{3.6}$$

Here A and L are linear operators and C is a homogeneous "cubic" operator, i.e., $C(\sigma u) = \sigma^3 C(u)$, for any scalar σ. C is obtained by evaluating $[f,u]$ entirely in terms of u. We shall show later how to reformulate this equation as a variational problem. For the time being, we merely note: (i) solutions of the von Kármán equations have the symmetry property that if (f,u) is one solution than (f,-u) is another solution (physically the plate can buckle up or down); (ii) Numerical studies of these equations by Bauer and Reiss [18] indicate that bifurcation always occurs from the eigenvalues of an associated linearized problem. This example will be studied later.

(b) As as example of the buckling of a curved elastic structure we consider the von Kármán equations for the buckling of an axially compressed cylindrical panel with initial constant curvature measured by the constant K.

$$\Delta^2 f = -\frac{1}{2}[u,u] + Ku_{xx} \quad \text{in } \Omega \tag{3.7a}$$

$$\Delta^2 u = -\lambda u_{xx} + [f,u] - Kf_{xx} \quad \text{in } \Omega \tag{3.7b}$$

$$u = u_x = u_y = f = f_x = f_y = 0 \quad \text{on } \partial\Omega \tag{3.7c}$$

Here Ω is a rectangular domain in R^2.

If $K = 0$, these equations reduce to a special case of (3.5). Following the approach of example (a), if we solve the first von Kármán equation for f as a function of u and substitute in the second equation we obtain an equation of the form

$$A'u + Qu + C'u = \lambda L'u$$

where A' and L' are linear operators, C' is a homogeneous cubic operator and Q' is a homogeneous quadratic operator, i.e. $Q(\sigma u) = \sigma^2 Q(u)$, for any scalar σ. Such an equation no longer has the symmetry property (i) of Example (a), and numerical studies indicate a much more complex structure for the totality of solutions.

Nonetheless this equation also has a formulation in terms of the calculus of variations. This example will be taken up in Lecture VII.

Example 4. (A boundary value problem with multiple solutions but no bifurcation). This example shows that bifurcation theory is only a first approximation to a theory of nonlinear equations. More specifically, the solutions of a nonlinear equation may form isolated branches that do not emanate from the eigenvalues of the linearized problem. Consider

$$\ddot{u} + \lambda u^2 = 0 \tag{3.8a}$$

$$u(0) = u(1) = 0 \tag{3.8b}$$

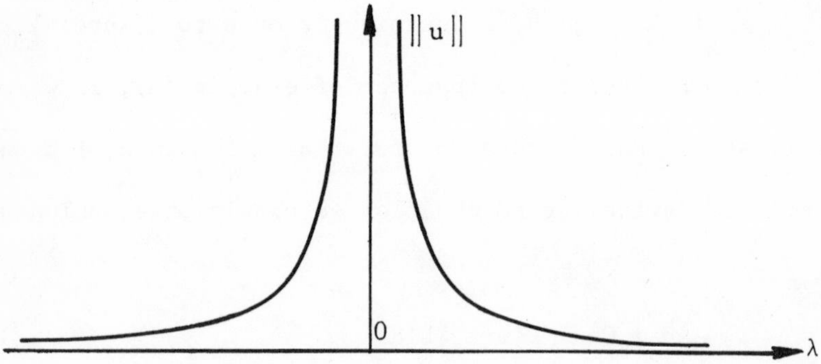

Figure 1.

All solutions must be either nonnegative or nonpositive as $\ddot{u}$ is necessarily nonnegative or nonpositive. Figure 1 indicates the solutions and the phenomenon of isolated solutions (cf. Lange-Emden equations of astrophysics).

Example 5. (Navier-Stokes equations for steady motions of an incompressible viscous fluid.) We consider the system of equations for $\underline{v}$ and p:

$$\Delta \underline{v} = R\{\text{grad } p + \underline{v}\cdot\text{grad } \underline{v} + \underline{f}(x)\} \quad \text{in } \Omega \tag{3.9a}$$

$$\text{div } \underline{v} = 0 \quad \text{in } \Omega \tag{3.9b}$$

$$\underline{v} = \underline{g}(x) \quad \text{on } \partial\Omega \tag{3.9c}$$

where $\underline{v}$ denotes the velocity field of the fluid, p, the pressure, R the Reynolds number (a given physical constant), $\underline{f}(x)$, some external given force, and Ω, a bounded domain in R^3 with boundary $\partial\Omega$. The components of $\underline{v}\cdot\text{grad } \underline{v}$ are $v_1 \frac{\partial v_k}{\partial x_1} + v_2 \frac{\partial v_k}{\partial x_2} + v_3 \frac{\partial v_k}{\partial x_3}$, $k = 1,2,3$. Leray [19] and Ladyzhenskaya [11] have shown the existence of a smooth solution for the system for all R, and that this solution is unique for small R. We shall consider the question of hydrodynamic instability, i.e. the existence of a second solution for sufficiently large values of R. It is important to note that in general no variational principle seems to be known for the Navier-Stokes equations due to energy dissipation inherent in the system.

Example 6. (Turbulence Models of J. Burgers and E. Hopf). In [20], E. Hopf studied the totality of real solutions of the following system as a function of the parameter μ:

$$\begin{aligned} u_t &= -v\cdot v - w\cdot w - u\cdot 1 + \mu\, u_{xx} \\ v_t &= v\cdot u + v\cdot a + w\cdot b + \mu\, v_{xx} \\ w_t &= w\cdot u - v\cdot b + w\cdot a + \mu\, w_{xx} \end{aligned} \tag{3.10}$$

Here the vector (u,v,w) is an analogue of the velocity field of a fluid, the functions a(x) and b(x) are given smooth even functions of period 2π, μ is the analogue of viscosity, and the convolution product $f \cdot g$ is defined by

$$f \cdot g = \frac{1}{2\pi} \int_{0}^{2\pi} f(x + y) g(y) dy.$$

Hopf found the real solutions of (3.10) to be even functions of x with period 2π and was able to show the following results. There are a countably infinite number of distinct numbers $\{\mu_n\}$ $\mu_1 > \mu_2 \ldots > \mu_n \ldots \to 0$, (which can be determined from an associated linear eigenvalue problem), such that bifurcation takes place from each μ_n. For $\mu \geq \mu_1$, every solution of (3.10) tends to $u = v = w = 0$, $t \to \infty$. For $\mu_1 > \mu > \mu_2$, "almost all" solutions of (3.10) tend to an explicit one-dimensional closed curve. In general for $\mu_n > \mu > \mu_{n+1}$, almost all solutions of (3.10) tend to an explicit n-dimensional torus-like manifold. Hopf also gave an analysis of the behavior of solutions as $\mu \to 0$.

This model gains interest by its close resemblance to the time-dependent Navier-Stokes equations for an incompressible fluid. We shall not discuss this example of bifurcation phenomena arising in parabolic nonlinear partial differential equations.

Example 7. (The Restricted 3-body problem). In 1914 G. D. Birkhoff completed the work of H. Poincaré on the problem of finding periodic solutions for a system describing the motion of a particle of mass zero moving subject to the attraction of two other bodies of positive mass. Birkhoff proved the existence of an infinite number of distinct periodic solutions for this problem by a fixed point theorem based on the area-preserving nature of a certain mapping. This latter property is, in turn, related to the fact that the system of differential equations involved is a variational system.

The following discussion is based on unpublished notes of J. Moser. Generally the masses of the two references bodies are taken as μ and $1-\mu$. For the limit case $\mu = 0$, we can put the system in the form

$$\begin{aligned} \frac{dw}{dT} &= i\{\frac{\nu}{C_o} \frac{|w-z|^2}{8} + \sqrt{C_o}\}w \\ \frac{dz}{dT} &= i\{\frac{\nu}{C_o} \frac{|w-z|^2}{8} - \sqrt{C_o}\}z \qquad (3.11) \\ |w|^2 &+ |z|^2 = 8 \end{aligned}$$

Here w and z are complex functions of the real argument r, and C_o is a constant > 0.

Two particular solutions of this problem are given by the circles $w = 0$, $|z|^2 = 8$, and $|w|^2 = 8$, $z = 0$.

We consider the periodic solutions of the system restricted to the neighborhood of each such circle. If we introduce the unknown period of tentative solutions into the equation by scaling the parameter T by $T = \lambda t$ and note that the variational problem associated with this system is invariant under the symmetry $(w,z) \to (e^{i\theta}w, e^{i\theta}z)$ for any θ, we have a system that falls into the class of those discussed in Section 10.

Example 8. (Analytic Perturbations of Rellich [21]). The following result on the perturbation of the spectrum of a self-adjoint operator by another self-adjoint operator depending on a small parameter is an important guide in our work.

Theorem. To an isolated eigenvalue λ_n of finite multiplicity p of the self-adjoint linear operator A there exists p eigenvalues $\lambda_i(\varepsilon)$ and eigenfunctions $u_i(\varepsilon)$, $(i = 1,\ldots,p)$ of the operator $A(\varepsilon) = A + B_\varepsilon$ depending analytically on ε (near $\varepsilon = 0$), provided B_ε is a self-adjoint linear operator depending analytically on ε.

We shall extent this result to nonlinear perturbations in Section 10. These perturbations will be chosen from a class whose linear analogue is a compact selfadjoint operator. This class consists of "variational operators with symmetry."

4. Nonlinear Operator Equations in Hilbert Space.

We outline the notation and concepts from functional analysis that we shall use in our subsequent work.

(a) Notation.

Let G denote a bounded domain in real Euclidean n-dimensional space R^n. Let the boundary of G be denoted ∂G and let $\bar{G} = G \cup \partial G$. All functions defined over G will be considered real valued. The following notation for differentiation is convenient: $D_j = \partial/\partial x_j$ $(j = 1,\ldots,n)$, and for any n-tuple of non-negative numbers $\alpha = (\alpha_1,\ldots,\alpha_n)$, the corresponding differential operator of order $|\alpha| = \alpha_1 + \alpha_2 + \ldots + \alpha_n$ is written $D^\alpha = D_1^{\alpha_1} D_2^{\alpha_2} \ldots D_n^{\alpha_n}$. Differentiation (where necessary) is to be taken in the generalized sense.

(b) Function spaces.

$C^m(\bar{G})$ is the collection of functions u(x) such that $D^\alpha u(x)$ for all $|\alpha| \leq m$ are defined, continuous and uniformly bounded on G. $C^m(\bar{G})$ is a Banach space with respect to the norm

$$||u||_{C^m(G)} = \sum_{|\alpha| \leq m} \sup_G |D^\alpha u(x)|$$

$L_p(G)$ (Lebesgue space) is the collection of

functions u(x) defined on G (up to a set of measure 0) such that $\int_G |u(x)|^p < \infty$. $L_p(G)$ is a Banach space with respect to the norm

$$\|u\|_{o,p} = [\int_G |u|^p]^{1/p}$$

$L_2(G)$ is a Hilbert space with respect to the inner product

$$(u,v)_{0,2} = \int_G u\ v.$$

$W_{m,p}(G)$ (Sobolev space) is the collection of functions u(x) in $L_p(G)$ such that $D^\alpha u$ lies in $L_p(G)$ for all $|\alpha| \leq m$. $W_{m,p}(G)$ is a Banach space with respect to the norm

$$\|u\|_{m,p} = [\sum_{|\alpha|\leq m} \|D^\alpha u\|^p_{o,p}]^{1/p}.$$

(In lectures IV, V, XII, $W_{m,p}(G)$ is denoted $W_p^{(m)}(G)$.)

$W_{m,2}(G)$ is a Hilbert space with respect to the inner product

$$(u,v)_{m,2} = \sum_{|\alpha|\leq m} (D^\alpha u, D^\alpha v)_{o,2}.$$

The relationship between these spaces is given by the Sobolev Imbedding Theorem. We say a Banach space X is imbedded in a Banach space Y ($X \subset Y$) if each element of X is an element of Y and the imbedding operator i: $X \to Y$ defined by $i(x) = x$, $x \in X$ is a continuous (1-1) mapping of **X** into

Y. If i is compact, (i.e., if i maps weakly convergent sequences in X into strongly convergent sequences in Y) we say that the imbedding i is compact.

Sobolev Imbedding Theorem. Let G be a bounded domain in R^N with a smooth boundary ∂G. Then

(i) $W_{m,p}(G) \subset W_{j,r}(G)$, for any number j satisfying the relation $1/p - (m-j)/N \leq 1/r \leq 1/p$. Thus there is a number $k_1 > 0$, independent of u, such that

$$||u||_{j,r} \leq k_1 ||u||_{m,p}$$

for any $u \in W_{m,p}(G)$. The imbedding is compact if

$$\frac{1}{p} - \frac{m-j}{N} < \frac{1}{r} \leq \frac{1}{p} .$$

(ii) $W_{m,p}(G) \subset C^j(\bar{G})$ for any number j satisfying the relation $1/p - (m-j)/N < 0$. Thus there is a number $k_2 > 0$, independent of u such that

$$||u||_j \leq k_2 ||u||_{m,p}$$

for any $u \in W_{m,p}(G)$. The imbedding is also compact. For the proof of this result we refer to Nirenberg [22] or Bers, John, Schechter [23].

(c) Some properties of Hilbert spaces.

It is important to distinguish carefully between the notions of weak and strong convergence in a Hilbert space H. We recall $x_n \to x$ strongly in H if $||x_n - x|| \to 0$ and $x_n \to x$ weakly in H if $(x_n, y) \to (x,y)$ for all $y \in H$. The following results on weak convergence are important:

(i) weak limits are unique.

(ii) if $y_n \to y$ weakly in H, $\{||y_n||\}$ are uniformly bounded.

(iii) any uniformly bounded set in H has a weakly convergent subsequence.

We also recall the following classical result:

Riesz Representation Theorem. Let $\ell(y)$ be a bounded linear functional defined on H. Then $\ell(y)$ has the unique representation $\ell(y) = (y,z)$ where z is a fixed element of H.

(d) Differential operators and their Hilbert space Representations.

A differential operator of order 2m, denoted $F(x,u,Du,\ldots,D^{2m}u)$ is a divergence expression of order m if it can be written:

$$F(x,u,Du,\ldots,D^{2m}u) = \sum_{|\alpha| \le m} D^\alpha (A_\alpha(x,u,\ldots,D^m u)).$$

An associated (nonlinear) Dirichlet form of such a divergence expression is given by the formula:

$$a(u,v) = \sum_{|\alpha| \le m} \int_G (-1)^{|\alpha|} A_\alpha(x,u,\ldots,D^m u) D^\alpha v$$

with $u,v \in W_{m,2}(G)$.

If $A_\alpha(x,u,\ldots,D^m u) \in L_2(G)$ for $|\alpha| \leq m$, $a(u,v)$ defines a continuous linear functional on $W_{m,2}(G)$ in v. Thus by the Riesz representation theorem, we may write $a(u,v) = (v,Au)_{m,2}$ where A is some operator (not necessarily linear) mapping $W_{m,2}(G)$ into itself.

It is also possible to incorporate boundary conditions associated with the differential operator $F(x,u,\ldots,D^{2m}u)$ into the abstract Hilbert space operator A. The simplest case arises from Dirichlet boundary conditions of the form

$$D^\alpha u = 0 \text{ on } \partial G, |\alpha| \leq m-1.$$

In such a case we consider the space $C_o^\infty(G)$, of all infinitely differentiable functions vanishing outside of a compact subset of G. Clearly $C_o^\infty(G)$ is included in $W_{m,2}(G)$, and if we complete $C_o^\infty(G)$ in $W_{m,2}(G)$, we obtain the closed subspace $\dot{W}_{m,2}(G)$. Then as in the last paragraph A can be defined as an operator from the Hilbert space $\dot{W}_{m,2}(G)$ into itself, by restricting u to $\dot{W}_{m,2}(G)$.

It will be important to deduce abstract properties of A from properties of the differential operator $F(x,u,\ldots,D^{2m}u)$, and its divergence representation involving $A_\alpha(x,n,\ldots,D^m u)$. For example, under what circumstances is

A continuous? bounded? compact? self-adjoint? For the present we merely note that from this point of view the iterated Laplacean $(-1)^m\Delta^m$ together with zero Dirichlet boundary conditions generates a bounded, linear, positive definite, self-adjoint operator A in $\dot{W}_{m,2}(G)$, and in $\dot{W}_{m+1,2}(G)$ another such operator A' which is also compact.

(e) Elliptic boundary value problems and associated operator equations.

We now give one procedure to reformulate a large class of elliptic boundary value problems as abstract operator equations in a Hilbert space H. It is the aim of our work to demonstrate the advantages of such a procedure.

Suppose we are given a boundary value problem of the form

$$\sum_{|\alpha|\leq m} D^{\alpha}(A_{\alpha}(x,u,\ldots,D^m u)) = 0 \qquad \text{in } G \qquad (4.1)$$

$$D^{\alpha}u = 0 \qquad |\alpha| \leq m-1 \qquad \text{on } \partial G \qquad (4.2)$$

A classical solution of this equation is a function $u \in C^{2m}(\Omega) \cap C^{m-1}(\bar{\Omega})$ satisfying (4.1) and (4.2) pointwise.

A generalized solution of the equation is a function $u(x) \in \dot{W}_{n,2}(G)$ satisfying the integral identity

$$\sum_{|\alpha|\leq m} \int_G (-1)^{|\alpha|} A_\alpha(x,u,\ldots,D^m u) D^\alpha v = 0 \qquad (4.3)$$

for all functions $v \in \dot{W}_{n,2}(G)$. (We assume throughout that $A_\alpha(x,u,\ldots,D^m u) \in L_2(G)$ for $u \in \dot{W}_{m,2}(G)$).

Our discussion in (d) shows that that the equation (4.3) is equivalent to the operator identity $(Au,v) = 0$ for any $v \in \dot{W}_{m,2}(G)$ i.e. $Au = 0$.

This defines an operator equation in a Hilbert space H associated with the boundary value problem (4.1), (4.2).

The next result gives a partial answer to the question of the relationship between the classical solution of (4.1), (4.2) and a solution of the operator equation $Au = 0$. To this end, we focus attention on elliptic boundary value problems with linear leading terms that can be written in divergence form. It is this class of problems that arise in our bifurcation theory. A differential operator of the form $\sum_{|\alpha|\leq m} D^\alpha A_\alpha(x,u,\ldots,D^m u)$ has linear principal part if all the terms $A_\alpha(x,u,\ldots,D^m u)$ with $|\alpha| = m$ are linear in $D^\alpha u$. We then consider the homogenous characteristic form associated with this operator, namely the polynomial

$$a(x,\xi) = \sum_{|\alpha|=2m} a_\alpha(x)\xi_1^{\alpha_1}\xi_2^{\alpha_2} \cdots \xi_2^{\alpha_n}$$

Such a differential equation is uniformly elliptic if there is a constant $c_o > 0$ such that

$$a(x,\xi) \geq c_o(\xi_1^2 + \cdots + \xi_n^2)^m$$

for every $x \in G$ and $\xi \in R^n$.

Regularity Theorem. Suppose the system (4.1), (4.2) is uniformly elliptic with linear leading part and that the operators $A_\alpha(x,u,\ldots,D^m u)\varepsilon L_2(G)$ for $u \in \dot{W}_{m,2}(G)$. Then any solution of the operator equation $Au = 0$ is a classical solution of (4.1), (4.2) in G and on all smooth portions of ∂G. Conversely, any classical solution of the equations (4.1), (4.2) can be considered a solution of the operator equation $Au = 0$. The proof of this result is based on the L_p regularity theory for linear elliptic boundary value problems of Agmon [24], and Agmon, Douglis and Nirenberg [25]. We refer to the paper [26] where the method of proof is discussed in detail.

The following example, although elementary, is illustrative of the approach described here. More difficult examples are discussed in Sections 11, 13, 15.

Example. We consider the problem

$$-\Delta u + f(u) = 0 \qquad \text{in } G, \tag{4.4}$$

$$u = 0 \qquad \text{on } \partial G, \tag{4.5}$$

where G is a bounded domain on R^n, and Δ denotes the Laplace operator.

Clearly this equation belongs to the class of problems discussed in this section. A generalized solution of this system satisfies the equation

$$\sum_{|\alpha|=1} \int_G D^\alpha u D^\alpha v + \int_G f(u)v = 0 \text{ for every } v \in \dot{W}_{1,2}(G) \tag{4.6}$$

The associated operator equation for the boundary value problem is

$$L_1 u + N_1 u = 0 \tag{4.7}$$

where

$$(L_1 u, v) = \sum_{|\alpha|=1} \int_G D^\alpha u D^\alpha v \quad \text{and} \quad (N_1 u, v) = \int_G f(u) v \tag{4.8}$$

provided $f(u) \in L_2(G)$ for $u \in \dot{W}_{1,2}(G)$. This last provision puts a growth restriction on the function f(u), and will be guaranteed if, for example,

$$|f(u)| \leq k\{1 + u^{n+2/n-2}\} \qquad n > 2$$

$$\leq k\, e^{u^2} \qquad n = 2$$

$$\text{unrestricted} \qquad n = 1$$

The theory of positive nonunique solutions of this system

can be discussed [1] by the methods outlined here; another quite different approach will be given in Lecture VIII.

5. Formulation of Bifurcation Problems.

We now discuss bifurcation theory in terms of operator equations in a real Hilbert space. We make the following customary assumptions.

(i) A bifurcation problem has a solution u_o for all values of a parameter λ, (which, without loss of generality, we take as identically zero).

(ii) The bifurcation problem has a linearization of the form $L_1u = \lambda L_2u$, where L_1 and L_2 are bounded linear operators in H.

(iii) The full bifurcation problem can be written in the form $L_1u + N_1u = \lambda(L_2u + N_2u)$ where N_1 and N_2 are strictly nonlinear operators in the sense that $N_i0 = 0$ and

$$\| N_iu\| \leq k\| u\|^{\sigma_i} + 0(\| u\|^{\sigma_i}) \quad \sigma_i > 1 \qquad (i = 1,2)$$

for sufficiently small $\|u\|$. (In most cases either N_1 or N_2 is identically zero.)

In addition to the questions of Existence, Multiplicity, and Spectral theory posed in the introduction we now consider the following problems:

(i) Validity of linearization. What facts concerning the full nonlinear problem are decidable on the basis of a complete knowledge of the linearized problem?

(ii) Nonlinear invariants. What quantities related to the nonlinear operators N_1 and N_2 are necessary to determine the structure of the solutions of the nonlinear problem for small norm?

A partial answer to Question (i) is given by

Theorem 5.1. The points of bifurcation of the nonlinear equation $L_1u + N_1u = \lambda(L_2u + N_2u)$ can occur only at points of the spectrum of the linearized equation $L_1u = \lambda L_2u$.

Proof. Suppose λ_o is not in the spectrum of the linear equation $L_1u = \lambda L_2u$. Then we shall show that for $|\lambda-\lambda_o|$ and $\|u\|$ sufficiently small, the nonlinear equation has only the trivial solution $u \equiv 0$.

Indeed, since

$$L_1u - \lambda_oL_2u = L_1u + N_1u - \lambda(L_2u + N_2u) - N_1u + \lambda N_2u + (\lambda-\lambda_o)L_2u,$$

we obtain

$$\|L_1u + N_1u - \lambda(L_2u + N_2u)\| \geq \|L_1u - \lambda_oL_2u\| - \|N_1u\| - |\lambda|\,\|N_2u\| - |\lambda-\lambda_o|\,\|L_2u\|.$$

Since $L_1u - \lambda_oL_2u$ is continuously invertible,

$$\|L_1u - \lambda_oL_2\| \geq k\|u\|$$

(for some $k > 0$, independent of u).

Also $\|N_1u\| \leq k_1\|u\|^{\sigma_1}$, $\|N_2u\| \leq k_2\|u\|^{\sigma_2}$. Furthermore L_2 is a bounded linear operator so that

$$|\lambda-\lambda_0|\,\|L_2u\| \leq k_3|\lambda-\lambda_0|\ \|u\|.$$

Thus, by choosing $|\lambda-\lambda_0|$ and $\|u\|$ sufficiently small, we have

$$\|L_1u + N_1u - \lambda(L_2u + N_2u)\| \geq k_4\|u\|$$

for some positive k_4 independent of u. Thus the full nonlinear equation can only have the solution $u \equiv 0$, if $\|u\|$ is sufficiently small.

This result, however, leaves unanswered the question as to the actual existence of bifurcation points. By Example 1 of Section 3 we know that this question cannot, in general, be answered by information derived strictly from the linearized problem.

We shall discuss question (ii) in the sequel, where we shall show that if the nonlinearity can be expanded in a power series of homogeneous nonlinear operators of degree p, $H_p(u)$, a significant role is played by the parity of the least integer p_0 such that $H_{p_0}(u) \not\equiv 0$.

6. <u>The spectrum of the linearized problem</u> $L_1u = \lambda L_2u$.

It is necessary to impose conditions on the spectrum of the linear operators L_1 and L_2 to ensure the reality and discreteness of the spectrum of the equation $L_1u = \lambda L_2u$.

We shall generally assume L_2 is a compact operator and that $\lambda = 0$ is not an eigenvalue of the equation $L_1u = \lambda L_2u$.

The following classes of operators are relevant for our work:

(a) L_1, L_2 are self-adjoint operators in a Hilbert space H. For this class of operators we have the following result.

Theorem 6.1. The spectrum of the equation $L_1u = \lambda L_2u$ consists of eigenvalues $\{\lambda_n\}$ forming a sequence of discrete real numbers tending possibly to $+\infty$, or $-\infty$ or both. The multiplicity of each λ_n is finite.

(b) L_1 and L_2 are Operators mapping the cone of positive functions into itself. This class of operators is related to systems of elliptic equations which possess a maximum principle, but which are not necessarily self-adjoint.

For this class of operators we have the following result:

Theorem 6.2. The "smallest" eigenvalue of $L_1u = \lambda L_2u$ is real and of multiplicity 1.

(c) L_1 and L_2 are Operators with Oscillatory Kernels (in the sense of Krein). A matrix A is oscillatory if all the minors of A are non-negative and if some iterate of A, A^q has all strictly positive minors. A kernel K(x,y) ($a \leq x, y \leq b$) is an oscillatory kernel if for arbitrary points

$x_1,\ldots,x_n \varepsilon [a,b]$ (at least one of which is in (a,b)) the matrix $A(x_1,\ldots,x_n) = (K(x_i,x_j))$ is oscillatory. For boundary value problems associated with such kernels that following result holds:

Theorem 6.3. All the eigenvalues of an operator with a continuous symmetric oscillating kernel are positive and of multiplicity one.

7. A Perturbation Method.

We study the solutions of small norm of the operator equation

$$(L_1 + N_1)u = \lambda(L_2 + N_2)u \tag{7.1}$$

in the neighborhood of a real isolated eigenvalue λ_n of finite multiplicity of the linearized problem

$$L_1 u = \lambda L_2 u \tag{7.2}$$

Throughout this section we impose mild restrictions on the operators N_1 and N_2. This work is intended to be used concurrently with some other method which exploits the particular properties of a given system. This approach enables us to prove new results. Our analysis is based on the work of Krasnosel'skii [27].

We set $\lambda = 1/\mu$ and we suppose $\lambda_n = 1/\mu_n$ is a real eigenvalue of multiplicity p of the linearized equation $L_1 u = \lambda L_2 u$ with $(1 \leq p < \infty)$. We choose p linearly independent eigenfunctions associated with $\lambda_n\{u_i\}$ $(i = 1,\ldots,p)$ and we assume

$(u_i, L_1 u_j) = \delta_{ij}$ (where δ_{ij} denotes the Kronecker delta).

We also assume that L_1 is a self adjoint and positive definite operator in a Hilbert space H. Let the subspace spanned by $(u_1,\ldots,u_p)$ be denoted $[u_1,\ldots,u_p]$ and its orthogonal complement in H be denoted $[u_1,\ldots,u_p]^{\perp}$. Let the mapping $P: H \to [u_1,\ldots,u_p]^{\perp}$ denote the projector of H onto $[u_1,\ldots,u_p]^{\perp}$.

Thus the totality of solutions of the equation $\mu(L_1 u + N_1 u) - L_2 u - N_2 u = 0$ can be obtained by solving the $(p + 1)$ equations:

$$
\begin{aligned}
&P(\mu(L_1 u + N_1 u) - L_2 u - N_2 u) = 0 \\
&(\mu(L_1 u + N_1 u) - L_2 u - N_2 u, u_i) = 0 \quad (i = 1,\ldots,p)
\end{aligned}
\tag{7.3}
$$

Furthermore any real solution u of system (7.3) can be written

$$u = y + \sum_{i=1}^{p} \varepsilon_i u_i$$

where $y \varepsilon [u_1,\ldots,u_p]^{\perp}$ and ε_i are real numbers to be determined.

Substituting this expression into (7.3), we obtain the following equations for y and ε_i

$$
\begin{aligned}
&y = (\mu L_1 - L_2)^{-1} P[-\mu N_1(w) + N_2(w)] \\
&\varepsilon_i(\mu - \mu_n) = (N_2(w) - \mu N_1(w), u_i)
\end{aligned}
\tag{7.4}
$$

where $w = y + \sum_{i=1}^{p} \varepsilon_i u_i$.

To proceed further we must assume that we are only concerned with solutions of small norm, i.e. we assume that $\|y\|$ and all the numbers ε_i are small compared to 1. Furthermore, for simplicity, we suppose that either (a)$N_1 \equiv 0$ or (b)$N_2 \equiv 0$, as these are the cases that will arise in our applications.

The basic idea of our method is to reduce the system (7.4) to the finite dimensional study of p equations (not necessarily linear) in p unknowns by showing that the first equation in (7.4) is uniquely solvable if ε_i are known. To this end we assume that the nonlinear operators N_1 and N_2 satisfy the following properties for $\|u\|$, $\|v\|$ sufficiently small:

$$N_i u = P_i u + R_i u \qquad (i = 1,2)$$

where P_i is a homogeneous operator of degree $p_i > 1$ (I.e., $P_i(\sigma u) = \sigma^{p_i} P_i(u)$, $p_i > 1$) and where

$$\|P_i u - P_i v\| \leq k_o \{\|u\|^{p_i - 1} + \|v\|^{p_i - 1}\} \|u-v\|$$

$$\|R_i u - R_i v\| \leq k_i \{\|u\|^{p_i} + \|v\|^{p_i}\} \|u-v\|$$

with k_o and k_1 constants independent of u and v.

Lemma 7.1. *Under the hypotheses stated above, if either* (a)$N_1(u) \equiv 0$ *or* (b)$N_2(u) \equiv 0$, *the first equation of* (7.4) *is uniquely solvable for y in terms of* $(\varepsilon_1, \ldots, \varepsilon_p)$.

<u>Furthermore the following estimate holds for the solution</u>

$y = y(\varepsilon_1,\ldots,\varepsilon_p)$:

$\|y\| \leq k_3|\varepsilon|^{p_i}$ <u>where</u> $|\varepsilon| = |\varepsilon|_1 + \cdots |\varepsilon_p|$ <u>and</u> $k_3 > 0$ <u>is</u> <u>independent of</u> $(\varepsilon_1,\ldots,\varepsilon_p)$.

<u>Proof</u>: It is sufficient to consider case (a), as case (b) is completely analogous. Furthermore it is sufficient to show that the mapping defined by

$$T_\varepsilon y = (\mu L_1 - L_2)^{-1} P(N_2(y + \sum_{i=1}^{p} \varepsilon_i u_i))$$

is a contraction mapping for $|\varepsilon| = |\varepsilon_1| + |\varepsilon_2| + \cdots |\varepsilon_p|$ sufficiently small and $\varepsilon = (\varepsilon_1,\ldots,\varepsilon_p)$ given with $\|y\| \leq |\varepsilon|$. To this end, we estimate as follows: let y and $\bar{y} \in H$ with $\|y\|, \|\bar{y}\| \leq |\varepsilon|$ and set $u = y + \sum_{i=1}^{p} \varepsilon_i u_i$, $\bar{u} = \bar{y} + \sum_{i=1}^{p} \varepsilon_i u_i$.

Then

$$\|T_\varepsilon y - T_\varepsilon \bar{y}\| \leq \|(\mu L_1 - L_2)\| \, \|N_2(u) - N_2(\bar{u})\|$$

$$\leq kk_1\{\|y\|^{p_i - 1} + \|\bar{y}\|^{p_i - 1} + |\varepsilon|^{p_i - 1}\}\|y - \bar{y}\|$$

$$\leq 3kk_1|\varepsilon|^{p_i - 1}\|y - \bar{y}\|$$

Thus for $|\varepsilon|$ sufficiently small it is possible to find a positive $\alpha < 1$ such that $\|T_\varepsilon y - T_\varepsilon \bar{y}\| \leq \alpha\|y - \bar{y}\|$. Thus the solution of $T_\varepsilon y = y$ exists and is unique, i.e. if $|\varepsilon|$ is sufficiently small, y is uniquely determined by $\varepsilon = (\varepsilon_1,\ldots,\varepsilon_p)$. Moreover, the solution of $T_\varepsilon y = y$ with

$\|y\| \leq |\varepsilon|$ satisfies

$$\begin{aligned}\|y\| &= T_\varepsilon y - T_o y + T_o y \\ &\leq \|T_\varepsilon y - T_o y\| + \|T_o y\| \\ &\leq k\{\|N_2(u) - N_2(y)\| + \|N_2 y\|\} \\ &\leq 2kk_1|\varepsilon|^{p_i}\end{aligned}$$

8. The case $p = 1$ (Bifurcation from a simple eigenvalue).

Here we give a rather complete analysis of the existence, multiplicity and spectral theory for the operator equations (7.1) under the hypotheses of Section 7.

Existence and Multiplicity Theorem 8.1. Let (7.1) satisfy the hypotheses of Section 7 and assume $(P_i u_1, u_1) \neq 0, (i=1,2)$ where u_1 is the normalized eigenfunction of the equation $L_1 u = \lambda_n L_2 u$. Then in either case (a) or case (b), (7.1) has a unique one parameter family of solutions of small norm with eigenvalue λ near λ_n.

Proof of Theorem: It is sufficient to consider the case (a), as (b) is completely analogous. By Lemma 7.1, we need only consider the second equation of the pair (7.4), provided we restrict $|\varepsilon|$ to be sufficiently small. Thus we need only consider real solutions ε for the equation

$$\varepsilon(\mu - \mu_n) = (P_2(w) + R_2(w), u_1) \tag{8.1}$$

where $w = y + \varepsilon u_1$.

Next we show that for sufficiently small ε, the solutions of

(8.1) can be completely described by studying the solutions of the simpler equation

$$\varepsilon(\mu-\mu_n) = (P_2(\varepsilon\mu_1),\ u_1) \tag{8.2}$$

To this end we note the following inequalities

$$|(P_2(w) - P_2(\varepsilon u_1),\ u_1)| \leq k_0|\varepsilon|^{p_2+1} \tag{8.3}$$

$$|(R_2(w),\ u_1)| \leq O(|\varepsilon|^{p_2}) \tag{8.4}$$

Thus for $|\varepsilon|$ sufficiently small, (8.1) can be written in the form

$$\begin{aligned}\varepsilon(\mu-\mu_n) &= (P_2(\varepsilon u_1) + P_2(w) - P_2(\varepsilon u_1) + R_2(w),\ u_1)\\ &= (P_2(\varepsilon u_1),u_1) + (P_2(w) - P_2(\varepsilon u_1),u_1) + (R_2(w),u_1)\\ &= (P_2(\varepsilon u_1),u_1)\ [1 + o(1)]\end{aligned} \tag{8.5}$$

We now study the solutions of (8.2). First note for $\varepsilon = 0$, $y = 0$ and so for $\lambda = \lambda_n$ equation (7.1) has only the trivial solution $u = 0$. For $\varepsilon \neq 0$, we have, by the homogeneity of P_2:

$$\varepsilon^{1-p_2}(\mu-\mu_n) = (P_2(u_1),u_1) = \text{constant} \tag{8.6}$$

Thus for $|\varepsilon|$ sufficiently small, the solutions of $(L_1 + N_1)u = \lambda(L_2 + N_2)u$ near $\lambda = \lambda_n$ can be described as a 1-parameter family $u(\varepsilon)$ such that $\lim\limits_{\varepsilon\to 0} \lambda(\varepsilon) = \lambda_n$ and $\lim\limits_{\varepsilon\to 0} ||u(\varepsilon)|| = 0.$

<u>Spectral Theorem</u> 8.2. <u>Under the hypotheses of Theorem 8.1, the local behavior of the one parameter families of solutions</u>

is qualitatively described by the parity of numbers p_1, p_2, the sign of the expressions $(P_i u_1, u_1)$ $(i = 1,2)$, and the sign of λ_n.

Proof: Case (a). By Theorem 8.1 we need only investigate the equation

$$\varepsilon^{1-p_2}(\mu-\mu_n) = (P_2(u_1),u_1).$$

By hypothesis $(P_2(u),u_1) \neq 0$ so

$$\varepsilon^{p_2-1} = (\mu-\mu_n)(P_2(u_1),u_1)^{-1}. \tag{8.7}$$

Thus the qualitative dependence of $\lambda = \lambda(\varepsilon)$ on ε near $\lambda = \lambda_n$ is determined by evenness or oddness of p_2 and the sign of $(P_2(u_1),u_1)$.

Case (b). As in case (a), equations (7.4) can be reduced to the equation

$$\varepsilon^{1-p_1}(\mu-\mu_n) = -\mu(P_1 u_1,u_1)$$

Thus $\varepsilon^{p_1-1} = \frac{1}{\mu}(\mu-\mu_n)(P_1 u_1,u_1)^{-1}$

and the conclusion of the theorem follows.

Corollary 8.4. Under the hypotheses of Theorem 8.1 no bifurcation will occur for $\lambda \leq \lambda_n$, (λ_n positive) in only the following circumstances:

in case (a) if $(P_2 u_1,u_1) < 0$, p_2 odd,

in case(b) if $(P_1 u_1,u_1) > 0$, $p_1$odd.

In these situations bifurcation always occurs for $\lambda > \lambda_n$.

Corollary 8.5. The following bifurcation pictures are valid under the hypotheses of Theorem 8.1.

Case (a) ($\lambda_n > 0$)	p_2 even	p_2 odd
$(P_2u_1,u_1) > 0$	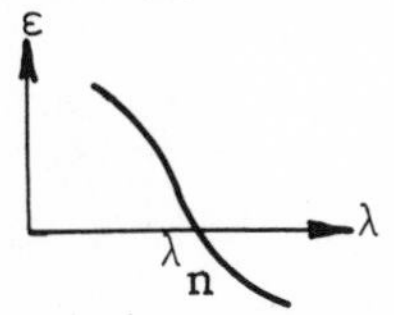	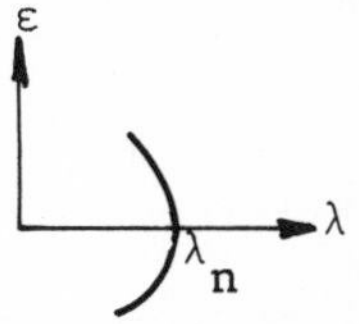
$(P_2u_1,u_1) < 0$	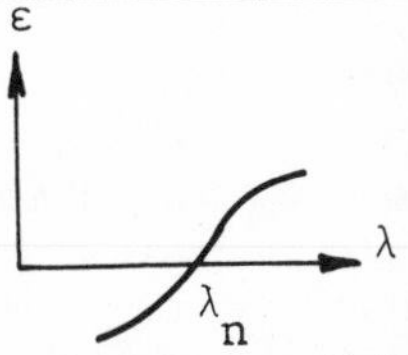	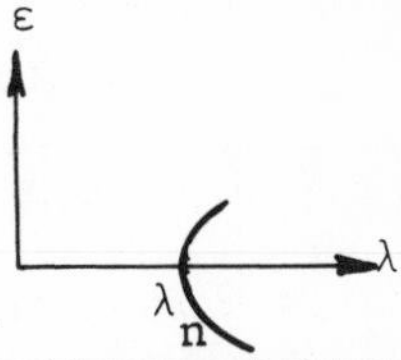
Case (b) ($\lambda_n > 0$)	**p_1 even**	**p_1 odd**
$(P_1u_1,u_1) > 0$	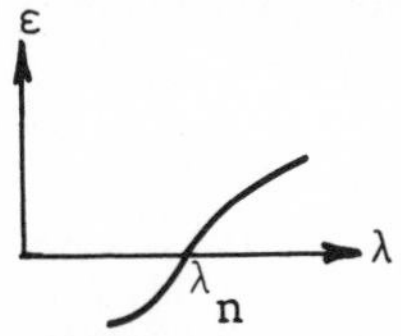	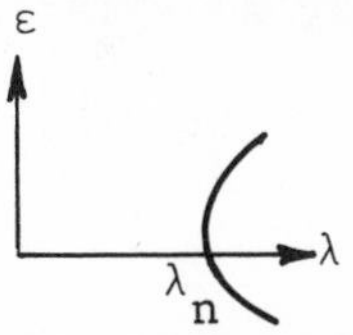
$(P_1u_1,u_1) < 0$	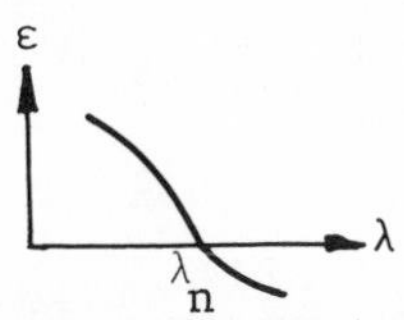	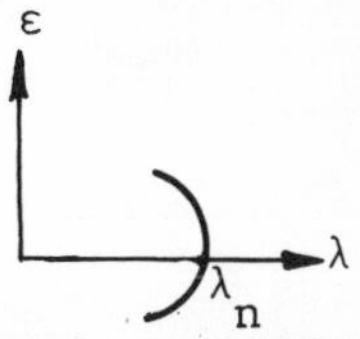

The proofs of these corollaries follow immediately from the equations:

case (a) $\varepsilon^{p_2-1} = (\mu-\mu_n)\,(P_2u_1,u_1)^{-1}$ (8.8) case (b) $\varepsilon^{p_1 - 1} = -\frac{1}{\mu}(\mu - \mu_n)(P_1 u_1, u_1)^{-1}$ (8.9)

We note that by Section 6 the analysis given here applies to any bifurcation question arising from a boundary value problem involving any differential operator associated with a Green's function which is an oscillating kernel or any differential operator with a positive Green's function (near the lowest eigenvalue).

9. The Case $p > 1$ (Bifurcation from multiple eigenvalues).

Multiple eigenvalues λ_n of the linearized equation $L_1 u = \lambda L_2 u$ require closer investigation and more detailed analysis than the case $p = 1$. This difficulty, known as "degeneracy", will be treated in our later work on the questions of existence and multiplicity. The possibility of meaningful results in this connection was indicated by Rellich's result of Example 8 Section 3. Here we present only a study of the spectral theory of such problems.

Theorem 9.1. *Let λ_n be an eigenvalue of multiplicity $p > 1$ of the equation $L_1 u = \lambda L_2 u$ with normalized eigenfunctions $u_1 \cdots u_n$. Then under the hypotheses of Theorem 8.1, the local behavior of the solutions of (7.1) (if they exist) can be described in cases (a) or (b) provided*

$$(P_i(\sum_{i=1}^{p} c_i u_i), \sum_{i=1}^{p} c_i u_i) \neq 0 \tag{9.1}$$

<u>for</u> $|\varepsilon| = |\varepsilon_1| + \cdots |\varepsilon_p|$ <u>sufficiently small</u> ($|\varepsilon| \neq 0$). <u>The local behavior is then one-sided in that bifurction takes place only for</u> $\lambda > \lambda_n$ <u>or for</u> $\lambda < \lambda_n$, <u>but not for both</u>.

<u>Proof:</u> Case (a) is considered ((b) is completely analogous). By Lemma 7.1, it is sufficient to study the p equations

$$\varepsilon_i(\mu-\mu_n) = (N_2(w),u_i) \quad (i = 1,\ldots,p) \tag{9.2}$$

where $w = y + \sum_{i=1}^{p} \varepsilon_i u_i$, and as in Theorem 8.1, it is actually sufficient to consider the equations

$$\varepsilon_i(\mu-\mu_n) = (P_2(\sum_{i=1}^{p} \varepsilon_i u_i),u_i) \quad i = 1,\ldots,p \tag{9.3}$$

Multiplying each of these equations by ε_1 and summing over i, we obtain

$$(\sum_{i=1}^{p} \varepsilon_i^2)(\mu-\mu_n) = (P_2(\sum_{i=1}^{p} \varepsilon_i u_i), \sum_{i=1}^{p} \varepsilon_i u_i). \tag{9.4}$$

Thus for $\mu = \mu_n$, (7.1) has a solution only if $\varepsilon_i=0$ i.e. if $y = 0$ and $u \equiv 0$.

Furthermore if $(P_2(\sum_{i=1}^{p} \varepsilon_i u_i), \sum_{i=1}^{p} \varepsilon_i u_i) \neq 0$ for sufficiently small $|\varepsilon|$ ($\neq 0$), the inner product, being a continuous function of $(\varepsilon_1,\ldots,\varepsilon_p)$, must not change sign. Thus (9.4) shows that bifurcation can only take place for $\lambda > \lambda_n$ or $\lambda < \lambda_n$ but not for both.

Corollary 9.2. <u>If</u> $p = 2$, <u>the solutions of the nonlinear</u>

problem of small norm in the neighborhood of λ_n can be determined from the solution of the one dimensional problem of finding the number of non zero real roots of an algebraic equation of degree $(p_i + 1)$.

Proof. By the theorem it is sufficient to study the roots of the two equations (in case (a))

$$(\mu-\mu_n)\varepsilon_1 = (P_2(\varepsilon_1 u_1 + \varepsilon_2 u_2), u_1) \tag{9.5}$$

$$(\mu-\mu_n)\varepsilon_2 = (P_2(\varepsilon_1 u_1 + \varepsilon_2 u_2), u_2) \tag{9.6}$$

Setting $\varepsilon_2 = k\varepsilon_1$ and using the homogeneity of P_i, we obtain for ε_1

$$(\mu-\mu_n)(1 + k^2) = \varepsilon_1^2(P_2(u_1 + ku_2), u_1 + ku_2),$$

i.e. under the hypotheses of the theorem, we get a pair of ε_1 values differing in sign. On the other hand to determine k we have the equation of degree $(p_i + 1)$

$$k(R_2(u_1 + ku_2), u_1) = (R_2(u_1 + ku_2), u_2).$$

Example. Let G be a bounded domain in R^3 and consider the boundary value problems

$$\Delta u + \lambda(e(x)u + f(u)) = 0 \qquad \text{in } G \tag{9.7}$$

$$\Delta u - f(u) + \lambda e(x)u = 0 \qquad \text{in } G \tag{9.8}$$

with the boundary condition

$$u = 0 \quad \text{on } \partial G. \tag{9.9}$$

Here $f(u) = \alpha_q u^q + \alpha_{q+1}u^{q+1} + \ldots$ (q an integer > 1, $\alpha_q \neq 0$)

and $e(x) > 0$. Then we have:

(i) all $\lambda_n > 0$, λ_1 is necessarily of multiplicity 1.

(ii) For (9.7), $(P_2 u,u) = \int_G \alpha_q u^{q+1}$.

For (9.8), $(P_1 u,u) = \int_G \alpha_q u^{q+1}$.

(iii) If q is odd and either $\alpha_q > 0$ or $\alpha_q < 0$, all the results of our study in this part, apply.

10. Variational Operators with Symmetry.

In this part of our work, we consider a large class of operator equations in a real Hilbert space H for which bifurcation always occurs, independent of the multiplicity index p. In addition, this class of equations has a rather remarkable multiplicity theory, analogous to the linear analytic perturbation theory of Rellich, mentioned in Section 3, Example 8.

The basic idea is to interpret $Au = \lambda Bu$ as an equation for the critical points of a functional $\phi_2(u)$ on a level surface $\phi_2(u) = R$, where the variational derivatives of ϕ_1 and ϕ_2 are A and B respectively, and R is some real number, which can vary. The class of operators, for which such an interpretation is valid, correspond to self-adjoint operators in the linear case and "variational" operators in general (we shall define this term formally later).

We consider the variational problem: <u>Find the critical points of</u> $\phi_2(u)$ <u>on the level surface</u> $\phi_1(u) = R$. The <u>automorphism group</u> of this variation problem consists of those mappings of the space H onto itself that leave the variational problem invariant. We say the variational problem possesses a symmetry if this automorphism group possesses some nontrivail element σ such that $\sigma u = u$ implies $u \equiv 0$. For example, for quadratic functionals the antipodal map i: $u \to -u$ is such an element σ. For simplicity, throughout this part we shall limit attention to problems with the antipodal map as symmetry. Another type of symmetry for complex function spaces was mentioned in Example 7 of Section 3, namely, $u \to e^{i\theta}u$ for all real Θ.

For bifurcation problems of this class, we introduce the idea of <u>nonlinear descent</u>. We find a countably infinite number of distinct normalized solutions $u_n(R)$ to the full nonlinear problem, associated with a parameter R(which can vary between 0 and ∞), and an "eigenvalue" $\lambda_n(R)$. This can be achieved, under suitable restrictions, by using results in [1b]. (Cf. J. Schwartz [28]). We then "descend to the linear problem" by letting $R \to 0$, to show that

$\lambda_n(R) \to \lambda_n$, the eigenvalues of the linearized problem counted according to multiplicity.

The appropriate nonlinear invariants for the bifurcation problems of this part will be certain critical points $c_n(R)$ $(n = 1,2,\ldots)$ of the variational problem calculated by a certain minimax principle. The construction of the appropriate constraints on the level surface $\phi_1(u) = R$ for $c_n(R)$, $n > 1$, will require the involutive symmetry of the variational problem and the homotopy invariant known as Lyusternik-Schnirelmann category. This system of nonlinear invariants can be calculated in the linear case by the Courant minimax principle, is stable under the nonlinear perturbations considered here, and measures the existence and multiplicity of real solutions of the nonlinear problem.

We now develop the concept of an abstract variational operator.

Definition: A functional $\phi(u)$ has a Gateaux derivative $\phi'(u,v)$ in the direction v if

$$\lim_{t \to 0} \left\{\frac{\phi(u + tv) - \phi(u)}{t}\right\} = \phi'(u,v).$$

Definition: A is a variational operator if there is a functional $\phi(u)$ defined on H such that the Gateaux derivative of $\phi(u)$ in the direction v is $\langle v,Au\rangle$ for every $v \in H$. Here $\langle\, ,\, \rangle$ denotes the inner product in H.

Lemma 10.1: *Let* A: $H \to H$ *be a mapping continuous from the strong topology of* H *into the weak topology of* H. *Then* A *is a variational operator if and only if for all* $u, v \in H$,

$$\int_0^1 \langle u, A(su)\rangle \, ds - \int_0^1 \langle v, A(sv)\rangle \, ds = \int_0^1 \langle u-v, A(v+s(u-v))\rangle \, ds. \tag{10.1}$$

Furthermore, the functional $\phi(u)$ *associated with* A(u) *can be written*

$$\phi(u) = \int_0^1 \langle u, A(su)\rangle \, ds. \tag{10.2}$$

Proof:

Clearly if conditions (10.1) and (10.2) hold, then

$$\phi(u + tv) - \phi(u) = t \int_0^1 \langle v, A(u + stv)\rangle \, ds. \tag{10.3}$$

Hence the Gateaux derivative of $\phi(u)$ in the direction v is $\langle v, Au\rangle$. On the other hand, if A is a variational operator, there is a functional $\phi(u)$ such that

$$\frac{d}{dt}[\phi(u+tv)] = \frac{d}{d\varepsilon}[\phi(u+tv+\varepsilon v)]_{\varepsilon=0} = \langle v, A(u+tv)\rangle. \tag{10.4}$$

Integrating (10.4) with respect to t between 0 and 1, we obtain

$$\phi(u) - \phi(v) = \int_0^1 \langle u-v, A(v+s(u-v)\rangle \, ds. \tag{10.5}$$

Setting $v = 0$, $\phi(0) = 0$ in (10.5), we get

$$\phi(u) = \int_0^1 \langle u, A(su)\rangle \, ds.$$

Example: If A is linear, and H is a Hilbert space, (10.1) clearly is equivalent to the fact that A is self-adjoint. Thus the operators satisfying (10.1), can be regarded as nonlinear generalizations of self-adjoint linear operators.

Using (10.2), we now define for each variational operator certain sets in H, that will be of interest throughout the present work.

Definition: Let R be a fixed positive number. Then

$$A_R \equiv \{u \mid u \in H, \int_0^1 \langle u, A(su)\rangle \, ds \leq R\}$$

$$\partial A_R \equiv \{u \mid u \in H, \int_0^1 \langle u, A(su)\rangle \, ds = R\}.$$

If A is a bounded linear self-adjoint operator and H is Hilbert space, ∂A_R represents a sphere in H with respect to the operator A for nonlinear operators A, ∂A_R is an infinite dimensional manifold and will serve as a nonlinear normalization for elements $u \in H$. It will be of interest to determine the relationship between the properties of the operator A and the associated set ∂A_R.

A variational principle to determine the totality of solutions of the operator equation $(L_1+N_1)u = \lambda(L_2+N_2)u$

can now be calculated. Under the assumption that $A = L_1+N_1$ and $B = L_2+N_2$ are variational operators this principle would be:

Find the critical points of the functional

$\frac{1}{2}(u,L_2u) + \int_0^1 (u,N_2(su))ds$ subject to the constraint

$\frac{1}{2}(u,L_1u) + \int_0^1 (u,N_1(su))ds = R$. Here R can be varied between 0 and ∞. We denote this variational principle by the symbol $\underline{V}(R)$.

Theorem 10.2. The totality of solutions of the nonlinear operator equation $(L_1+N_1)u = \lambda(L_2+N_2)u$ are identical with the critical points determined by the variational principle $\underline{V}(R)$ for some R, provided the operators L_1,L_2 are self-adjoint and N_1,N_2 are variational. The proof is immediate by definition and by Lemma 10.1.

Thus the existence of bifurcation from $u \equiv 0$ at $\lambda = \lambda_n$ will be guaranteed by finding a critical point for the variational problem $\underline{V}(R)$ with arbitrarily small norm and associated eigenvalue $\lambda(R) \to \lambda_n$ as $\|u(R)\| \to 0$.

Definition: Let the operator $A = L_1 + N_1$: $H \to H$ be a variational operator. Then A is of Class I if

(i) L_1 is a bounded, positive definite, self-adjoint linear operator.

(ii) $A(-u) = -A(u)$

(iii) N_1 is a bounded operator defined on H continuous from the weak topology of H to the strong topology of H.

(iv) $\|N_1u - N_1v\| \leq k\{\|u\|^{p_1-1} + \|v\|^{p_1-1}\}\|u-v\|$, for $\|u\| \leq \kappa_3$ (where k and κ_3 are constants independent of u,v and p_1 is an integer).

(v) $(N_1u,u) \geq 0$.

The next result demonstrates the geometric consequences of the above definition on the nature of the level surface ∂A_R. We assure throughout that R is a positive number > 0.

Theorem 10.3. *The set ∂A_R is a closed, bounded starlike set in H, homeomorphic to the sphere $\partial\sum_R = \{u|(L_1u,u) = 2R\}$ by a mapping along rays through the origin, provided $R(\neq 0)$ is sufficiently small. Furthermore $\|u\| \geq k(R) > 0$ for $u \in \partial A_R$ where $k(R)$ is a constant independent of u; ∂A_R is symmetric with respect to the origin.*

Proof. Let $u_n \in \partial A_R$ $u_n \to u$ strongly in H. Then $N_1(u_n) \to N_1u$ strongly by (iii) and thus

$$\frac{1}{2}(L_1u,u) + \int_0^1 (u,N_1(su))ds = R, \text{ i.e. } u \in \partial A_R.$$

Thus ∂A_R is closed.

To show ∂A_R is bounded for sufficiently small non-zero R, we note that for $u \in \partial A_R$

$$\frac{1}{2}(L_1u,u) + \int_0^1 (u,N_1(su))ds = R$$

$$\frac{1}{2}(L_1u,u) \leq R \quad \text{by (v).}$$

By the positive definiteness of L_1, there is a constant $\kappa > 0$, such that

$$||u||^2 \leq 2\kappa R.$$

On the other hand if ∂A_R is not uniformly bounded away from 0, there is a bounded sequence $\{u_n\} \varepsilon \partial A_R$ with $||u_n|| \to 0$. As H is a Hilbert space, there is a weakly convergent sequence $\{u_{n_j}\} \varepsilon \partial A_R$ with $||u_{n_j}|| \to 0$. Thus $u_{n_j} \to 0$ strongly and since ∂A_R is closed, $0 \in \partial A_R$ this is impossible since $A(0) = 0$.

We now prove that ∂A_R is starlike. First note that any line through the origin necessarily intersects ∂A_R. Indeed if $u \neq 0$

$$f(t) = t^2 \frac{1}{2}(L_1u,u) + t\int_0^1 (u,N_1(stu))ds$$

is a continuous function of t varying between 0 and $+\infty$ as t varies in $(0,\infty)$, i.e. there is a positive number t_R such that $t_R u \in \partial A_R$ for every R. To prove that ∂A_R is starlike we show that any line through the origin intersects ∂A_R

exactly twice. Suppose $u \in \partial A_R$ and in addition $tu \in \partial A_R$ for some real scalar t distinct from ± 1. Then $\frac{1}{2} t^2(L_1u,u) + t\int_0^1 (u,N_1(stu))ds = R$. Setting $\sigma = 1-t^2$ and $st = \tau$, we find that if $t = +\sqrt{1-\sigma}$, then

$$\frac{1}{2}(1-\sigma)(L_1u,u) + \int_0^{+\sqrt{1-\sigma}} (u,N_1(\tau u))d\tau = R.$$

As $u \in \partial A_R$,

$$-\sigma \frac{1}{2}(L_1u,u) + \int_0^{+\sqrt{1-\sigma}} (u,N_1(\tau u))d\tau = 0.$$

By the properties of ∂A_R in the definition, this last equation can hold if and only if $\sigma = 0$. On the other hand if $t = -\sqrt{1-\sigma}$,

$$(1-\sigma)\frac{1}{2}(L_1u,u) + \int_0^{-\sqrt{1-\sigma}} (u,N_1(\tau u))d\tau = R$$

implies

$$-\sigma \frac{1}{2}(L_1u,u) + \int_1^{-\sqrt{1-\sigma}} (u,N_1(\tau u))d\tau = 0.$$

Thus once more this equation can hold if and only if $\sigma = 0$.

To prove that ∂A_R is homeomorphic to $\partial\sum_R$ along rays through the origin, assume $u \in \partial A_R$ and $tu \in \partial\sum_R$. Then

$$\frac{1}{2}(L_1u,u) + \int_0^1 (u,N_1(su))ds = R$$

and

$$\frac{t^2}{2}(L_1u,u) = R.$$

Thus, solving for t^2, we find

$$\frac{1}{t^2} = 1 - (\frac{1}{R})\int_0^1 (u,N_1(su))ds > 0 \text{ (for all } u \in \partial A_R).$$

The mapping $u \to tu$ therefore defines a (1-1) bicontinuous mapping of ∂A_R onto $\partial\sum_R$ because ∂A_R is starlike.

The fact that ∂A_R is symmetric with respect to the origin follows immediately from the fact that $u \in \partial A_R$ implies $-u \in \partial A_R$ since $A = L_1 + N_1$ is an odd operator.

<u>Definition</u>. Let the operator $B = L_2 + N_2$: $H \to H$ be a variational operator. Then B is of Class II if

(i) L_2 is a bounded, compact, positive, self-adjoint linear operator.

(ii) $B(-u) = -B(u)$.

(iii) N_2 is a bounded operator continuous from the weak topology of H to the strong topology of H.

(iv) There is a constant $\kappa_3 > 0$, such that

$$\|N_2u - N_2v\| \leq \kappa_3\{\|u\|^{p_2-1} + \|v\|^{p_2-1}\}\|u-v\|$$

$$\text{for } \|u\|, \|v\| \leq \kappa_3.$$

(v) For $\|u\|$ sufficiently small, $(Bu,u)>0$, $u\neq 0$.

Lemma 10.4. Let A be an operator of Class I and B an operator of Class II. Then the associated variational problem V(R) invariant under the antipodal mapping i: $u \to -u$.

Proof. The lemma is a direct consequence of the oddness of the operators A and B.

We now proceed to calculate the nonlinear invariants for bifurcation problems associated with operators of Class I or II. As mentioned at the beginning of this section, these invariants will be certain critical points $c_n(R)$ of the variational principle V(R). To define appropriate constraints for these critical points we study "curved" subspaces of the unit sphere and of the manifold ∂A_R by utilizing the properties of the topological invariant described in the next few paragraphs.

In the Hilbert space H, we denote by P_R^∞, the infinite dimensional real projective space obtained by identifying antipodal points of the sphere

$$\partial\Sigma_R = \{u | \frac{1}{2} ||u||^2 = R\}.$$

We now define the Lyusternik-Schnirelmann category of a closed subset A relative to P_R^∞, denoted $\text{cat}_{P_R^\infty} A$, as the least integer K for which there is a covering of A By closed sets $A_1, A_2, \ldots, A_k$ of P_R^∞ each of which is homotopic to a point relative to P_R^∞. If no such integer exists we write

$\text{cat}_{P_R^\infty} A = \infty$. This definition is related to that of J. Schwartz [28], where many of the properties of this invariant are discussed. The space P_R^∞ has, however, special properties with respect to category. (These are mentioned in [1(b)], and were known to Lyusternik [29] in the 1930's.) In particular,

(i) $\text{cat}_{P_R^\infty} P_R^\infty = \infty$.

(ii) P_R^∞ contains sets of every catogory $n = 1, \ldots,$. Indeed $\text{cat}_{P_R^\infty} P_R^m = m + 1$.

(iii) If X and Y are projective spaces $X \subset Y$, $\text{cat}_X A = \text{cat}_Y A$; in particular $\text{cat}_{P_R^\infty} P_R^m = \text{cat}_{P_R^m} P_R = m + 1$.

However Lyusternik-Schnirelmann category is a topological quantity and so it can be defined for the space $\partial\bar{A}_R$, namely the set ∂A_R with antipodal points identified. This space is then homeomorphic to P_R^∞ and thus the properties (i)-(iii) mentioned above hold for it as well as for P_R^∞. It is also important to notice that category is invariant under the homeomorphism, $\bar{T}: \partial\bar{A}_R \to P_R^\infty$ induced by the homeomorphism $T: \partial A_R \to \partial\sum_R$, mentioned in Theorem 10.3.

The importance of category in the present work is

its applicability in the study of the perturbation of degenerate critical points of quadratic functionals defined by multiple integrals. Indeed the homotopy classes generated by the Ljusternik-Schnirelmann category on ∂A_R provide a nonlinear analogue of orthogonal complement. The further properties of category will be mentioned as they arise.

We are now in a position to define the nonlinear invariants for bifurcation problems arising from operators of Class I or II. These invariants are the numbers

$$c_n(R) = \sup_{[V]_n} \min_{V} [\frac{1}{2} (L_2u,u) + \int_o^1 (u,N_2(su))ds]$$

where V is a closed compact set of $\partial\bar{A}_R$ such that $\text{cat}_{\partial\bar{A}_R} V \geq n$. $[V]_n$ is the collection of all such sets on $\partial\bar{A}_R$ for fixed integral n. In order to justify our claim that these numbers are indeed a set of nonlinear invariants for our problem we shall show:

(i) for that the linearized equation $L_1u = \lambda L_2u$, the invariants $c_n(R)$ are the related eigenvalues $R\lambda_n^{-1}$ counted according to multiplicity.

(ii) the existence of a solution to full nonlinear equation $Au = \lambda Bu$ in each class $[V]_n$ on ∂A_R for sufficiently small R, with associated "eigenvalue" $\lambda_n(R)$.

(iii) the "stability" of the numbers $c_n(R)$ under the nonlinear perturbations generated by the operators N_1

and N_2.

(iv) that $\lim_{R\to 0} \lambda_n(R) = \lambda_n$, thus demonstrating the existence of at least p branches of solutions of the nonlinear equation near an eigenvalue of multiplicity p of $L_1 u = \lambda L_2 u$. (This fact will be proven in the bifurcation theorem below.

Lemma 10.5. *Let* S *denote an n-dimensional subspace of elements* {u} *in a Hilbert space* H *of infinite dimension, and* $T = \{u | u \in S, \frac{1}{2}||u||^2 = R\}$. *Let* $P_R(n-1)$ *be the set of elements obtained by identifying antipodal points of T and regarded as a subspace of* P_R^∞. *Then* $\text{cat}_{P_R^\infty} P_R(n-1) = n$.

The proof of this result is an immediate consequence of properties (2.3) of Lyusternik-Schnirelmann category and the fact that $\text{cat}_{P^n} P^n = n + 1$.

Remark: In this notation the usual Courant-Fischer minimax principle can be written

$$(\lambda_n)^{-1} = \sup_{[T]_n} \min_T \frac{1}{2} (Lu,u)$$

where T is defined in the above lemma and $[T]_n$ is the class of all such sets in P^∞, for fixed n.

This principle is also valid for eigenvalues of multiplicity greater than 1 provided we count λ_n according to its multiplicity. The analogue of this fact for "curved" subspaces of sphere as allowable sets is stated in the following result:

Lemma 10.6. (Generalized Courant Minimax Principle for Quadratic Functionals). The eigenvalues λ_n of the equation $L_1u = \lambda L_2u$ can be characterized as follows:

$$R(\lambda_n)^{-1} = \sup_{[V]_n} \min_{V} \frac{1}{2} (Lu,u)$$

where

a) V is a closed set in P_R^∞ such that $\operatorname{cat}_{P_R^\infty} V \geq n$.

(Here P_R^∞ is obtained by identifying antipodal points of the sphere $\partial\sum_R = \{u|\frac{1}{2} (L_2u,u) = R\}$).

b) $[V]_n$ is the class of all such sets V in P_R^∞ for fixed integral n. Thus $c_n(R) = (\lambda_n)^{-1}R$.

Proof. By applying the results of [1b] or [28], we know that the numbers defined by $R\lambda_n^{-1} = \sup_{[V]_n} \min_{V} \frac{1}{2} (L_2u,u)$ are critical points of the functional $\frac{1}{2} (L_2u,u)$ on $\partial\sum_R$. Furthermore the completeness of the eigenvalues of $L_1u = \lambda L_2u$ implies that $\lambda_n^{-1}(R) = \lambda_m^{-1}$ for some m. By Lemma 10.5, we have $\lambda_m^{-1} \geq \lambda_n^{-1}$, and by definition $\lambda_1^{-1}(R) = \lambda_1$. So we have:

$$\begin{array}{ccccccc} \lambda_1^{-1}(R) & \geq & \lambda_2^{-1}(R) & \geq & \lambda_3^{-1}(R) & \ldots & \\ \| & & \vee| & & \vee| & & \\ \lambda_1^{-1} & \geq & \lambda_2^{-1} & \geq & \lambda_3^{-1} & \ldots . & \end{array} \qquad (10.6)$$

Now suppose the first eigenvalue λ_1 is of multiplicity m, i.e. $\lambda_1 = \lambda_2 = \ldots = \lambda_m \neq \lambda_{m+1}$. Then necessarily $\lambda_1(R) = \lambda_2(R) = \ldots \lambda_m(R) \neq \lambda_{m+1}(R)$ by virtue of (10.6) and the fact that if $\lambda_m(R) = \lambda_{m+1}(R)$, then the first eigenvalue λ_1 would be of multiplicity m + 1 by corollary 14 of Schwartz [28]. We proceed by induction. Suppose the first n distinct eigenvalues, which we label $\lambda^{(1)}, \lambda^{(2)}, \ldots, \lambda^{(n)}$ have $\lambda_i = \lambda_i(R)$ and the (n + 1)st distinct eigenvalue $\lambda^{(n+1)} = \lambda_k$ has multiplicity p and $\lambda_k \neq \lambda_k(R)$. On the other hand, let $\lambda_k(R) = \lambda_{k'}$ for some $k' > k$. Suppose $\lambda_{k'}$ is of multiplicity q. Then $\lambda_k(R) = \lambda_{k+1}(R) = \ldots = \lambda_{k'+q}(R)$. A second application of Lemma 14 of Schwartz [28] show that $\lambda_k(R)$ corresponds to an eigenvalue of multiplicity > q. This contradiction then completes the induction proof.

We now study the solution of the nonlinear equation $Au = \lambda Bu$ for $[V]_n$ on ∂A_R.

Theorem 10.7. (A Sturm-Liouville Theorem). For each fixed number $R > 0$, there exists a countable number of distinct solutions $u_n(R) \in \partial A_R$ of the equation $Au = \lambda Bu$ with associated eigenvalues $\lambda_n(R) \to \infty$. Each solution $u_n(R)$ is characterized as a critical point of the functional $\frac{1}{2}(L_2u,u) + \int_0^1 (u,N_2(su))ds$ on the manifold ∂A_R by the formula

$$c_n(R) = \sup_{[V]_n} \min_V \left[\frac{1}{2}(Lu,u) + \int_0^1 (u, N_2(su))ds\right]$$

where a) <u>V is a closed set of $\partial\bar{A}_R$ such that</u> $\text{cat}_{\partial\bar{A}_R} V \geq n$.

b) <u>$[V]_n$ is the collection of all such sets on $\partial\bar{A}_R$ for fixed integral n.</u>

<u>Proof</u>. This result is a direct consequence of the author's previous work [1b] (Theorem IV.3.1) or Browder's [30] and, in a slightly different form, is related to papers of J. Schwartz [28], R. Palais [31], and M. Krasnosel'skii [10]. We omit the proof.

We now examine the stability of the numbers $c_n(R)$. Denote by $\tilde{c}_n(R)$, the values of the critical points on $\partial\sum_R$ of the functional $\frac{1}{2}(L_2u,u)$ as calculated by the Generalized Courant minimax principle (Lemma 10.6) and by $\bar{c}_n(R)$ the related critical points of $\frac{1}{2}(L_2u,u) + \int_0^1 (u,N_2(su))ds$ on $\partial\bar{A}_R$ as calculated by the Sturm-Liouville Theorem 10.7. For simplicity, we shall consider only the cases (a) $N_1 \equiv 0$ or (b) $N_2 \equiv 0$ as discussed in Section 7. The stability of the critical numbers $c_n(R)$ in each case is expressed by the following result.

<u>Lemma</u> 10.7. $|\tilde{c}_n(R) - \bar{c}_n(R)| \leq KR^\sigma$

<u>where</u> σ <u>is a constant</u> > 1.

<u>Proof</u>. We begin by considering case (a). By definition

$$|\tilde{c}_n(R)-\bar{c}_n(R)| = \Big| \sup_{[V]_n} \min_V \frac{1}{2}(L_2u,u) - \sup_{[V]_n} \min_V \{\frac{1}{2}(L_2u,u)$$

$$+ \int_0^1 (u,N_2(su))ds)\} \le \Big|\sup_{[V]_n} \min_V \frac{1}{2}(L_2u,u) - \sup_{[V]_n} \min_V [\frac{1}{2}(L_2u,u)$$

$$+ KR^{\frac{p+1}{2}}]$$

where K is a constant independent of $u \in \partial\sum_R$.

Thus $|\tilde{c}_n(R) - \bar{c}_n(R)| \le KR^{\frac{p+1}{2}}$.

In case (b),

$$|\tilde{c}_n(R)-\bar{c}_n(R)| = \Big|\sup_{[V]_n} \min_V \frac{1}{2}(L_2u,u) - \sup_{[V]_n} \min_{V'} \frac{1}{2}(L_2u,u)\Big|$$

$$= \Big|\sup_{[V]_n} \min_V \frac{1}{2}(L_2u,u) - \sup_{[V]_n} \min_V 2\frac{1}{t^2}(L_2u,u)\Big|$$

$$= \Big|\sup_{[V]_n} \min_V \frac{1}{2}(L_2u,u) - \sup_{[V]_n} \min_V \frac{1}{2}(L_2u,u) \{1 - \frac{\int_0^1 (u,N_1(su))ds}{R}\}\Big|.$$

These last two equality signs are valid since the classes $[V]_n$ and $[V']_n$ are preserved under the homeomorphism $t\colon \partial A_R \to \partial\sum_R$. Thus

$$|\tilde{c}_n(R)-\bar{c}_n(R)| \leq |\sup_{[V]_n} \min_{V} \frac{1}{2}(Lu,u)-\sup_{[V]_n} \min_{V} (\frac{1}{2}(L_2u,u) - KR^{\sigma})| \leq KR^{\sigma}$$

where $\sigma > 1$.

The work of this section culminates in the following result which demonstrates the manner in which the numbers $c_n(R)$ measure the existence and multiplicity of real "small" solutions of the nonlinear equation $Au = \lambda Bu$.

Theorem 10.8. In cases (a) or (b), from each eigenvalue of the equation $L_1u = \lambda L_2u$ there bifurcates at least one branch of nontrivial solutions of the nonlinear equation $(L_1 + N_1)u = \lambda(L_2 + N_2)u$. From an eigenvalue λ_n of multiplicity p, there bifurcates at least p such branches.

Proof. We shall prove the first part of this result by showing in either case (a) or (b) that

$$\lim_{R \to 0} |\lambda_n - \lambda_n(R)| = 0$$

where λ_n is the nth eigenvalue of $L_1u = \lambda L_2u$ and $\lambda_n(R)$ is the "eigenvalue" associated with the solution of $Au = \lambda Bu$ on ∂A_R calculated in the homotopy class $[V]_n$.

We consider first case (a)(i.e. $N_1 \equiv 0$). We have

$$|\lambda_n^{-1} - \lambda_n^{-1}(R)| = |\frac{\frac{1}{2}(L_2u,u)}{R} - \frac{\frac{1}{2}(L_2u',u') + \frac{1}{2}(N_2(u'),u')}{R}|$$

where u is any eigenfunction of $L_1 u = \lambda L_2 u$ on $\partial\sum_R$ with eigenvalue λ_n and u' is any eigenfunction of $Au = \lambda Bu$ on ∂A_R with eigenvalue $\lambda_n(R)$. Thus

$$|\lambda_n^{-1}-\lambda_n^{-1}(R)| \leq \frac{1}{R} \{|\tilde{c}_n(R)-\bar{c}_n(R)|+|\int_0^1 (u',N_2(su))ds - \frac{1}{2}(N_2(u'),u')|\}$$

By Lemma 10.7 and the estimates on N_2

$$|\lambda_n^{-1} - \lambda_n^{-1}(R)| \leq \frac{1}{R} \{(K_1 R^\sigma) + K_2 R^\beta\}$$

where $\sigma,\beta > 1$, K are constants independent of $u \in \partial A_R$.

Hence

$$\lim_{R \to 0} |\lambda_n^{-1} - \lambda_n^{-1}(R)| = 0.$$

Turning now to case (b) (i.e. $N_2 \equiv 0$), we obtain

$$|\lambda_n^{-1}-\lambda_n^{-1}(R)| = \left| \frac{\frac{1}{2}(L_2 u,u)}{R} - \frac{\frac{1}{2}(L_2 u',u')}{R+\frac{1}{2}(N_1 u',u')-\int_o^1 (N_1(su'),u')ds} \right|.$$

We set

$$b(u) = \frac{\frac{1}{2}(N_1 u,u) - \int_o^1 (u,N_1(su))ds}{R}.$$

Then for sufficiently small $\|u\|$, we have $|b(u)| < 1$ since $L_1 + N_1$ is in class I. Thus for R sufficiently small

$$|\lambda_n^{-1}-\lambda_n^{-1}(R)| = \frac{1}{R} \left|\frac{1}{2}(L_2 u,u) - \frac{1}{2}(L_2 u',u')[1+b(u')]^{-1}\right|$$

$$= \frac{1}{R} \left| \frac{1}{2} (L_2 u,u) - \frac{1}{2} (L_2 u',u')[1 - \frac{b(u')}{1+b(u')}] \right|$$

$$\leq \frac{1}{R} \left| \bar{c}_n(R) - \tilde{c}_n(R) \right| + \frac{1}{2} (L_2 u',u') \left| \frac{b(u')}{1+b(u')} \right| .$$

Since $u' \varepsilon \partial A_R$

$$(1 + b(u'))R = \frac{1}{2} (L_1 u',u') + \frac{1}{2} (N_1 u,u) \geq \frac{1}{2} (L_1 u',u')$$

Thus

$$0 < \frac{1}{2} (L_2 u',u) \left| \frac{b(u')}{1+b(u')} \right| \leq \left| \frac{1}{2} (N_1 u,u) - \int_0^1 (u,N_1(su))ds \right|$$

$$\leq K_1 \| u \|^{p_1+1}$$

where K_1 is some constant independent of u. Since

$$\| u \|^2 \leq \frac{1}{2} \bar{K}(L_1,u,u), \text{ we have } \frac{1}{2} \bar{K}(\|u\|^{p_1+1}) \leq \frac{1}{2} \bar{K} R^{\frac{p+1}{2}} .$$

Thus by this last estimate and Lemma 10.6

$$|\lambda_n^{-1} - \lambda_n^{-1}(R)| \leq \frac{1}{R} \frac{1}{2} [(KR^{\sigma}) + \bar{K}K_1 R^{\frac{p_1+1}{2}}]$$

Thus, as σ and $\frac{p_1+1}{2}$ are greater than 1,

$$\lim_{R \to 0} |\lambda_n^{-1} - \lambda_n^{-1}(R)| = 0.$$

On the other hand, suppose $c_n(R) = c_{n+i}(R)$ for some i and some small number R. Then, by Lemma 14 of Schwartz [28], these branches do not disappear, rather they form a continuum of solutions "joining $u_n(R)$ and $u_{n+i}(R)$", i.e. the distinct branches form an (n+1) dimensional surface.

11. Applications of the Bifurcation Theory for Variational Operators with Symmetry.

Here we consider only two distinct but fundamental problems. The first example, taken from nonlinear elasticity, is illustrative of a bifurcation problem of case (b), the second, taken from the theory of periodic solutions of autonomous system, illustrates problems of case (a).

Example 1. The von Kármán equations for a thin clamped elastic plate.

The von Kármán equations for a thin clamped plate were given in Section 3. They are written

$$\begin{aligned} \Delta^2 w &= \lambda[F,w] + [w,f] \\ \Delta^2 f &= -[w,w] \end{aligned} \qquad \text{in } \Omega \qquad (11.1)$$

$$\begin{aligned} w &= w_x = w_y = 0 \\ f &= f_x = f_y = 0 \end{aligned} \qquad \text{on } \partial\Omega \qquad (11.2)$$

where Ω is a bounded domain in R^2, $[f,g] = f_{xx}g_{yy} + f_{yy}g_{xx} - 2f_{xy}g_{xy}$, and F is a given smooth function.

The boundary value problem (11.1), (11.2) has the following self-adjoint linearization

$$\Delta^2 w = \lambda[F,w] \qquad \text{in } \Omega \qquad (11.3)$$

$$\begin{aligned} w &= w_x = w_y = 0 \\ f &= f_x = f_y = 0 \end{aligned} \qquad \text{on } \partial\Omega. \qquad (11.4)$$

If we assume that only compressive forces act on $\partial\Omega$, then

$$\int_{\Omega}[F,w] \geq 0.$$

We note that the form [f,g] is a divergence expression i.e.

$$[f,g] = (f_{yy}g_x - f_{xy}g_y)_x + (f_{xx}g_y - f_{xy}g_x)_y.$$

We write (11.1), (11.2) in the form

$$\begin{aligned} w &= \lambda Lw + C(w,f) \\ f &= -C(w,w) \end{aligned} \tag{11.5}$$

Here L is a linear self-adjoint operator $H \to H$, and C(w,f) is an operator arising from the term [w,f]. If we set $C(w) = C(w,C(w,w))$, the equations (11.5), take the simplified form

$$w + Cw = \lambda Lw \tag{11.6}$$

where C is a cubic operator of degree 3, and the equation $f = -C(w,w)$ is regarded as an equation uniquely determining f once w is known. We study (11.6) in the Hilbert space $H = \dot{W}_{2,2}(\Omega)$ having the norm

$$\|u\|_{2,2} = \sum_{|\alpha|=2} \int_{\Omega} |D^{\alpha}u|^2$$

Using the procedure of Section 10, we can reformulate (11.6) as the Euler-Lagrange equations of the following associated variational problem:

<u>Find the critical points of the functional</u> $\frac{1}{2}$ (Lw,w) <u>on the level surface</u> $\frac{1}{2}$ (w,w) + $\frac{1}{4}$ (Cw,w) = R. The proof of this equivalence is a consequence of the following symmetry property of C(f,g).

<u>Lemma</u> 11.1. <u>Let</u> f,g,h ε $W_{2,2}(\Omega)$. <u>Then</u> I(f,g,h) = (C(f,g),h) <u>is a symmetric trilinear form in</u> f,g,h. <u>In particular</u> (Cw,w) = $\|C(w,w)\|^2$.

By means of the regularity theorem of Section 4, all solutions obtained by such a procedure are automatically smooth in Ω, and at all smooth portions of $\partial\Omega$.

Furthermore it can be shown that (Cw,w) $\geq$ 0, $\|Cw - Cv\| \leq K\{\|w\|^2 + \|v\|^2\} \|u-v\|$.

In summary, we study the von Kármán equations (11.1) and (11.2) as a bifurcation problem of type (b) with $A = L_1 + N_1 = I + C$ and $B = L_2 + N_2 = L$. Here I denotes the identify operator.

<u>Theorem</u> 11.2. <u>For the von Kármán equation</u> u + C = λLu <u>the following results hold:</u>

<u>Existence Theory</u>.

(i) From each eigenvalue of the linear equation u = λLu there bifurcates at least one branch of nontrivial solutions of the nonlinear equation. These are the only points λ at which bifurcation takes place with respect to u = 0.

(ii) The solution branches of (i) can be continued for large norms.

Multiplicity Theory.

(iii) From simple eigenvalues of $u = \lambda Lu$ bifurcates exactly one distinct branch of solutions.

(iv) From an eigenvalue λ_n of multiplicity p of $u = \lambda Lu$ bifurcates at least p branches of solutions.

Spectral Theory.

(v) For $\lambda \leq \lambda_1$ there is no solution different from $u \equiv 0$.

In the neighborhood of λ_n and $u \equiv 0$,

(vi) there are no nonzero solutions for $\lambda \leq \lambda_n$, and

(vii) there are always nonzero solutions for $\lambda > \lambda_n$.

Other Results.

(viii) The potential energy $V(u) < 0$ for any bifurcated solution.

(ix) For a circular uniformly compressed plate, radially symmetric eigenfunctions of the linear problem remain radially symmetric for small deflections.

We indicate proofs of these results:

(i) is a consequence of the abstract Theorems 5.1 and 10.8, as the operator $A = L_1 + C$ is of class I and $B = L_2$ is of class II.

(ii) is a consequence of the Sturm Liouville Theorem 10.7.

(iii) is a consequence of Theorem 8.1.

(iv) is a consequence of Theorem 10.8.

(v) requires an additional proof. Suppose there is some solution $u \varepsilon W_{2,2}(\Omega)$ with $\|u\| \neq 0$; then the variational characterization of λ_1, implies $(u,u) - \lambda(Lu,u) \geq 0$ for $\lambda \leq \lambda_1$. For u to be a solution for such a λ, we must have $(Cu,u) = 0$, i.e.

$$\int_\Omega (u_{xx}u_{yy} - u_{xy}^2)^2 = 0 \text{ (by Lemma 11.1).}$$

Thus $u = u(x,y)$ is a solution of the Monge Ampere equation $u_{xx}u_{yy} - u_{xy}^2 = 0$, subject to boundary condition $u = 0$ on ∂G. Since $u = u(x,y)$ is a classical solution of von Kármán equations, the surface defined by $u = u(x,y)$ has zero Gaussian curvature and by the null boundary conditions defines a ruled surface that must coincide with $u(x,y) \equiv 0$.

(vi) and (vii) are consequences of the bifurcation theorem.

(viii) Apart from a constant factor, the potential energy $V(u)$ defined by a deflection $u(x,y)$ is given by

$$V(u) = (u,u) + \frac{1}{2}(Cu,u) - \lambda(Lu,u).$$

Thus the unbuckled state u_o of the plate has potential energy $V(u_o) = 0$. For any buckled state, $(u,u) + (Cu,u) = \lambda(Lu,u)$. Thus we obtain

$$V(u) = -\frac{1}{2}(Cu,u) < 0 \text{ as } \|u\| \neq 0.$$

(ix) is a consequence of (iii) and of a result due to Keller, Keller and Reiss [37], to the effect that radially symmetric solutions exist for small norms near simple eigenvalues with radially symmetric eigenvalues.

Example 2. Periodic Solutions of Autonomous Systems of Ordinary Differential Equations.

We consider the following system of ordinary differential equations:

$$\ddot{x} + Ax + f(x) = 0 \tag{11.7}$$

where A is self-adjoint positive definite real matrix with constant coefficients, $x = (x_1,\ldots,x_n)$ is a real n-vector, f(x) is a holomorphic function in a neighborhood of the origin, representable as a power series in $x_1,\ldots,x_n$ beginning with terms of the second order. We also assume that $f(-x) = -f(x)$ and that f(x) is the gradient of some scalar function F(x). (This assumption merely states that (11.7) is representable as a Hamiltonian system (See Example 2 of Section3.)

Let $(x,y) = \sum_{i=1}^{n} x_i y_i$.

We seek non-trivial periodic solutions of this system near periodic solutions of the linearized equations

$$\ddot{x} + Ax = 0 \tag{11.8}$$

In this case, we do not make any assumptions on

the eigenvalues of A, and thus the nondegeneracy conditions of Section 3, Example 2 do not hold. Indeed we shall prove that from every periodic solution of (11.8) with minimal period $2\pi\lambda$ not identically zero there bifurcates periodic solutions of (11.7) with period near $2\pi\lambda$.

It is sufficient to study 2π periodic solutions of the equations

$$\ddot{x} + \lambda^2[Ax + f(x)] = 0 \tag{11.9}$$

$$\ddot{x} + \lambda^2[Ax] = 0 \tag{11.10}$$

since these equations are obtained from (11.7) and (11.8) by the reparametrization $t = \lambda\tau$, where λ is to be determined and t varies over $[0,2\pi]$.

To define an appropriate function space for equations (11.9), (11.10), we introduce the space of real valued trigonometric polynomials of the form

$$u(x) = \sum_{k=-n}^{n} a_k e^{ikx}$$

where the (complex-valued) coefficients a_k are subject to the condition $a_{-k} = \bar{a}_k$. We define the scalar product

$$(u,v)_{1,2} = 2\pi \sum_{k=-n}^{n} (1+k^2) a_k b_{-k} \text{ where } v(x) = \sum_{k=-n}^{n} b_k e^{ikx}.$$

Completing the space of trigonometric polynomials

in the natural norm $\|u\|_1 = \sqrt{(u,u)_{1,2}}$, we obtain a separable Hilbert space which we call $H_{1,2}$. $H_{1,2}$ is the space of 2π periodic functions having generalized L_2 derivatives up to order 1.

To find an operator formulation of equations (11.9), (11.10), we consider an n-fold direct product of Hilbert spaces

$$H = \prod_{i=1}^{n} H_{1,2}$$

with the scalar product for $u = (u_1,\ldots,u_n)$ $v = (v_1,\ldots,v_n)$ defined as

$$(u,v)_H = \sum_{i=1}^{n} (u_i,v_i)_{1,2}.$$

By the prodedure of Section 5, using the periodicity of the functions instead of the null boundary conditions, we may define operator equations related to equations (11.9) and (11.10) in the form

$$x = \lambda^2[L_1x + N_1x] \qquad (11.11)$$

$$x = \lambda^2(L_1x) \qquad (11.12)$$

where $$(L_1x,x)_H = \int_0^{2\pi} (Ax.x)dt$$

$$(N_1x,x)_H = \int_0^{2\pi} (f(x)\cdot x)dt$$

$$(x,x)_H = \int_0^{2\pi} (\dot{x}.\dot{x})dt$$

By the hypotheses on f(x), the operator equation is a variational operator equation with involution as symmetry in the Hilbert space H in the form of case (a). Thus the abstract theory of Section 10 applies. Furthermore we note the regularity of the solutions of (11.9) and (11.10) follows without the use of the elaborate regularity theorems. Indeed applying the result of Theorem 10.8 we obtain

Theorem 11.3. The equation (11.7) has at least n real one-parameter families of non-zero periodic solutions. If the minimal period of the jth family is denoted by $\tau_j(R)$, then

$$\lim_{R \to 0} \tau_j(R) = 2\pi\lambda_j^{-1}$$

where λ_j denotes an eigenvalue of the matrix A (i.e. $\lambda_j^{-1}Ax_j = x_j$).

Bibliography

[1] M. Berger, (a), An eigenvalue problem for nonlinear elliptic partial differential equations, Trans. A. M. S. Vol. 120, 145-84. (1965). (b), A Sturm-Liouville Theorem for nonlinear elliptic partial differential equations, Ann. Scuola di Pisa, XX (1966), 543-582.

(c), On von Kármán's equations and the Buckling of a thin elastic plate, Comm. Pure and Applied Math. (d), An application of the calculus of variations in the large to the equations of nonlinear elasticity, Bull. A. M. S. to appear.

[2] E. Schmidt, Zur Theorie der linearen und nicht linearen Integralgleichungen, III Teil, Math. Ann. 65, (1910), 370-399.

[2'] H. Poincare, Sur l'equilibre d'une mass fluid...Acta Math VII (1885).

[3] A Hammerstein, Nichtlineare Integralgleichungen nebst Anwendungen, Acta Math 54 (1930) 117-176.

[4] R. Bartle, Singular points of functional equations, Trans. Amer. Math. Soc. 75 (1953) 366-384.

[5] J. Cronin, Branch points of solutions in Banach space I, II, Trans. Amer. Math. Soc. 69 (1950) 208-231, 76 (1954) 207-222.

[6] M. Vainberg and V. Tregonin, The methods of Lyapunov and Schmidt in the theory of nonlinear equations, Uspekhi Math Nauk

[7] H. Poincaré, Les methodes nouvelles de la mecanique celeste Vol. 1,2,3, Gauthier-Villars, Paris 1892-99.

[7'] G. D. Birkhoff, The restricted problem of 3 bodies,

Rendiconti del Circolo Math. di Palermo XXXIX (1915) (1-46).

[8] K. Friedrichs and J. Stoker, The nonlinear boundary value problem of the buckled plate, Amer. J. Math. (1941), 839-888.

[9] M. Vainberg, Variational methods for the study of nonlinear operators Holden Day (English Edition) 1964.

[10] M. Krasnosel'skii, Topological methods in the theory of nonlinear integral equations, Pergamon, New York (1964).

[11] O. Ladyzhenskaya, The mathematical theory of viscous incompressible Flow, Gordon and Breach, New York, (1963).

[12] W. Velte, Stabilätsverhalten und Verzweigung stationer Lösungen der Navier Stokesschen Gleichungen, Arch. Rat. Mech. (17) 97-125 (1964).

[13] V. Yudovich, The bifurcation of a Rotating Flow of Fluid, Dokl. Akad. Nauk USSR Vol. 169, No. 2 pp. 306-309 (1966.)

[14] A. Harnack, Über die Vielheiligkeit der ebenen algebraischen Kurven, Math. Annalen X, (1876).

[15] D. Hilbert, Über die reele Zuge algebraischer Kurven, Math. Annalen XXXVIII, (1891).

[16] C. L. Siegel, Lectures on Celestial Mechanics (John Hopkins University) (1953).

[17] J. Moser, Notes on Ordinary Differential Equations (Stanford) (1966).

[18] L. Bauer, and E. Reiss, Nonlinear buckling of rectangular plates, Journal S. I. A. M. 13 (1965), 603-627.

[19] J. Leray, Etude de diverses equation integrales nonlineares, Journal Math. Pure Appl. 12 (1933) 1-82.

[20] E. Hopf, A mathematical example displaying the features of turbulence, Comm. Pure Applied Math. p. 303-322 (1948).

[21] F. Rellich, Störungstheorie der Spektralzerlegung I, Math. Ann 113, 600-619 (1936).

[22] L. Nirenberg, Estimates and existence of solutions of elliptic equations, Comm. Pure and Appl. Math. (1956) 509-530.

[23] L. Bers, F. John, M. Schechter, Partial Differential Equations, Interscience (New York) 1964.

[24] S. Agmon, The L_p approach to the Dirichlet problem, Ann. Scuola di Pisa, 13 (1959), 405-448.

[25] S. Agmon A. Douglis and L. Nirenberg, Estimates near the boundary for solutions of elliptic equations, Comm. Pure and Appl. Math 2 (1959) 623-727.

[26] Reference [1(a)].

[27] Reference [10].

[28] J. Schwartz, Generalizing the Lyusternik-Schnirelmann theory of critical points, Comm. Pure Appl. Math 17 (1964).

[29] L. Lyusternik and L. Schnirelmann, Methodes topologique dans les problems variationels, Hermann, Paris, (1934).

[30] F. Browder, Lyusternik-Schnirelmann category and nonlinear elliptic eigenvalue problems, Annals of Math. 72 (1965), 559-477.

[31] R. Palais, Lyusternik-Schnirelmann theory of Banach manifolds, Topology 15 (1966), 115-132.

[32] H. Keller, J. Keller, and E. Reiss, Buckled states of circular plates, Quart. Appl. Math. 20 (1962), 55-65.

VII. A Bifurcation Theory for Nonlinear Elliptic Partial Differential Equations (continued)

Melvyn S. Berger

12. Variational Operators Without Symmetry Assumptions.

In this lecture we show that some of the bifurcation results of Section 10 can be extended to variational operators independent of any symmetry assumptions. A somewhat different formulation of this fact is due to M. Krasnosel'skii [1]. However the multiplicity theory of Part 10 does not carry over to this case. The following example clarifies this point.

Example. (An operator equation having multiplicity index $p = 2$ at an eigenvalue having only one branch of real solutions bifurcating from it.)

Let the Hilbert space $H = R^2$. We consider the equation

$$x = \lambda(x + x^2 - y^2),$$
$$y = \lambda(y + 2xy). \tag{12.1}$$

If we set $z = x + iy$, (12.1) is equivalent to $z = \lambda(z + z^2)$. Clearly $\lambda = 1$ is an eigenvalue of multiplicity 2 for the linearized problem. On the other hand setting $\lambda = 1 + \varepsilon$ for ε real, we see that the only real solutions of (12.1) are of the form $z(\varepsilon) = (x(\varepsilon), y(\varepsilon)) = (-\frac{\varepsilon}{1+\varepsilon}, 0)$. This $z(\varepsilon)$ determines a one parameter family of solutions and thus only one branch of solutions bifurcates from $\lambda = 1$.

This observation has also been confirmed for certain boundary value problems in ordinary differential equation by E. Reiss in [2]. In theoretical and numerical studies Reiss showed that in a specific case from some eigenvalues of multiplicity 2 there bifurcates only one branch of solutions for the nonlinear equation, while other eigenvalues have three such branches.

Throughout this work we shall follow the notation and definitions of Lecture VI. Full proofs of our results can be found in [3].

We first study bifurcation from the lowest eigenvalue λ_1.

We consider operator equations of the form

$$u = \lambda(L_2 u + N_2 u) \tag{12.2}$$

$$u + N_1 u = \lambda L_2 u. \tag{12.3}$$

In conformity with the notation of Lecture VI, we call equations of type (12.2) case (a) and equations of type (12.3) case (b). The linearized equation

$$u = \lambda L_2 u \tag{12.4}$$

has a smallest eigenvalue $\lambda_1 > 0$, provided L_2 is positive, compact and self-adjoint. The direct method of the calculus of variations enables us to show that bifurcation always occurs from the first eigenvalue λ_1, independent of its multiplicity and of any symmetry properties of the nonlinearity, provided this nonlinearity determines a variational operator. Moreover, this branch of solutions can be continued for large norms subject to very mild restrictions on the nonlinearity.

Bifurcation Theorem 12.1. Let the operator equation $Au = \lambda Bu$ have the following properties: $A = L_1 + N_1$ is an operator of class I and $B = L_2 + N_2$ is an operator of class II (See Section 10). Then in cases (a) and (b), from the smallest eigenvalue λ_1 of $L_1 u = \lambda L_2 u$ there bifurcates at least a one parameter family of solutions to the nonlinear equation

$Au = Bu.$

Sketch of proof. We consider case (b). (Case (a) can be treated similarly.)

Set $c_1(R) = \inf \Phi_1(u)$ for small positive R

$\Phi_2(u) = R$

where $\Phi_1(u) = \frac{1}{2}(L_1u,u) + \int_0^1 (u,N_1(su))ds, \ \Phi_2(u) = \frac{1}{2}(L_2u,u).$

Let $\tilde{c}_1(R) = \inf \frac{1}{2}(L_1u,u).$

$\Phi_2(u) = R$

From Lemma 10.7 we have $|c_1(R) - \tilde{c}_1(R)| \leq KR^\sigma$ for $\sigma > 1$, where K is a constant independent of R.

In the Hilbert space H, the extremum problems which define $c_1(R)$ and $\tilde{c}_1(R)$ have solutions $u_1(R)$ and $\tilde{u}_1(R)$ with associated eigenvalues $\lambda_1(R)$ and λ_1 which determine solutions of the associated Euler-Lagrange equations:

$$Au_1(R) = \lambda_1(R)Bu_1(R), \tag{12.5}$$

$$L_1\tilde{u}_1(R) = \lambda_1 L_2\tilde{u}_1(R). \tag{12.6}$$

The solutions $u_1(R)$ and $\tilde{u}_1(R)$ lie on the surface $\Phi(u) = R$ because this surface is weakly closed in H. To see this we note that L_2u is a compact linear operator. Thus if $u_n \to u$ weakly in H, then $L_2u_n \to L_2u$ strongly. Therefore,

$$\Phi_2(u_n)-\Phi_2(u)= \frac{1}{2}(u_n,Lu_n)- \frac{1}{2}(u,Lu)= \frac{1}{2}(u_n-u,Lu)- \frac{1}{2}(u_n,Lu-Lu_n).$$

By the Schwarz inequality and the weak convergence of $\{u_n\}$, we have

$$|\Phi_2(u_n) - \Phi_2(u)| \leq \frac{1}{2}|(u_2-u, Lu)| - \frac{1}{2}\|u_n\| \, \|Lu - Lu_n\| .$$

Thus, as $n \to \infty$, $\Phi_2(u_n) \to \Phi_2(u)$ so that if $\Phi_2(u_n) = R$, then $\Phi_2(u) = R$. As in the proof of Theorem 10.8 we can show that $\lim_{R \to 0} |\lambda_n(R) - \lambda_n| \to 0$. Here it is important to note that no topological argument is needed. Indeed, the solution of the minimum problems for $c_1(R)$ and $\tilde{c}_1(R)$ follows from the weak lower semicontinuity of the functionals $\Phi_1(u)$ and $\frac{1}{2}(L_1u,u)$ and from the generalized Weierstrass theorem which states that such a functional bounded from below on a weakly compact set, achieves its infinimum there. That the solution of the extremum problem is actually a solution of the operator equation follows as in [4] PART III.

Corollary 12.2. *In case (b) let* $\Phi_1(u) \geq 0$ *for all* $u \in H$. *Then the family of solutions* $u_1(R)$ *bifurcating from* λ_1 *exists for all values of R.*

Proof: This fact follows immediately from the proof of the theorem since the functional $\Phi_1(u)$ is then bounded from below by 0 for all $u \in H$, and thus the functional $\Phi_1(u)$ achieves its infinimum on the surface $\Phi_2(u) = R$ for all values R.

We now show that an existence theory for bifurcation is valid for the class of variational operators considered in Theorem 12.1 at all eigenvalues λ_n of the associated linearized problem. For clarity, we distinguish two possible circumstances.

Case I: (cf. The Perturbation Theory of Section 9.) The branching equations near an eigenvalue $\frac{1}{\mu_n}$ of multiplicity p:

$$(P_2(\sum_{j=1}^{n} \varepsilon_i u_i), u_i) = \varepsilon(\mu - \mu_n) \quad (i = 1,\dots,n)$$

are non degenerate, i.e.,

$$(P_2(\sum_{j=1}^{p} \varepsilon_i u_i), u_i) \neq 0$$

for some values of $(\varepsilon_1, \varepsilon_2, \dots, \varepsilon_p)$ and P_2 a variational operator.

Case II: The branching equations are degenerate, i.e.,

$$(P_2(\sum_{i=1}^{p} \varepsilon_i u_i), u_i) = 0 \qquad i = 1,\dots,p$$

for all values $\varepsilon = (\varepsilon_1, \dots, \varepsilon_p)$.

By using only elementary arguments, we now show that a result analogous to the Theorem 12.1 is valid in Case I.

<u>Theorem</u> 12.2. <u>Let the operator equation</u> $Au = \lambda Bu$ <u>have the following properties</u>: $A = L_1 + N_1$ <u>is an operator of Class I and</u> $B = L_2 + N_2$ <u>is an operator of Class II</u>. <u>In cases (a)</u>

<u>and (b), if the assumptions of Case I are satisfies at an eigenvalue</u> λ_n, <u>then a one-parameter family of solutions to the full nonlinear equations</u> $Au = \lambda Bu$ <u>branches from</u> λ_n.

<u>Proof</u>: According to the arguments of Theorem 9.1 on perturbation theory it is sufficient to study the structure of the solutions $(\varepsilon_1,\ldots,\varepsilon_p)$ for the branching equations

$$(P_2(\sum_{k=1}^{p} \varepsilon_k u_k), u_i = \varepsilon_1(\mu - \mu_n) \quad (i=1,\ldots,p) \quad (12.7)$$

where $\frac{1}{\mu_n}$ is an eigenvalue of multiplicity p with associated orthonormal eigenvectors $(u_1,\ldots,u_p)$. According to the assumptions of Case I we note that the functional

$$(P_2(\sum_{i=1}^{p} \varepsilon_i u_i), \sum_{i=1}^{p} \varepsilon_i u_i) = f(\varepsilon_1,\ldots,\varepsilon_p)$$

is not identically zero and has as gradient the left hand side of (12.7). Thus the branching equations (12.7) can always be solved for $|\varepsilon|^2 = |\varepsilon_1|^2 + \ldots |\varepsilon_p|^2$ sufficiently small. Indeed, these equations can be considered as determining the critical points in R^p of the continuous function $f(\varepsilon_1,\ldots,\varepsilon_p)$ on the sphere $\sum_{i=1}^{p} \varepsilon_i^2 = K$ where K is a small fixed number. Furthermore, a continuous function, not identically zero, on this sphere has a maximum and minimum, both of which cannot be zero. It is this nonzero critical point that determines a one parameter family of solutions of the equations (12.7) for $0 < K < K_o$, for K_o sufficiently small.

We now ask if Theorem 12.2 is valid in Case II. We shall complete this Section by giving an affirmative answer to this question. The proof, however, is not elementary and will be found in the author's forthcoming paper [3].

Theorem 12.3. Let the operator equation $Au = \lambda Bu$ have the following properties: $A = L_1 + N_1$ is an operator of Class I and $B = L_2 + N_2$ is an operator of Class II. Then in cases (a) and (b), bifurcation always takes place from each eigenvalue λ_n of the linearized equations.

13. The von Kármán Equations for The Buckling of Thin Elastic Shells.

As an application of the results of Section 12, we show how the results of Section 11, Example 1, can be extended to curved elastic structures. (The notation of this example is retained.) Full proofs appear in [4]. The von Kármán equations for the buckling of a thin cylindrical shell of constant initial curvature K subjected to appropriate boundary conditions to guarantee buckling can be written:

$$\begin{aligned} \Delta^2 f &= -\frac{1}{2}[w,w] + Kw_{xx}, \\ & \qquad\qquad\qquad\qquad \text{in } \Omega \qquad (13.1) \\ \Delta^2 w &= -\lambda w_{xx} + [f,w] - Kf_{xx}, \end{aligned}$$

$$\left.\begin{aligned} w &= w_x = w_y = 0, \\ f &= f_x = f_y = 0, \end{aligned}\right\} \quad \text{on } \partial\Omega \qquad (13.2)$$

where Ω is a rectangular domain in R^2 and $[f,g] = f_{xx}g_{yy} + f_{yy}g_{xx} - 2f_{xy}g_{xy}$.

The linearization of this system can be written

$$\left.\begin{aligned} \Delta^2 f &= Kw_{xx} \\ \Delta^2 w &= -w_{xx} - Kf_{xx}, \end{aligned}\right\} \quad \text{in } \Omega \qquad (13.3)$$

$$\left.\begin{aligned} w &= w_x = w_y = 0 \\ f &= f_x = f_y = 0 \end{aligned}\right\} \quad \text{on } \partial\Omega \qquad (13.4)$$

The system (13.3)-(13.4) is self adjoint and possesses a countably infinite number of eigenvalues $\lambda_n \to \infty$. Bifurcation from each eigenvalue λ_n is guaranteed by the following result:

Theorem 13.1. *In the vicinity of each eigenvalue* λ_n *of the system* (13.3)-(13.4), *there is a number* $\lambda_n(R)$ *for which the system* (13.1)-(13.2) *has a corresponding nontrivial solution* $(w_n(R), f_n(R))$. *Here* R *is a sufficiently small positive number. As* $R \to 0$, $\lambda_n(R) \to \lambda_n$ *and* $(w_n(R), f_n(R)) \to (0,0)$ *in the* L_2 *sense*.

Proof. This results follows from Theorem 12.3 once the systems (13.1)-(13.2) and (13.3)-(13.4) are reformulated as operator equations in the Hilbert space $\dot{W}_{2,2}(\Omega)$. To accomplish this task we again use the divergence structure of the von Kármán equations (as in Section 11) to obtain the operator equation

$$f = -\frac{1}{2} C(w,w) - KLw$$
$$w = \lambda Lw + C(w,f) + KLf. \tag{13.5}$$

(Note that these equations differ from the von Kármán equations for plates only by the presence of a linear term at the end of each equation.)

As before we eliminate f from these equations; f is uniquely determined once w is known. We thus obtain the equation

$$w + K^2L^2w + \frac{1}{2} Cw + KC(w,Lw) + \frac{K}{2} LC(w,w)=\lambda Lw \tag{13.6}$$

and its linearization

$$w + K^2L^2w = \lambda Lw. \tag{13.7}$$

Theorem 12.3 can now be applied to this system of equations since the operator $w + K^2L^2w + \frac{1}{2} C w + KC(w,Lw) + \frac{K}{2} LC(w,w)$ is an operator of Class I, L is a self-adjoint positive operator, and the equation (13.6) is of type (b).

The bifurcation Theorem 12.1 can also be applied in this case to study the spectral theory near λ_1, the lowest eigenvalue of (13.3)-(13.4). A result in this direction is the following

Theorem 13.2. From the lowest eigenvalue λ_1 of the system (13.3)-(13.4) bifurcates a one parameter family of nontrivial solutions $u_1(R)$ with associated eigenvalue $\lambda_1(R)$ for the system (13.1)-(13.2). This family exists for all values of the parameter R, and $\lambda_1(R) \to 0$ as $R \to 0$. Furthermore for small $R(\neq 0)$, $\lambda_1(R) < \lambda_1$.

14. Operators Representable as Compact Perturbations of the Identity.

We now define a nonlinear invariant useful in the study of the bifurcation theory of operator equations that are not necessarily of variational type. This invariant is known as the degree of mapping and assigns to each mapping for which the invariant is defined a definite integer which may be positive, negative, or zero. The finite dimensional case was studied initially by L. Brouwer in the early part of this century. The extension to the infinite dimensional case is due to J. Schauder and J. Leray [5].

a. The Definition of Degree of a Mapping.

Finite Dimensional Case. Let D be any open bounded set in R^n with boundary ∂D. For any given $p \in R^n$, we consider the number of solutions in D of the equation $f(x) = p$, where f is a continuous function mapping $D \to R^n$. We "measure" the number of solutions of this equation by an integer $d(p,f,D)$

which is defined in the following manner. (Throughout we assume $f(x) \neq p$ for $x \in \partial D$.)

Step 1. Suppose $f(x) = (f_1(x), f_2(x), \ldots, f_n(x)) \in C^1(D)$, i.e., f is a continuously differentiable function on D, and the Jacobian $\det\left(\frac{\partial f_i}{\partial x_j}\right) \neq 0$ at those values of $x \in D$ for which $f(x) = p$. Then we define $d(p,f,D) = \sum_{x:f(x)=p} \text{sign} \det\left(\frac{\partial f_i}{\partial x_j}\right)$. This sum is finite since the set $\{x | f(x) = p\}$ is discrete. This follows from the implicit function theorem and from the compactness of $\bar{D} \equiv D \cup \partial D$.

Step 2. If the $\det\left(\frac{\partial f_i}{\partial x_j}\right) = 0$ at some value of x for which $f(x) = p$, we use a theorem due to A. Sard (cf. [6]) that asserts we can find a sequence $\{p_n\} \to p$ in D such that $\det\left(\frac{\partial f_i}{\partial x_j}\right) \neq 0$ for any $\{x | f(x) = p_n, n = 1,2,\ldots,\}$. Thus we define $d(p,f,D)$ by approximation as follows:

$$d(p,f,D) = \lim_{n \to \infty} d(p_n,f,D).$$

(It can be shown that this definition is independent of the approximating sequence of points p_n.)

Step 3. If $f \in C(D)$, i.e., if f is merely continuous, we again define $d(p,f,D)$ by approximating as follows: Since $C^1(D)$ is dense in $C(D)$, we let $\{f_n\}$ be any uniformly convergent sequence of function tending to f everywhere in D. Then we define

$$d(p,f,D) = \lim_{n \to \infty} d(p,f_n,D).$$

Again it can be shown that this definition is independent of the approximating sequence $\{f_n\}$.

Infinite Dimensional Case. Let X be a Banach space over the real numbers. Then the degree of a mapping cannot be defined for all continuous mappings of $X \to X$. However it can be defined for all mappings that are compact perturbations of the identity, i.e., all mappings of the form $I + C$. Here I is the indentity map of $X \to X$ defined by $I(x) = x$ and C is a compact (not necessarily linear) mapping of $X \to X$, i.e., if $\{x_n\}$ is any bounded sequence in X, $\{Cx_n\}$ has a convergent subsequence. To formulate such a definition we need the following two results:

(i) Compact mappings can be approximated by finite dimensional operators in the following sense:

Theorem 14.1. *A mapping* $C: X \to X$ *is compact if and only if for every* $\varepsilon > 0$ *there is a mapping* $C_\varepsilon: X \to E_n$ *where* E_n *is a finite dimensional subspace of* X *such that*

$$||Cx - C_\varepsilon x|| \leq \varepsilon ||x||$$

for every $x \in X$. (A proof of this result is given in [5].)

(ii) _If_ $f(x)$ _maps the domain_ $D \subset R^n$ _into a subspace_ R^m _of_ R^n, _then the degree of the mapping_ $x + f(x)$, $d(p, x + f(x), D)$, _does not change when restricted to the subspace_ R^m (_provided, of course, that the degree is defined_).

The properties (i) and (ii) imply that there is a sequence of finite dimensional operators $\{F_n\}$ with range in R^n approximating an infinite dimensional operator of the form $(I + C)$, such that for sufficiently large n, $d(p, F_n, D_n)$ becomes a constant (independent of n). Here $D_n = D \cap R^n$.) This constant is the degree $d(p, I+C, D)$ of the infinite dimensional operator $I + C$ where $p \in X$ and D is a bounded open set in X.

b. Properties of the Degree of a Mapping.

The degree $d(p, I + C, D)$ of a mapping $I + C: X \to X$ relative to the point p and bounded domain $D \subset X$ is defined whenever $(I + C)(x) = p$ has no solutions $x \in \partial D$. The degree is an integer and has the following properties:

(i) If $(I + C)(x) \neq p$ in $\bar{D}$, then $d(p, I + C, D) = 0$.

(ii) If $(I + C)(x) = p$ has a finite number of solutions $x_1, x_2, \ldots, x_n \in D$ then $d(p, I + C, D) = \sum_{i=1}^{n} d(p, I + C, D)$ where $D_i \subset D$ is a sphere of sufficiently small radius inscribed about $x_i (i = 1, \ldots, n)$ such that D_i encloses x_i and no other x_j, $j \neq i$.

(iii). $d(p,I+C,D)$ is continuous in p and C (in the norm topology).

(iv). (Invariance under homotopy). Let $H(x,t)$: $X \times [0,1] \to X$ be such that $H(x,t) \neq p$ for any $x \in \partial D$ and $t \in [0,1]$. If $H(x,t)$ is uniformly continuous in t with respect to X, then $d(p,H(x,t),D)$ is a constant independent of t, provided it is defined for all values of $t \in [0,1]$.

(v). If the mappings $I + C$ and $I + \tilde{C}$ do not point in opposite directions at any point on $\| x \| = 1$, then $d(p,I+\tilde{C},D) = d(p,L+C,D)$, (provided both sides of the equation are defined). (This is the Poincare-Bohl theorem.)

(vi). (Borsuk's Theorem). If the mapping $(I + C)(x)$ has the property that $C(-x) = -C(x)$ for all x on the unit sphere $\| x \| = 1$, then $\deg(0,L+C,\| x \| \leq 1)$ is an odd number. (For the proof of these results we refer to the lecture notes of J. Schwartz [6].)

The relevance of the degree for bifurcation theory is expressed in the following way. We consider nonzero solutions of the equation $x = \lambda Cx$, where C is compact with $C(0) = 0$ and λ is a real parameter. We wish to find those values λ at which the number of solutions to $x = \lambda Cx$ changes. Then we utilize the following three propositions, which we shall not prove

(i) If $d(0,I-\lambda C,\| x \| \leq \delta)$ is different for $\lambda > \lambda_o$ and

$\lambda < \lambda_o$, the equation $u = \lambda Cu$ must have some nontrivial solution of small norm in the neighborhood of $\lambda = \lambda_o$.

(ii) Suppose $Cu = Lu + Du$ where L is a compact linear operator and D is a compact operator of higher order i.e. $\|Du\| \leq k\|u\|^{1+\varepsilon}$ for $\varepsilon > 0$. Then for sufficiently small $\delta > 0$

$$d(0, I-\lambda(L+D), \|x\| \leq \delta) = d(0, I-\lambda L, \|x\| \leq \delta)$$

(iii) Let L be a compact linear operator and λ_o a real positive eigenvalue of L. Then for sufficiently small $\varepsilon > 0$,

$$d(0, I-(\lambda_o+\varepsilon)L, \|x\| \leq \delta) - d(0, I-(\lambda_o-\varepsilon)L, \|x\| \leq \delta) = (-1)^{\beta}$$

where β is the multiplicity of the eigenvalue λ_o. Thus we have the following principle for the existence of bifurcation:

Theorem 14.2. *Let L be a compact linear mapping of the Banach space X into itself. Suppose λ_o is a real positive eigenvalue of odd multiplicity for L. Then λ_o is a bifurcation point for any equation of the form $x = \lambda(Lx + Cx)$ where C is a nonzero compact operator mapping $X \to X$ with $\|C_x\| \leq k\|x\|^{1+\varepsilon}$ for some $\varepsilon > 0$.*

Proof: This result follows immediately from the properties (i), (ii), (iii) directly above.

15. An Application of the Degree of a Mapping.

An outstanding problem in theoretical hydrodynamics can be stated as follows. Can the nonlinear stationary problem associated with the Navier-Stokes equations for viscous incompressible fluid flow have more than one smooth solution for large Reynolds numbers? A celebrated special case of this problem is known as Taylor instability. This problem is concerned with viscous fluid motions between two concentric rotating cylinders. (See Section 3, Example 5 and Lecture XIV). Experimental facts with reference to this problem have been carefully studied and are well summarized in the article of Cole [7]. An important theoretical investigation is due to Velte [8] who showed that if only the inner cylinder rotates, then at a sufficiently large angular velocity a new steady solution, known as a Taylor vortex, bifurcates from the so-called Couette flow. This result is in accord with experiments. In the proof of his result Velte made essential use of the degree of a mapping in the form given in Theorem 14.2. Velte's result was almost simultaneously extended by Yudovich [9]. We intend to discuss Yudovich's results from the viewpoint of Theorem 14.2.

To apply Theorem 14.2 in the present case we show:

(i) The difference between any possible steady secondary flow and the Couette flow satisfies a nonlinear elliptic eigenvalue problem of the type considered in Section 7. Here the eigenvalue is the Reynolds number R, which is, in turn, determined by the angular velocities of the rotating cylinders.

(ii) The associated operator equation has the form

$$u = \lambda(Lu + Qu),$$

where L is a real linear non self-adjoint compact operator mapping a Hilbert space H into itself and Q is a compact homogeneous quadratic operator mapping H into itself.

(iii) The linearized problem $u = \lambda Lu$ can be reduced to a linear integral equation with an oscillating kernel mentioned at the very end of Section 6.

(iv) By the Theorem 6.3 of Krein, the associated eigenvalues λ_n of this integral equation are real and are of multiplicity 1.

(v) Since 1 is an odd number, Theorem 14.2 is applicable and one can demonstrate the existence of a countably infinite number of distinct steady motions bifurcating from the Couette flow at various Reynolds numbers.

We consider the flow of a viscous incompressible fluid between two rotating concentric cylinders. This flow is governed by the Navier-Stokes equations and the continuity equation which determine the velocity vector v' and the pressure p'. We employ cylindrical coordinates (r,θ,z) in which v' has components (u',v',w'). The equations hold in the domain G consisting of the volume between the cylinders

$r = r_1$ and $r = r_2 (r_1 < r_2)$. The angular velocities of the inner and outer cylinders are denoted ω_1 and ω_2. The boundary conditions are that the velocities of the fluid at the rigid rotating boundaries equal the velocities of the boundaries.

A solution of these equations satisfying the boundary conditions is the Couette flow:

$$u' = 0, \; v' = v_o = A_r + B/r, \; w' = 0, \; p' = p_o = \int_{r_1}^{r_2} [v_o(r)/r]\,dr + K$$

where

$$A = -\frac{\omega_2 r_2^2 - \omega_1 r_1^2}{r_2^2 - r_1^2}, \qquad B = \frac{(\omega_2 - \omega_1) r_1^2 r_2^2}{r_2^2 - r_1^2},$$

and K is some constant.

To study the bifurcation of solutions from the Couette flow, we set

$$\underset{\sim}{v}' = \underset{\sim}{v} + \underset{\sim}{v}_o, \qquad p' = R^{-1} p + p_o.$$

Here $\underset{\sim}{v} = (u,v,w)$ and R is the Reynolds number. We wish such bifurcating solutions to exhibit the experimentally observable properties of Taylor vortices. We therefore assume that

(i) The flow is axisymmetric and steady.

(ii) The flow has period $2\pi/\alpha_o$ in z.

(iii) There is no net mass flow in the z-direction.

(iv) Coordinates can be selected so that u and v are even functions of z and w is an odd function of z.

(See Figure 1).

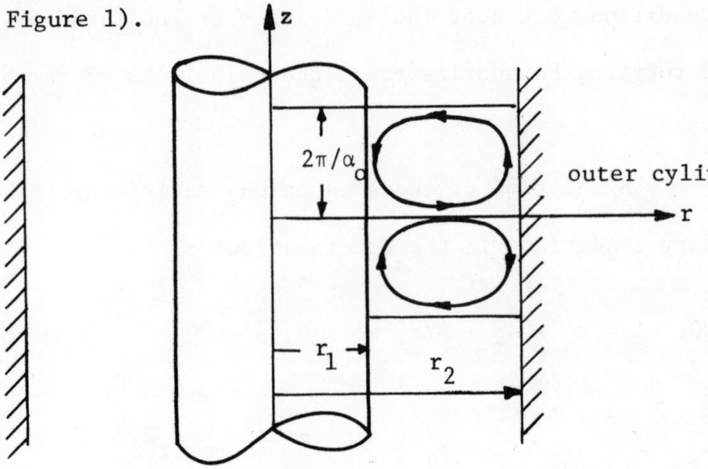

Figure 1.

These conditions can be expressed mathematically in the form

$$\underset{\sim}{v} = \underset{\sim}{v}(r,z), \qquad \underset{\sim}{v}(r,z + 2\pi/\alpha_o) = \underset{\sim}{v}(r,z)$$

$$\int_{r_1}^{r_2} w(r,z)r\,dr = 0, \; u(r,z) = u(r,-z), \; v(r,z) = v(r,-z), \; w(r,z) = -w(r,-z).$$

We obtain the following boundary value problem for $\underset{\sim}{v}$ and p:

$$\Delta u - \frac{u}{r^2} - p_r = R[uu_r + wu_z - (\frac{1}{r})v^2 - \frac{2}{r} v_o v]$$

$$\Delta v - \frac{v}{r^2} = R[uv_r + wv_z + \frac{1}{r} uv + \frac{1}{2}(v_o + rv_{or})u] \tag{15.1}$$

$$\Delta w - p_z = R[uw_r + ww_z]$$

$$(ru)_r + rw_z = 0 \tag{15.2}$$

$$u, v, w = 0 \text{ for } r = r_1, r_2 \tag{15.3}$$

$$\underset{\sim}{v}(r, z + 2\pi/\alpha_o) = \underset{\sim}{v}(r,z).$$

where $\Delta = \frac{\partial^2}{\partial r^2} + \frac{1}{r}\frac{\partial}{\partial r} + \frac{\partial^2}{\partial z^2}$.

We write (15.1) as the system

$$A\underset{\sim}{v} - \text{grad } p = R\{L(\underset{\sim}{v}_o)\underset{\sim}{v} + N\underset{\sim}{v}\}$$

where A and $L(\underset{\sim}{v}_o)$ are linear operators and N is a quadratic nonlinear operator.

The associated linear system can then be written

$$A\underset{\sim}{v} - \text{grad } p = RL(\underset{\sim}{v}_o)\underset{\sim}{v}. \tag{15.4}$$

together with the equations (15.2), (15.3).

We associate with the system (15.1)-(15.3) generalized solutions and operator equations in an appropriate Hilbert space. We consider the set M of twice continuously differentiable solenoidal vectors $\underset{\sim}{v}$ defined in the domain $\{r_1 \leq r \leq r; -\infty < z < \infty\}$ satisfying the conditons (i)-(iv). To obtain a Hilbert space H from the set M we complete M with respect to the norm obtained from the inner product:

$$(\underset{\sim}{v}_1, \underset{\sim}{v}_2)_H = -\int_{\pi/\alpha_o}^{\pi/\alpha_o}\int_{r_1}^{r_2}\{[\Delta u_1 - \frac{u_1}{r^2}]u_2 + [\Delta v_1 - \frac{v_1}{r^2}]v_2 + [\Delta w_1]w_2\}rdr \tag{15.5}$$

Here it is understood that we integrate the above

formula by parts using the boundary conditions to obtain a formula involving only first derivatives of $\underset{\sim}{v}_1$ and $\underset{\sim}{v}_2$.

We then find that the equations (15.1)-(15.3) can be written in the operator formulation in H as

$$\underset{\sim}{v} = R(L\underset{\sim}{v} + Q\underset{\sim}{v}) \tag{15.6}$$

where L is a compact linear operator (H → H) and Q is a compact quadratic operator (H → H). We note that pressure gradient terms disappear because we are considering solutions in the subspace of solenoidal vectors which is perpendicular to the subspace of gradients.

To find properties of the linearized problem (15.2)-(15.4) we write tentative solutions $\tilde{u},\tilde{v},\tilde{w},\tilde{\phi}$ as Fourier series, i.e. linear combinations of solutions of the form

$$\tilde{u} = U(r) \cos \alpha_o nz$$
$$\tilde{v} = V(r) \cos \alpha_o nz$$
$$\tilde{w} = W(r) \sin \alpha_o nz$$
$$\tilde{p} = P(r) \cos \alpha_o nz$$

After substitution, we find that W(r) and P(r) are determined once U(r), V(r) and R are obtained from the following system:

$$[L - (\alpha_o n)^2]^2 U = 2\alpha_o^2 n^2 R\omega(r)V \tag{15.7}$$

$$[L - (\alpha_o n)^2]V = -Rg(r)U$$

$$U = V = \frac{dU}{dr} = 0 \qquad \text{for } r = r_1, r_2$$

where $\omega(r) = \frac{v_o}{r}$

$$g(r) = -\left(\frac{dv_o}{dr} + \frac{v_o}{r}\right)$$

$$L = \left(\frac{d}{dr^2} + \frac{1}{r}\frac{d}{dr} - \frac{1}{r^2}\right).$$

Now to apply Krein's theory of oscillating kernels to this system we note that the differential operators occuring in (15.7) can be written as follows

$$-r(L - \alpha^2)U = \rho_o \frac{d}{dr}\{\rho_1[\frac{d}{dr}(\rho_2 U)]\}$$

$$r(L - \alpha^2)^2 U = \rho_o \frac{d}{dr}\{\rho_1 \frac{d}{dr}[\rho_2 \rho_o \frac{d}{dr}\{\rho_1[\frac{d}{dr}(\rho_2 U)]\}]\}.$$

Here ρ_o, ρ_1, ρ_2 are positive functions of r. Thus by a result of Krein [3], the Green's functions for these operators with the given boundary conditions are oscillatory kernels.

The system (15.7) is then found to be equivalent to the uncoupled system of integral equations:

$$\begin{aligned} U &= \mu G_2[g(r)G_1(\omega(r)U)] \\ V &= \mu G_1\{\omega(r)G_2[g(r)V]\} \end{aligned} \qquad (15.8)$$

where G_1, and G_2 are integral operators with kernels associated with differential operators of (15.7). A simple eigenvalue $\mu > 0$ of the first equation in (15.8) is then found to be a simple eigenvalue R of (15.4) where

$R = \pm\sqrt{\dfrac{\mu}{2\alpha_o^2 n^2}}$. Set $\Lambda_i(\alpha) = \left(\dfrac{\mu_i(\alpha)}{\alpha^2}\right)^{1/2}$. We consider the set of those α_o for which

$$\Lambda_{ikrs}(\alpha_o) = \Lambda_i(k\alpha_o) - \Lambda_r(s\alpha_o) = 0$$

It can be shown that this set is countably infinite since Λ_{ikrs} is analytic in α_o and thus has at most a countably infinite number of zeros provided the function itself is not identically zero.

Theorem 15.1 ([9]). Suppose $\omega_1 > 0$, $\omega_2 \geq 0$ and $\omega_1 r_1^2 > \omega_2 r_2^2$. Then for any positive number α_o (with the exception of a countably infinite set) the system (15.2)-(15.4) has a sequence of positive simple eigenvalues $0 < R_1(\alpha_o) < R_2(\alpha_o) < \ldots$ each of which is a bifurcation point of the system (15.1)-(15.3). Furthermore $\min\limits_{0<\alpha<\infty} R_1(\alpha) > 0$ and is attained for some value α_o.

Sketch of proof. The conditions $\omega_1 > 0$, $\omega_2 \geq 0$, $\omega_1 r_1^2 > \omega_2 r_2^2$ are precisely those that guarantee the positivity of the functions $\omega(r)$ and $g(r)$ of (15.7) and thus that kernels associated with G_1 and G_2 are oscillatory. The omission of the countable set α_o guarantees that no eigenvalue of the form $\left(\dfrac{\mu_i(k\alpha_o)}{k^2\alpha_o^2}\right)^{1/2}$ is multiple. Thus Theorem 14.2 is directly applicable to yield the first part of the bifurcation theorem. To prove the second part of the theorem we note that $R_1(\alpha)$ is continuous in α for $\alpha \varepsilon (0,\infty)$ and we can then show that $R_i(\alpha) \to \infty$ as $\alpha \to 0$ or ∞. For example to show $R_i(\alpha) \to \infty$ as $\to \infty$ 0 we note that from above, $R_1(\alpha) = \frac{\sqrt{\mu_1(\alpha)}}{\alpha}$ and $\mu_1(\alpha)$ is continuous over the real axis with $\mu_1(0) > 0$.

Thus $\lim_{\alpha \to 0} R_1(\alpha) = \lim_{\alpha \to 0} \frac{\sqrt{\mu_1(\alpha)}}{\alpha} = \infty.$

Bibliography

[1] M.Krasnosel'skii (see [10] Lecture 6).

[2] E. Reiss, Bifurcation Buckling of Spherical Caps, Comm. Pure and Appl. Math 65-82 Vol. XVIII (1965).

[3] M. Berger, A New Bifurcation Theory for a Class of Nonlinear Elliptic Partial Differential Equations (forthcoming paper).

[4] M. Berger, An Application of the Calculus of Variations in the Large to the Equations of Nonlinear Elasticity (forthcoming paper).

[5] J. Leray and J. Schauder, Topologie et Equations Fonctionelles, Ann. Sci. Ecole Norm Sup. 3(51), 1934 45-78.

[6] J. T. Schwartz, Lectures on Nonlinear Functional

Analysis (NYU Lecture Notes)

[7] D. Cole, Transition in circular Couette-flow, Journal of Fluid Mechanics 21, 1965, 385-425.

[8] W. Velte, Stabilität und Verzweigung stationärer Lösungen der Navier-Stokesschen Gleichungen beim Taylorproblem. Arch. Ratl. Mech. Anal. 22, 1966,1-14.

[9] V. Yudovich, See [13] Lecture 6.

[10] M. Krein, On asymmetric oscillatory Green's functions of ordinary differential operators, Dokl. Akad. Nauk Vol. 25, #8, 1939.

VIII. Some Positone Problems Suggested by Nonlinear Heat Generation

H. B. Keller*

1. Introduction.

There is much current interest in boundary value problems containing positive linear differential operators and monotone functions of the dependent variable, see for example, M. A. Krasnosel'ski [1] and H. H. Schaefer [2]. We call such problems "positone" and shall examine here a particular class of them.

---

*This lecture is based on a paper by H. B. Keller and D. S. Cohen [10]. Section 5 is based on a paper by D. S. Cohen [11].

One physical motivation for the problems we study concerns the temperature distribution in a body heated by the application of a uniform electric current, $i = \sqrt{\lambda}$, (Joule heating). If the body is inhomogeneous with thermal conductivity $K(x)$, if its electrical resistance $R(x,T)$ is a function of the temperature $T(x,t)$, and if radiation is negligible, the resulting problem can be formulated, in some dimensionless form, as

$$\frac{\partial T}{\partial t} - \nabla \cdot (K(x) \nabla T) = \lambda R(x,T) \tag{1.1}$$

subject to appropriate initial and boundary conditions. In particular, we are interested in the steady states, their "stability," and their dependence upon the current λ. This leads to problems of the form

$$-\nabla \cdot (K(x) \nabla T) = \lambda R(x,T), \tag{1.2}$$

subject to appropriate boundary conditions. In many cases of physical interest $R(x,T)$ is a monotone function of T(i.e. the resistance increases with temperature) and only positive solutions are physically meaningful. In some such cases it is known that a limiting current exists beyond which positive steady states do not exist. The value of this limiting current is of great interest.

The boundary conditions will always be assumed homogeneous. If in the physical problem they are not, e.g. if T is a prescribed function on the boundary, then we solve the steady state problem with zero current, $\lambda = 0$, to obtain the state $T_o(x)$. We then subtract this from the desired state, $T(x)$, to obtain a problem with homogeneous boundary conditions for the difference, $u \equiv (T-T_o)$. This in effect changes the resistance term since $R(x,T)=R(x,u+T_o)\equiv f(x,u)$, say. It is also intuitively clear from these considerations that positive solutions, $u > 0$, are of interest (i.e. the temperature increases when current is applied) and that the resistance should <u>not</u> vanish when $u \equiv 0$, i.e. $f(x,0) = R(x,T_o) > 0$.

For our study it is of no additional difficulty to treat more general equations of the form

$$Lu = \lambda f(x,u), \qquad x \in D, \tag{1.3}$$

where $x = (x_1,x_2,\ldots,x_m)$ and L is the uniformly elliptic, self-adjoint, second order operator

$$Lu \equiv - \sum_{i,j=1}^{m} \frac{\partial}{\partial x_i} (a_{ij}(x) \frac{\partial u}{\partial x_j}) + a_o(x)u. \tag{1.4}$$

The coefficients $a_{ij}(x) = a_{ji}(x)$ are continuously differentiable, $a_o(x) \geq 0$ is continuous and for all unit vectors $\xi = (\xi_1,\xi_2,\ldots,\xi_m)$,

$$\sum_{i,j=1}^{m} a_{ij}(x)\xi_i\xi_j \geq a > 0, \quad x \in D. \tag{1.5}$$

The boundary conditions will be taken as

$$Bu \equiv \alpha(x)u(x) + \beta(x)\frac{\partial u(x)}{\partial\nu} = 0, \quad x\varepsilon\,\partial D. \tag{1.6}$$

$$\alpha(x) \geq 0, \not\equiv 0; \ \beta(x) \geq 0.$$

Here $\partial/\partial\nu$ is the conormal derivative:

$$\frac{\partial u}{\partial\nu} \equiv \sum_{i,j=1}^{m} n_i(x)a_{ij}(x)\frac{\partial u}{\partial x_j}, \tag{1.7}$$

where $n(x) \equiv (n_1(x),\ldots,n_m(x))$ is the outer unit normal to ∂D at x. The functions $\alpha(x)$ and $\beta(x)$ are assumed piecewise continuous on ∂D; in fact, we require $\alpha(x) \equiv 1$, $\beta(x) \equiv 0$ on ∂D_1 where $\partial D_1 + \partial D_2 = \partial D$ and the measure of ∂D_1 is positive. The boundary is assumed so smooth that the strong maximum principle for L on D is valid, see [3].

In Section 2 we establish necessary and sufficient conditions for the existence of positive solutions to certain linear problems involving L and B. This yields the Positivity Lemma which is basic for all of our later results.

In Section 3 we investigate the nonlinear boundary value problem (1.3), (1.6) under rather mild monotonicity conditions on $f(x,u)$. The set Λ consisting of those values of λ for which positive solutions exist is completely characterized by means of an iteration procedure which yields the least or minimal positive solution when it converges.

By means of a comparison theorem we show that Λ is an interval and that the minimal solution is an increasing function of λ. We obtain upper and lower bounds on the least upper bound λ^* of Λ.

The cases when $f(x,u)$ is concave and convex in u are treated in Section 4 where more precise estimates for Λ are obtained. In particular, for concave nonlinearities Λ is shown to be open and its upper limit λ^* is determined. Furthermore for a class of nonlinearities, which include concave nonlinearities, the positive solutions are shown to be unique. These results are in marked contrast with special cases of convex $f(x,u)$ for which it is known that nonunique positive solutions exist and for which Λ is closed above.

In Section 5 we establish an alternate iteration scheme for concave nonlinearities which converges monotonically to the unique solution from above, in contrast to the aforementioned iteration procedure which converges to the solution from below.

Finally, in Section 6, we examine the stability of the positive solutions when considered as steady states of corresponding time dependent (parabolic) problems. We show that for $0 < \lambda < \lambda^*$ the minimal solutions are always stable and that for convex f they are more stable than any other positive solutions. Furthermore, as λ increases the relative stability of these minimal solutions increases if f is concave and decreases if f is convex.

2. A Lemma on Positive Operators.

It is easy to show that the operator L defined by (1.4)-(1.5) subject to homogeneous Dirichlet boundary conditions is positive. That is, if $\phi(x)$ is twice continuously differentiable and satisfies $L\phi(x) \geq 0$, $\not\equiv 0$, in D and $\phi(x) = 0$ on ∂D, then $\phi(x) > 0$ in D. This result is a consequence of the maximum principle for elliptic operators [3]. (Note the minus sign in (1.4).) However, we shall require a somewhat sharper and more general result which we state as the

Positivity Lemma. Let $\rho(x)$ be positive and continuous on D and let $\phi(x)$ be twice continuously differentiable and satisfy:

$$\begin{aligned} L\phi - \lambda\rho(x)\phi &> 0, \quad x \in D, \\ B\phi &= 0, \quad x \in \partial D. \end{aligned} \tag{2.1}$$

Then $\phi(x) > 0$ on D if and only if $\lambda < \mu_1$, where μ_1 is the principal (i.e., least) eigenvalue of

$$\begin{aligned} L\psi - \mu\rho(x)\psi &= 0, \quad x \in D, \\ B\psi &= 0, \quad x \in \partial D. \end{aligned} \tag{2.2}$$

Proof. The sufficiency part of this lemma follows from the fact that the Green's function, G_λ, for $L-\lambda\rho(x)$ on D subject to $BG_\lambda = 0$ on ∂D is positive on D if $\lambda < \mu_1$. A proof of this fact follows from the work of Aronszajn and Smith [4] on reproducing kernels. However, by using a variational characterization of the solution of the appropriate boundary value problem, Bellman [5] has given a neat proof of the fact that G_λ is non-negative for a special ordinary differential operator. This idea can easily be extended and generalized to prove sufficiency in the present case, and we shall indicate it here.

Let us write (2.1) as

$$\begin{aligned} L\phi - \lambda\rho(x)\phi &= p(x), & x \in D, \\ B\phi &= 0, & x \in \partial D, \end{aligned} \tag{2.3}$$

where $p(x) > 0$ on D and is continuous there. The solution $\phi(x)$ of this boundary value problem is also the function that minimizes the quadratic functional

$$I[\psi] \equiv Q[\psi] + \int_{\partial D_2} \frac{\alpha(x)}{\beta(x)} \psi^2(x)ds,$$

where

$$Q[\psi] \equiv \int_D \{ \sum_{i,j=1}^{m} a_{ij}(x) \frac{\partial\psi}{\partial x_i} \frac{\partial\psi}{\partial x_j} + [a_o(x)-\lambda\rho(x)]\psi^2 - 2p(x)\psi\}dx,$$

over the class of admissible functions: $A \equiv \{$all piecewise continuously differentiable functions $\psi(x)$ on D which vanish on $\partial D_1\}$. By using the variational characterization of μ_1, we can easily show that if $\lambda < \mu_1$, the quadratic terms in $I[\psi]$ are positive definite for the class of admissible functions A. This fact ensures the existence of a unique minimum which can then be shown to be a twice continuously differentiable solution of the boundary value problem (2.3). Conversely, any twice continuously differentiable solution of (2.3) is known to minimize $I[\psi]$ over A.

To show that the minimizing function, say $\phi(x)$, is positive, suppose to the contrary that it is negative somewhere in D. Then, define an admissible function $\psi(x)$ by

$$\psi(x) \equiv |\phi(x)|.$$

This does not affect the quadratic terms in $I[\psi]$, but it clearly diminishes the contribution from the term involving $p(x)$. This contradicts the fact the $\phi(x)$ is the minimizing function, from which it follows that $\phi(x) \geq 0$ on D if $\lambda<\mu_1$. To show that $\phi(x) > 0$ on D if $\lambda < \mu_1$, suppose that $\phi(x) = 0$ at some point $x \in D$. Such a point would be a relative minimum at which $\partial\phi(x)/\partial x_i = 0$, $i = 1,2,\ldots,m$ and at which the matrix $(\partial^2\phi(x)/\partial x_i\partial x_j)$ must be positive semi-definite. At this minimum the equation (2.3) reduces to

$$- \sum_{i,j=1}^{m} a_{ij}(x) \frac{\partial^2 \phi(x)}{\partial x_i \partial x_j} = p(x) > 0,$$

which contradicts the fact that $(a_{ij}(x))$ is positive definite. Thus, $\phi(x) > 0$ on D if $\lambda < \mu_1$.

To show necessity let $\phi(x) > 0$ on D be a solution of (2.3) and let $\psi_1(x)$ be an eigenfunction of (2.2) corresponding to μ_1. It is well known that $\psi_1(x) \neq 0$ on D. Now, form the quantity $(\psi_1 L\phi - \phi L\psi_1)$, integrate it over D, and obtain, by partial integration and a use of the boundary value problems (2.2) and (2.3) satisfied by $\psi_1(x)$ and $\phi(x)$, the relation

$$(\mu_1 - \lambda) \int_D \rho(x)\phi(x)\psi_1(x)dx = \int_D p(x)\psi_1(x)dx.$$

Since both integrals are of the same sign, it follows that $\mu_1 > \lambda$, thus completing the proof. Q.E.D.

We shall also require a slightly different form of the Positivity Lemma:

Weak Form of Positivity Lemma: *Let $\rho(x)$ be positive and continuous on D and let $\phi(x)$ be twice continuously differentiable and satisfy*

$$\begin{aligned} L\phi - \lambda\rho(x)\phi &\geq 0, & x \in D \\ B\phi &= 0, & x \in \partial D. \end{aligned} \tag{2.4}$$

Then $\phi(x) \geq 0$ on D if $\lambda < \mu_1$.

The proof of this lemma easily follows from the proof of the Positivity Lemma and is omitted.

3. Existence and Nonexistence of Positive Solutions.

Under certain conditions on $f(x,u)$ we seek those values of λ for which the boundary value problem

$$\begin{aligned} Lu &= \lambda f(x,u), & x &\in D, \\ Bu &= 0, & x &\in \partial D, \end{aligned} \tag{3.1}$$

has positive solutions, $u(x) > 0$, $x \in D$. We denote the set $\{\lambda\}$ of real values of λ for which positive solutions of (3.1) exist by Λ, and the least upper bound of Λ by λ^*. The conditions to be imposed on f will frequently include one or more of the following:

H - 0: $f(x,\phi)$ is continuous for $x \in D$, $\phi \geq 0$;

H - 1: $f(x,0) \equiv f_0(x) > 0$ on D;

H - 2: $f(x,\phi) > f(x,\psi)$ on D if $\phi > \psi \geq 0$.

The last condition is the first monotonicity requirement to be imposed on $f(x,u)$. Stronger restrictions will be imposed in Section 4.

We first show that only positive λ are in Λ for a large class of nonlinearities including those satisfying H-0,1,2. More precisely, we have

Theorem 3.1. *Let* $f(x,\phi) > 0$ *on* D *if* $\phi > 0$ *and let* $f(x,\phi)$ *satisfy* H-0. *Then only positive* λ *can be in* Λ.

Proof: The proof is by contradiction. Assume that $u(x) > 0$ is a solution of (3.1) with $\lambda < 0$. Then, $\lambda f(x,u) < 0$ on D, and hence $-u(x)$ satisfies $L(-u) > 0$ on D, $B(-u) = 0$ on ∂D. From the Positivity Lemma (with $\lambda = 0$), we conclude that $-u(x) > 0$ on D which contradicts our assumption. The only solution of (3.1) with $\lambda = 0$ is $u(x) \equiv 0$, and the theorem follows. Q.E.D.

The existence of positive solutions for a large class of monotone nonlinearities is covered by

Theorem 3.2. *Let* $f(x,\phi)$ *satisfy* H-0,1,2. *For any* $\lambda > 0$ *define the sequence* $\{u_n(\lambda;x)\}$ *by*:

$$u_o(x) \equiv 0,$$

$$\left.\begin{aligned} Lu_n(x) &= \lambda f(x,u_{n-1}(x)), && x \in D, \\ Bu_n(x) &= 0, && x \in \partial D. \end{aligned}\right\} \quad n = 1,2,3,\ldots \qquad (3.2)$$

Then $\lambda > 0$ *is in* Λ *if and only if the sequence* $\{u_n(\lambda;x)\}$ *is uniformly bounded*. *For* λ *in* Λ *this sequence converges uniformly and its limit, say*

$$\lim_{n \to \infty} [u_n(\lambda;x)] = \underline{u}(\lambda;x),$$

is the minimal positive solution of (3.1); *that is*, $u(\lambda;x) > 0$ *and* $\underline{u}(\lambda;x) \leq u(\lambda;x)$ *on* D *for any positive solution* $u(\lambda;x)$.

Proof. We first show, by induction, that the sequence

defined in (3.2) is monotone increasing for $\lambda > 0$; that is,

$$u_{n+1}(\lambda;x) > u_n(\lambda;x), \qquad x \in D,\ n=0,1,2,\ldots\ .$$

By condition H - 1 we have, recalling that $u_o(x) \equiv 0$,

$$Lu_1(x) = \lambda f_o(x) > 0 \text{ in } D,$$
$$Bu_1 = 0 \text{ on } \partial D.$$

Hence by the Positivity Lemma it follows that $u_1(x) > 0$ on D. Assume the monotonicity established for all $n \leq \nu$, say. Then, by condition H - 2 and the inductive assumption we have

$$L[u_{\nu+1}-u_\nu] = \lambda[f(x,u_\nu)-f(x,u_{\nu-1})] > 0 \text{ on } D,$$
$$B[u_{\nu+1}-u_\nu] = 0 \text{ on } \partial D;$$

Now, the Positivity Lemma implies $u_{\nu+1} > u_\nu$ on D to conclude the induction.

If the iterates (3.2) are uniformly bounded then they converge, and their limit, say $\underline{u}(\lambda;x)$, is a positive function on D which is also uniformly bounded. That is, $\underline{u}(\lambda;x) \leq M$ on D for some positive number M. We now employ the Green's function $G_o(x,\xi)$ for L on D subject to $BG_o = 0$ for $x \in \partial D$ to write the iteration scheme (3.2) in the equivalent form:

$$u_o(x) \equiv 0;$$
$$u_n(\lambda;x)=\lambda\int_D G_o(x,\xi)f(\xi,u_{n-1}(\lambda;\xi))d\xi, \quad n = 1,2,3,\ldots, \qquad (3.3)$$

Now, $u_n(\lambda;x) \leq \underline{u}(\lambda,x) \leq M$ on D, $n = 1,2,3,\ldots$, and

$G_o(x,\xi)f(\xi,u_{n-1}) < G_o(x,\xi)f(\xi,M)$ with

$$\int_D G_o(x,\xi)f(\xi,M)d\xi < \infty.$$

Thus, the Lebesgue bounded convergence theorem for Riemann integrals implies that the limit can be taken under the integral in (3.3) to yield

$$\underline{u}(\lambda;x) = \lambda \int_D G_o(x,\xi)f(\xi,\underline{u}(\lambda;\xi))d\xi.$$

It follows that $\underline{u}(\lambda;x)$ is a positive solution of (3.1), and so the sufficiency part of the theorem follows. Note that since $\underline{u}$ is continuous, the sequence $\{u_n(\lambda,x)\}$ is a sequence of continuous monotone functions converging to a continuous limit. Thus, Dini's Theorem implies that the convergence is uniform.

Now, assume that $\lambda > 0$ is in Λ and let $u(\lambda;x)$ be some corresponding positive solution. Clearly, $u(\lambda;x) > u_o(\lambda;x) \equiv 0$ on D. Furthermore, if $u(\lambda;x) > u_{n-1}(\lambda;x)$ on D, then by H - 2,

$$L[u-u_n] = \lambda[f(x,u)-f(x,u_{n-1})] > 0 \text{ on } D,$$

$$B[u-u_n] = 0 \text{ on } \partial D.$$

The Positivity Lemma and an induction now yield $u(\lambda;x) > u_n(\lambda;x)$ on D, $n = 0,1,2,\ldots$. Hence, the monotone sequence $[u_n(\lambda;x)]$ is uniformly bounded and as above converges uniformly to a positive solution, $\underline{u}(\lambda;x)$, which satisfies $u(\lambda;x) \geq \underline{u}(\lambda;x)$ on D. We see that $\underline{u}(\lambda;x)$ is the minimal positive solution and the necessity part of the theorem has also been proved. Q.E.D.

The iteration scheme and characterization of the minimal solution in Theorem 3.2 lead to a variety of results on the existence and dependence of the minimal solution on λ. First, we have the basic comparison theorem,

Theorem 3.3. *Let* $f(x,\psi)$ *satisfy* H - 0,1,2. *Let* $F(x,\phi)$ *satisfy*

$$F(x,\phi) > f(x,\psi) \text{ on } D \text{ if } \phi > \psi \geq 0,$$

and for some $\lambda > 0$ *let a positive solution* $v(\lambda;x)$ *exist for the problem*

$$\begin{aligned} Lv &= \lambda F(x,v), \quad && x \in D, \\ Bv &= 0, && x \in \partial D. \end{aligned} \tag{3.4}$$

Then, λ *is in* Λ, *and the minimal positive solution of* (3.1) *satisfies*

$$\underline{u}(\lambda;x) \leq v(\lambda;x) \text{ on } D.$$

Proof. We prove, by induction, that the monotone increasing sequence of iterates in (3.2) satisfies $u_n(\lambda;x) < v(\lambda;x)$ on D. This follows as in the proof of Theorem 3.2 since $v(\lambda;x) > u_o(\lambda;x) \equiv 0$ and if $u_{\nu-1}(\lambda;x) < v(\lambda;x)$, then

$$L[v-u_\nu] = \lambda[F(x,v) - f(x,u_{\nu-1})] > 0 \text{ in } D,$$

$$B[v-u_\nu] = 0 \text{ on } \partial D.$$

Thus, $\lim_{n \to \infty} [u_n(\lambda;x)] = \underline{u}(\lambda;x)$ exists, is the minimal positive solution of (3.1), and satisfies $\underline{u}(\lambda;x) \leq v(\lambda;x)$ in D.

Q.E.D.

It is now a simple matter to show that Λ is an interval and that the minimal positive solution increases with λ. We state these results as the

Corollary 3.3.1. *Let* $f(x,\phi)$ *satisfy* H - 0, 1,2 *and* $\lambda' > 0$ *be in* Λ. *Then the interval* $0 < \lambda \leq \lambda'$ *is in* Λ *and* $\underline{u}(\lambda,x)$ *is an increasing function of* λ *on* Λ *for each* $x \in D$.

Proof. For any fixed value of λ in the open interval $0 < \lambda < \lambda'$ we define

$$F(x,\phi) \equiv \frac{\lambda'}{\lambda} f(x,\phi).$$

Then for this value of λ the hypothesis of Theorem 3.3 is satisfied, say with $v(\lambda,x) \equiv \underline{u}(\lambda',x)$. Hence λ is in Λ. We also have by this theorem that

$$\underline{u}(\lambda;x) \leq \underline{u}(\lambda';x).$$

But then using H - 2 it follows that

$$\begin{aligned} L[\underline{u}(\lambda';x) - \underline{u}(\lambda;x)] &= \lambda' f(x,\underline{u}(\lambda';x)) - \lambda f(x,\underline{u}(\lambda;x)), \\ &\geq (\lambda'-\lambda)\, f(x,\underline{u}(\lambda;x)) \\ &> 0, \text{ on } D. \end{aligned}$$

Of course $B[\underline{u}(\lambda';x) - \underline{u}(\lambda;x)] = 0$ on ∂D and so by the Positivity Lemma: $\underline{u}(\lambda';x) > \underline{u}(\lambda;x)$ on D. Clearly this holds for any two values $\lambda' > \lambda$ in Λ. Q.E.D.

Some results concerning the extent of Λ also follow from the above theorem.

Corollary 3.3.2. *Let* $f(x,\phi)$ *satisfy* H- 0,1,2 *and in addition, for some positive function* $F(x)$ *on* D,

$$f(x,\phi) < F(x) \quad \text{if } \phi > 0.$$

Then, all $\lambda > 0$ *are in* Λ *and thus* $\lambda^* = \infty$.

Proof. If we use the function $F(x)$ in place of $F(x,v)$ in problem (3.4), then we are assured that a positive solution exists for all $\lambda > 0$, namely

$$v(\lambda;x) = \lambda \int_D G_o(x,\xi)\, F(\xi)d\xi,$$

where $G_o(x,\xi)$ is the (positive) Green's function used in (3.3). The corollary now follows from Theorem 3.3. Q.E.D.

Corollary 3.3.3. *Let* $f(x,\phi)$ *satisfy* H - 0,1,2, *and for some positive functions* $F(x)$ *and* $\rho(x)$:

$$f(x,\phi) < F(x) + \rho(x)\phi \text{ on } D \text{ for } \phi > 0.$$

Then Λ *contains all* λ *in* $0 < \lambda < \mu_1\{\rho\}$, *where* $\mu_1\{\rho\}$ *is the principal eigenvalue of* (2.2). *The least upper bound* λ^* *on* Λ *is then bounded below by*

$$\mu_1\{\rho\} \leq \lambda^*.$$

Proof. By the Positivity Lemma the problem (3.4) with the choice $F(x,v) \equiv F(x) + \rho(x)\, v$ has a positive solution,

$v(\lambda;x)$, for each λ in $0 < \lambda < \mu_1\{\rho\}$. An application of Theorem 3.3 now yields the result. Q.E.D.

Note that Corollary 3.3.2 is a limiting form of Corollary 3.3.3 since, by the variational characterization of the principal eigenvalue of (2.2), we have in an obvious notation $\lim_{\rho \to 0} [\mu_1\{\rho\}] = \infty$.

A result on nonexistence is contained in

Corollary 3.3.4. Let $f(x,\psi)$ and $F(x,\phi)$ satisfy the hypothesis of Theorem 3.3. Let $\lambda^* < \infty$ be the least upper bound on Λ. Then, the problem (3.4) has no positive solutions for $\lambda > \lambda^*$. In particular, if $f(x,\phi)$ satisfies $f(x,\phi) > F(x) + \rho(x)\phi$ on D for $\phi > 0$, with $F(x)$ and $\rho(x)$ positive, then $\lambda^* \leq \mu_1\{\rho\}$, where $\mu_1\{\rho\}$ is the principal eigenvalue of (2.2).

Proof. Assume that (3.4) has a positive solution for some $\lambda > \lambda^*$. Then, by Theorem 3.3 the problem (3.1) would have a positive solution for this value of λ. This contradicts the definition of λ^*, and the first part of the corollary follows.

To prove the second part of the corollary we note that the Positivity Lemma implies that the problem $L\phi = \lambda[F(x) + \rho(x)\phi]$ has no positive solutions for $\lambda>\mu_1\{\rho\}$. Now, an application of the first part of this corollary yields the result. Q.E.D.

Another nonexistence result which illustrates the importance of condition H - 1 when $f(x,\phi)$ is dominated by a linear function of ϕ is clearly shown in

Theorem 3.4. *Let* $f(x,\phi)$ *satisfy* H - 0 *and in addition, for some* $\rho(x) > 0$ *assume that* $f(x,\phi) < \rho(x)\phi$ *on* D *for* $\phi > 0$. *Then a positive solution of (3.1) does not exist for any* λ *in* $0 < \lambda < \mu_1\{\rho\}$ *where* $\mu_1\{\rho\}$ *is the principal eigenvalue of* (2.2).

Proof. Assume to the contrary that a positive solution, u, of (3.1) does exist for some λ in $0 < \lambda < \mu_1\{\rho\}$. For this solution we have $Bu = 0$ on ∂D and

$$Lu - \lambda\rho(x)\, u = \lambda\, [f(x,u) - \rho(x)u\} < 0 \text{ on } D.$$

An application of the Positivity Lemma to (-u) yields that $(-u) > 0$ on D which contradicts the assumed positivity of u(x). Q.E.D.

4. Concave and Convex Nonlinearities.

In this section we shall require that f(x,u) satisfy the strong monotonicity condition

$$\text{H - 2}': \quad \frac{\partial f(x,\phi)}{\partial \phi} > 0 \text{ and continuous on D for } \phi > 0.$$

Clearly this implies condition H - 2. Now, we have

Theorem 4.1. *Let* $f(x,\phi)$ *satisfy* H - 0, 1,2' *and be such that (3.1) has positive solutions for all* λ *in* $0 < \lambda < \lambda^*$. *Then each* λ *in this interval must satisfy* $\lambda \leq \mu_1(\lambda)$ *where*

$\mu_1(\lambda) \equiv \mu_1\{f_u(x,\underline{u}(\lambda;x))\}$ *is the principal eigenvalue of*

$$\begin{aligned} L\psi - \mu f_u(x,\underline{u}(\lambda;x))\psi &= 0, \qquad x \in D, \\ B\psi &= 0, \qquad x \in \partial D. \end{aligned} \tag{4.1}$$

*Proof**: We first show that $\underline{u}(\lambda;x)$ is continuous on the left at each $\lambda \in \Lambda$. In fact for any fixed $\lambda \in \Lambda$ let $\{\lambda_\nu\}$ be a monotone increasing sequence with $\lambda_\nu \varepsilon \Lambda$ and $\lambda_\nu \uparrow \lambda$. Then by Corollary 3.3.1 it follows that $\underline{u}(\lambda_\nu;x) \leq \underline{u}(\lambda;x)$ on D and hence the monotone sequence of functions $\{\underline{u}(\lambda_\nu;x)\}$ is bounded above and hence converges; say $\underline{u}(\lambda_\nu;x) \to \underline{\underline{u}}(\lambda;x)$. Since

$$\underline{u}(\lambda_\nu;x) = \lambda_\nu \int_D G_o(x,\xi) f(\xi,\underline{u}(\lambda_\nu;\xi))d\xi,$$

the bounded convergence theorem implies upon taking the limit that $\underline{\underline{u}}(\lambda;x)$ is also a positive solution of (3.1). But clearly $\underline{\underline{u}}(\lambda;x) \leq \underline{u}(\lambda;x)$ and since $\underline{u}(\lambda;x)$ is the minimal positive solution it follows that $\underline{u}(\lambda_\nu;x) \to \underline{u}(\lambda;x)$.

Now take any λ' and λ both in Λ with $\lambda' < \lambda$. It easily follows with the definition

$$f_u(\lambda,\lambda';x) \equiv \int_o^1 f_u(x,\theta\underline{u}(\lambda;x) + (1-\theta)\underline{u}(\lambda';x))d\theta$$

---

*An error in the original version of this theorem, which stated erroneously that $\lambda < \mu_1(\lambda)$, was found by Dr. T. Laetsch. The present proof is due to Laetsch.

that on D:

$$L[\underline{u}(\lambda;x)-\underline{u}(\lambda';x)]-\lambda f_u(\lambda,\lambda';x)[\underline{u}(\lambda;x)-\underline{u}(\lambda';x)]$$

$$= (\lambda-\lambda')f(x,\underline{u}(\lambda';x) > 0. \qquad (4.2)$$

Thus by Positivity Lemma it follows, since $[\underline{u}(\lambda;x)-\underline{u}(\lambda';x)] > 0$, that

$$\lambda < \mu_1\{f_u(\lambda,\lambda';x)\}$$

where $\mu_1\{ - \}$ is the principal eigenvalue of (4.1) with $f_u(x,\underline{u}(\lambda;x))$ replaced by $f_u(\lambda,\lambda';x)$. By the continuity of $\underline{u}(\lambda,x)$ from the left it follows that

$$\lim_{\lambda'\uparrow\lambda} f_u(\lambda,\lambda';x) = f_u(x;\underline{u}(\lambda;x))$$

and thus $\lambda \leq \mu_1\{f_u(x,\underline{u}(\lambda;x))\}$. Q.E.D.

With the notation $\underline{u}(0;x) \equiv 0$ as the minimal non-negative solution of (3.1) for $\lambda = 0$ we may use (4.1) to define the eigenvalue $\mu_1(0) \equiv \mu_1\{f_u(x,0)\}$, even though $\lambda = 0$ cannot be in Λ.

Theorem 4.1 required only the strong monotonicity of f(x,u). If in addtion the nonlinearity is concave or convex the function $\mu_1(\lambda)$ can be studied in more detail. We say that f(x,u) is (a) <u>concave</u> or (b) <u>convex</u>, respectively, if it satisfies H - 2' and

H-3a: $f_u(x,\phi) < f_u(x,\psi)$ on D if $\phi > \psi \geq 0$ (concave),

or

H-3b: $f_u(x,\phi) > f_u(x,\psi)$ on D if $\phi > \psi \geq 0$ (convex).

If f(x,u) satisfies H-0,1 and is concave, then clearly

$$f(x,\phi) < f_o(x) + f_u(x,0)\phi, \qquad \phi > 0, \tag{4.3a}$$

or if it satisfies H-0,1 and is convex, then

$$f(x,\phi) > f_o(x) + f_u(x,0)\phi, \qquad \phi > 0. \tag{4.3b}$$

An application of Corollary 3.3.3 to the case of concave f reveals that Λ contains the interval $0 < \lambda < \mu_1(0)$ and that $\lambda^* \geq \mu_1(0)$. On the other hand, for f convex the Corollary 3.3.4 and the bound (4.3b) imply that $\lambda^* \leq \mu_1(0)$. To improve these bounds we have

<u>Corollary</u> 4.1.1. <u>Let</u> $f(x,\phi)$ <u>satisfy</u> H-0,1,2', 3a (<u>or</u> 3b). <u>If</u> Λ <u>is the open interval</u> $(0,\lambda^*)$, <u>then</u> $\mu_1(\lambda)$ <u>is an increasing (or decreasing) function of</u> λ <u>on this interval</u>. <u>Furthermore, for</u> f <u>concave</u> $\mu_1(\lambda) < \lambda^*$, <u>and for</u> f <u>convex</u> $\mu_1(\lambda) > \lambda^*$, <u>on</u> $0 < \lambda < \lambda^*$. (<u>See Figure 1</u>)

<u>Proof</u>. From the variational characterization of the principal eigenvalue, $\mu_1(\lambda)$, of the problem (4.1) we can write

$$\mu_1(\lambda) = \min_{\psi(x)\varepsilon M}\left[\frac{(\psi,L\psi)}{(\psi,f_u(x,\underline{u}(\lambda;x))\psi)}\right], \tag{4.4}$$

where the obvious inner product used is

$$(\psi,\phi) = \int_D \psi(x)\phi(x)dx,$$

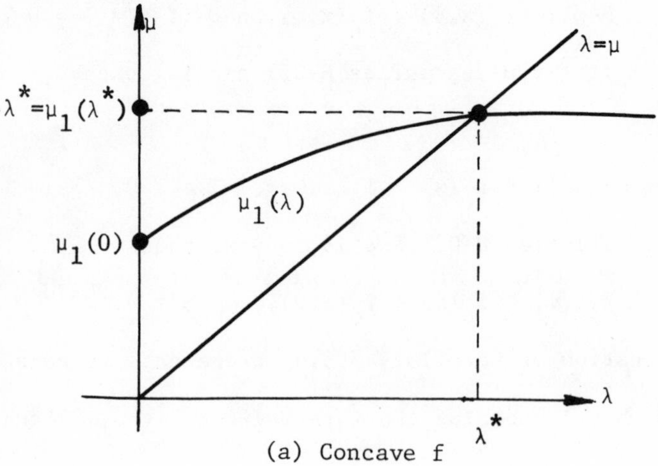

(a) Concave f

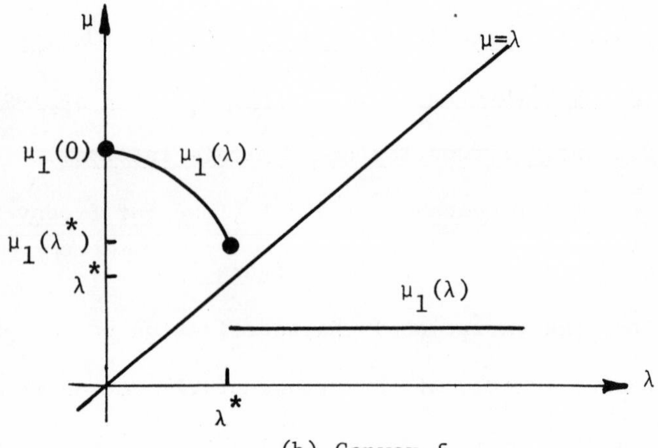

(b) Convex f

Figure 1.

and the class M of admissible functions can be taken as

$M \equiv \{\psi(x) \mid \psi(x) > 0 \text{ on } D,\ \psi(x) \in C(\bar{D}) \cap C'(D),\ \psi(x) = 0 \text{ on } \partial D_1\}$.

(We recall that ∂D_1 is that portion of ∂D on which $\beta(x) \equiv 0$ and $\alpha(x) \equiv 1$.)

From Corollary 3.3.1 we know that the minimal positive solutions are increasing functions of λ on $0 < \lambda < \lambda^*$. Thus, if $f(x,u)$ is concave and if $0 < \lambda < \lambda' < \lambda^*$ we must have

$$f_u(x,\underline{u}(\lambda;x)) > f_u(x,\underline{u}(\lambda';x)) \quad \text{on } D.$$

Moreover, since $\psi \in M$ implies $\psi(x) > 0$ on D, it follows from this result and (4.4) that $\mu_1(\lambda) < \mu_1(\lambda')$. The opposite inequality for convex f follows in an obvious manner.

We have observed, just before the statement of this corollary, that $\mu_1(0) \geq \lambda^*$ in the case of convex f. But by Theorem 4.1 it follows that $\lambda \leq \mu_1(\lambda)$ in $0 < \lambda < \lambda^*$. Thus, since $\mu_1(\lambda)$ is a decreasing function of λ, we may conclude that $\mu_1(\lambda) > \lambda^*$ on $0 \leq \lambda < \lambda^*$ for convex f.

If f is concave, then $\mu_1(0) \leq \lambda^*$ as previously indicated. However, in this case, for any λ in $0 < \lambda < \lambda^*$ and any $\phi(x) > 0$ on D we must have

$$\begin{aligned} f(x,\phi) &\leq f(x,\underline{u}) + (\phi-\underline{u})f_u(x,\underline{u}) \qquad (4.5) \\ &< f_o(x) + [f_u(x,0)-f_u(x,\underline{u})]\underline{u}(\lambda;x) \\ &\qquad + f_u(x,\underline{u})\phi. \end{aligned}$$

Now, we apply Corollary 3.3.3 to conclude that $\mu_1(\lambda) \leq \lambda^*$ on $0 < \lambda < \lambda^*$ for concave f. Q.E.D.

The function $\mu_1(\lambda)$ has been defined only for $0 \leq \lambda < \lambda^*$. However, under the hypotheses of Theorem 4.1 we may define a function $\mu_1(\lambda)$ for all $\lambda \geq 0$ which agrees with the previous definition when $\lambda < \lambda^*$. For this purpose let $\{u_n(\lambda;x)\}$ be the sequence defined in (3.2) for any $\lambda \geq 0$. Then, define $\mu_{1,n}(\lambda)$ to be the principal eigenvalue of the problem

$$L\psi - \mu f_u(x,u_n(\lambda;x))\psi = 0. \qquad x \in D \qquad (4.6a)$$

$$B\psi = 0, \qquad x \in \partial D.$$

Finally, we define $\mu_1(\lambda)$ as

$$\mu_1(\lambda) = \lim_{n \to \infty} [\mu_{1,n}(\lambda)]. \qquad (4.6b)$$

To show that (4.6) defines $\mu_1(\lambda)$ for all λ we write the equivalent variational characterization

$$\mu_1(\lambda) = \lim_{n \to \infty} \min_{\psi \varepsilon M} \left[\frac{(\psi, L\psi)}{(\psi, f_u(x,u_n(\lambda;x))\psi)}\right].$$

Clearly, if $\lambda < \lambda^*$, then by Theorem 3.2 the sequence $\{u_n(\lambda;x)\}$ converges to $\underline{u}(\lambda;x)$ and we obtain the same values defined in Theorem 4.1. If $\lambda > \lambda^*$, the sequence does not converge, but since it is monotone increasing and the $u_n(\lambda;x)$ are uniformly continuous on $\bar{D}$, we must have

$\lim_{n \to \infty} [u_n(\lambda;x)] = \infty$ on D. Now either $\lim_{K \to \infty} [f_u(x,K)] = \infty$ or $\lim_{K \to \infty} [f_u(x,K)] = r(x) \geq 0$. In the former case $\mu_1(\lambda) = 0$ if $\lambda > \lambda^*$, and in the latter case $\mu_1(\lambda) = m$ if $\lambda > \lambda^*$, where m is the principal eigenvalue of $L\psi - \mu\, r(x)\psi = 0$ on D, $B\psi = 0$ on ∂D. Thus in any event, $\mu_1(\lambda)$ is constant for all $\lambda > \lambda^*$. The behavior of this extended function $\mu_1(\lambda)$ is sketched in Figure 1 for both concave and convex f. (See however Corollary 4.1.2, Theorem 4.3 and the remark following.)

Some important facts concerning the limit of Λ for the case of concave f are contained in

Corollary 4.1.2. *Let $f(x,\phi)$ satisfy H-0,1,2', 3a (i.e. f is concave). Then*

$$\lim_{\lambda \uparrow \lambda^*} \mu_1(\lambda) = \lambda^*, \tag{4.7}$$

and λ^* does not belong to Λ. (I.e., Λ is open.)

Proof. It is clear from the continuous dependence of $\underline{u}(\lambda;x)$ on λ from the left and from the characterization (4.4) that $\mu_1(\lambda)$ is also a continuous function of λ from the left on $0 < \lambda < \lambda^*$. From Theorem 4.1 and Corollary 4.1.1 we have for concave f and $\lambda < \lambda^*$ that:

$$\lambda \leq \mu_1(\lambda) < \lambda^*.$$

Now (4.7) follows on letting λ approach λ^* from the left.

Suppose that λ^* is in Λ. Then a corresponding minimal positive solution $\underline{u}(\lambda^*,x)$ exists and is finite. By (4.7) and the continuous dependence on λ from the left we have that

$$\lambda^* = \mu_1\{f_u(x,\underline{u}(\lambda^*,x)\}.$$

Now since $f(x,\phi)$ is concave it follows, just as in the derivation of (4.5), that

$$f(x,\phi) < F(x) + \rho(x)\phi \quad \text{on } D \text{ for } \phi > 0,$$

where for any $\psi(x) > 0$ on D:

$$F(x) \equiv f_o(x) + [f_u(x,0) - f_u(x,\psi(x))]\psi(x),$$

$$\rho(x) \equiv f_u(x,\psi(x)).$$

Pick some smooth bounded function $\psi(x) > \underline{u}(\lambda^*,x)$ on D and now apply Corollary 3.3.3 to conclude that $\lambda^* \geq \mu_1\{f_u(x,\psi(x))\}$. However this is a contradiction since $f_u(x,\underline{u}(\lambda^*,x)) > f_u(x,\psi(x))$ on D and the variational characterization of the principal eigenvalue μ_1 then implies

$$\mu_1\{f_u(x,\underline{u}(\lambda^*,x))\} < \mu_1\{f_u(x,\psi(x))\}. \qquad \text{Q.E.D.}$$

The above proof suggests that the minimal positive solutions become unbounded for concave f as $\lambda \to \lambda^*$. Then the extended function $\mu_1(\lambda)$ would be continuous as is conjectured and indicated in Figure 1a. However in cases of convex f which have been solved explicitly [6], the solutions remain bounded as $\lambda \to \lambda^*$ while $\partial\underline{u}/\partial\lambda \to \infty$. In these cases λ^* is a point of Λ. There is reason to conjecture that (4.7) also holds for convex nonlinearities.

Another fundamental difference between concave and convex nonlinearities concerns the uniqueness of positive solutions. For the concave case we have uniqueness as in

Corollary 4.1.3. *Let* $f(x,\phi)$ *satisfy* H-0,1,2' *and* 3a (*i.e. f is concave*). *Then positive solutions of* (3.1) *are unique for each* λ *in* $0 < \lambda < \lambda^*$.

Proof. Let $\underline{u}(\lambda;x)$ be the minimal positive solution of (3.1) for some fixed λ in $0 < \lambda < \lambda^*$. If some other positive solution $u(\lambda;x)$ exists for this value of λ it must satisfy

$$u(\lambda;x) - \underline{u}(\lambda;x) \geq 0, \not\equiv 0 \text{ on } D.$$

Furthermore $B[u-\underline{u}] = 0$ on D and from the concavity of f we deduce that in D,

$$\begin{aligned} L[u-\underline{u}] &= \lambda[f(x,u) - f(x,\underline{u})] \\ &= \lambda f_u(x,\underline{u} + \theta[u-\underline{u}])[u-\underline{u}], \quad 0 < \theta(x) < 1, \\ &\leq \lambda f_u(x,\underline{u})[u-\underline{u}]. \end{aligned}$$

From Theorem 4.1 it follows that $\lambda \leq \mu_1\{f_u(x,\underline{u})\}$ and so we may apply the Weak Form of the Positivity Lemma to conclude that $u(\lambda;x)-\underline{u}(\lambda;x) \leq 0$. It therefore follows that $u-\underline{u} \equiv 0$.

Q.E.D.

In some special cases of convex nonlinearities [6] the positive solutions are known to be nonunique. A criterion that ensures uniqueness for certain convex nonlinearities and for more general types of nonlinearities is contained in the following

Theorem 4.2: Let $f(x,u)$ satisfy H-0,1,2' and the condition

$$0 < f_u(x,u) \leq \rho(x). \tag{4.8}$$

Then the positive solutions of (3.1) are unique for each λ in $0 < \lambda < \mu_1\{\rho\}$.

Proof: We repeat the development in the beginning of the proof of Corollary 4.1.3 and obtain, by using (4.8) rather than the concavity of $f(x,u)$, that

$$L[u-\underline{u}] \leq \lambda\rho(x)[u-\underline{u}].$$

An application of the Weak Form of the Positivity Lemma gives the conclusion of the theorem. Q.E.D.

Note that Corollary 3.3.3 implies that $\mu_1\{\rho\} \leq \lambda^*$.

Finally we may actually determine λ^* for many concave nonlinearities by means of

Theorem 4.3: Let $f(x,\phi)$ satisfy H-0,1,2', 3a and in addition:

$$\lim_{\phi \to \infty} f_\phi(x;\phi) = \rho(x) \quad \text{on } D.$$

Then $\lambda^* = \mu_1\{\rho\}$ where we understand that $\mu_1\{\rho\} = \infty$ if $\rho(x) \equiv 0$.

Proof. By the concavity of f and the limit condition it easily follows that there exist positive functions $F_1(x)$ and $F_2(x)$ such that, on D,

$$F_1(x) + \rho(x)\phi < f(x,\phi) < F_2(x) + \rho(x)\phi,$$

for all $\phi > 0$. The upper bound is determined as in (4.5) and we may take $F_1(x) \equiv f(x,0)$. Corollaries 3.3.3 and 3.3.4 immediately imply that $\lambda^* \geq \mu_1\{\rho\}$ and $\lambda^* \leq \mu_1\{\rho\}$, respectively, so that $\lambda^* = \mu_1\{\rho\}$. In addition it follows from Corollary 3.3.2 that $\lambda^* = \infty$ if $\rho(x) \equiv 0$. Q.E.D.

It should be observed that if, as we have previously conjectured, $\lim_{\lambda \uparrow \lambda^*} \underline{u}(\lambda;x) = \infty$ for concave f then the limit in (4.7) gives the same value for λ^* as that in Theorem 4.2.

5. A Newton Iteration Scheme for Strictly Concave Nonlinearities.

In this section we introduce an alternative iteration scheme for strictly concave nonlinearities that converges monotonically to the unique positive solution from above. The iterates of this procedure and those of (3.2) "pinch" the solution and furnish pointwise upper and lower bounds for it which improve with each iteration. Our procedure is the Newton iteration technique used by Bellman and Kalaba (See [7] and [8] for references) and by Wendroff [9].

We require that f(x,u) satisfy H-0,1,2', 3a, and be strictly concave, i.e., H-4: $f(x,\phi)$ is twice continuously differentiable in ϕ on D for $\phi > 0$ and $f_{uu}(x,\phi) < 0$ on D.

Theorem 5.1. *Let* $f(x,\phi)$ *satisfy* H-0,1,2',3a,4. *For any* $\lambda > 0$ *define the sequence* $\{v_n(\lambda;x)\}$ *by*

$$v_o(x) = 0$$

$$Lv_n = \lambda[f(x,v_{n-1}) + f_u(x,v_{n-1})(v_n - v_{n-1})], \quad x \in D \tag{5.1}$$

$$n=1,2,3,\ldots$$

$$Bv_n = 0, \qquad x \in \partial D$$

Then $v_n(\lambda;x) > 0$ *on* D, $n \geq 1$, *for all* λ *in* $0 < \lambda < \mu_1(0) \equiv \mu_1\{f_u(x,0)\}$.

Proof: The proof is by induction. From (5.1) and H-1, we have

$$Lv_1 - \lambda f_u(x,0)v_1 = \lambda f(x,0) > 0, \quad x \in D$$

$$Bv_1 = 0, \qquad x \in \partial D.$$

Hence by the Positivity Lemma it follows that $v_1(\lambda;x) > 0$ on D since $0 < \lambda < \mu_1(0)$. Assume $v_\nu(\lambda;x) > 0$ on D for all $\nu \leq n-1$. Then

$$\begin{aligned} Lv_n - \lambda f_u(x,v_{n-1})v_n &= \lambda[f(x,v_{n-1}) - f_u(x,v_{n-1})v_{n-1}] \\ &= \lambda[f(x,0) - \tfrac{1}{2} f_{uu}(x,\theta v_{n-1})v_{n-1}^2], \quad 0 < \theta < 1 \end{aligned} \tag{5.2}$$

We now use H-4 in (5.2) to get

$$Lv_n - \lambda f_u(x,v_{n-1})v_n > 0 \text{ on } D, \qquad Bv_n = 0 \text{ on } \partial D.$$

Thus, by the Positivity Lemma it follows that $v_n(\lambda;x) > 0$ on D if $0 < \lambda < \mu_1\{f_u(x,v_{n-1})\}$. Now H-3a implies that $f_u(x,v_n) < f_u(x,0)$ on D for all $n \geq 1$. Thus, it follows from (4.4) (the variational characterization of μ_1) that

$$\mu_1\{f_u(x,0)\} < \mu_1\{f_u(x,v_n)\}, \ n \geq 1$$

which concludes the proof. Q.E.D.

Theorem 5.2. *Let* $f(x,\phi)$ *satisfy* H-0,1,2',3a,4. *Then for all* λ *in* $0 < \lambda < \mu_1\{f_u(x,0)\}$ *the sequence* $\{v_n(\lambda;x)\}$ *defined by* (5.1) *is monotone nonincreasing; that is,*

$$v_{n+1}(\lambda;x) \leq v_n(\lambda;x), \ x \in D, \ n = 1,2,3,\dots .$$

Proof. The strict concavity property of $f(x,u)$ implies that

$$f(x,v_n) \leq f(x,v_{n-1}) + f_u(x,v_{n-1})(v_n-v_{n-1}). \quad (5.3)$$

This follows easily, geometrically as a consequence of the fact that f lies below its tangent, or analytically from H-4 and a Taylor's series expansion of $f(x,v_n)$ about $v = v_{n-1}$. Thus, (5.1) and (5.3) imply

$$Lv_n = \lambda[f(x,v_{n-1}) + f_u(x,v_{n-1})(v_n-v_{n-1})] \geq \lambda f(x,v_n). \quad (5.4)$$

From (5.1) we have

$$Lv_{n+1} = \lambda[f(x,v_n) + f_u(x,v_n)(v_{n+1}-v_n)]. \quad (5.5)$$

Subtracting (5.5) from (5.4) and using (5.3), we obtain

$$L(v_n-v_{n+1})-\lambda f_u(x,v_{n-1})(v_n-v_{n+1}) \geq 0 \text{ on } D. \quad (5.6)$$

Furthermore, it is clear that $B(v_n-v_{n+1}) = 0$ on ∂D. Hence, from the Weak Form of the Positivity Lemma we conclude that $v_n(\lambda;x) \geq v_{n+1}(\lambda;x)$ on D if $0 < \lambda < \mu_1\{f_u(x,v_{n-1})\}$. However, as we showed in the proof of Theorem 5.1 we have

$\mu_1\{f_u(x,0)\} < \mu_1\{f_u(x,v_n)\}$ for all $n \geq 1$. Therefore, we have $v_n(\lambda;x) \geq v_{n+1}(\lambda;x)$, $x \in D$, $n = 1,2,3,\ldots$, for all λ in $0 < \lambda < \mu_1\{f_u(x,0)\}$. Q.E.D.

Theorem 5.3. Let $f(x,\phi)$ satisfy H-0,1,2',3a,4. Then the sequence $\{v_n(\lambda;x)\}$ defined by (5.1) converges to the unique solution, $\underline{u}(\lambda;x)$ of (3.1) for all λ in $0 < \lambda < \mu_1\{f_u(x,0)\}$.

Proof. Having demonstrated in Theorems 5.1 and 5.2 that the sequence $\{v_n(\lambda;x)\}$ is monotone nonincreasing and bounded from below, we may immediately conclude that there is a limit function, say

$$\lim_{n \to \infty} [v_n(\lambda;x)] = \underline{u}(\lambda;x).$$

To show that $\underline{u}(\lambda;x)$ is a solution of (3.1), we write the iteration scheme (5.1) equivalently as

$$v_n(\lambda;x)=\lambda\int_D G_o(x,\xi)[f(\xi,v_{n-1}(\lambda;\xi))+f_u(\xi,v_{n-1}(\lambda;\xi))(v_n(\lambda;\xi) - v_{n-1}(\lambda;\xi))]d\xi \qquad (5.7)$$

$$n = 1,2,3,4,\ldots,$$

where $G_o(x,\xi)$ is the Green's function for L on D subject to BG = 0 for $x \in \partial D$. Clearly, $v_n(\lambda;x) \leq M$ on D, for all $n \geq 1$, for some positive number M. Thus, $f(x,v_n) \leq f(x,M)$ on D for all $n \geq 1$. Moreover, H-3a implies that $f_u(x,v_n) \leq f_u(x,0)$ on D for all $n \geq 1$. Therefore, the integrand in (5.7) is bounded by

$$G_o(x,\xi)[f(\xi,M) + f_u(\xi,0)(2M)]$$

with

$$\int_D G_o(x,\xi)[f(\xi,M) + f_u(\xi,0)(2M)]d\xi < \infty.$$

Thus, the Lebesgue bounded convergence theorem for Riemann integrals implies that the limit can be taken under the integral in (5.7) so that

$$\underline{u}(\lambda;x) = \lambda\int_D G(x,\xi)f(\xi,\underline{u}(\lambda;\xi))d\xi.$$

It follows that $\underline{u}(\lambda;x)$ is a positive solution of (3.1). By Corollary 4.1.3, $\underline{u}$ is unique. Q.E.D.

Remark: It can be shown, just as in Bellman and Kalaba [7] that the sequence $\{v_n(\lambda;x)\}$ converges quadratically; that is for $x \in D$,

$$\max_x|v_{n+1}-v_n| \leq k_1 \max_x|v_n-v_{n-1}|^2,$$

where k_1 is a constant independent of n, whereas the Picard iteration scheme which defines the sequence $\{u_n(\lambda;x)\}$ will in general converge only geometrically; i.e.,

$$|u_{n+1}-u_n| \leq k_2|u_n-u_{n-1}|.$$

Note that we have also given another proof that Λ contains the interval $0 < \lambda < \mu_1(0) \equiv \mu_1\{f_u(x,0)\}$ with $\lambda^* > \mu_1(0)$.

6. Stability of Positive Solutions.

Any solution $u(\lambda;x)$ of the boundary value problem

(3.1) may be regarded as a steady state solution of the mildly non-linear parabolic problem

$$\begin{aligned} \frac{\partial U}{\partial t} + LU &= \lambda f(x,U), && x \in D,\ t > 0, \\ BU &= 0, && x \in \partial D,\ t > 0, \\ U(x,0) &= U_o(x), && x \in D. \end{aligned} \tag{6.1}$$

We shall give a more precise definition later, but roughly, we say that $u(\lambda;x)$ is stable if for all initial data of the form

$$U_o(x) = u(\lambda;x) + \varepsilon V(x), \tag{6.2}$$

the solution of (6.1) decays exponentially in t to $u(\lambda;x)$ to first order in ε.

Assuming a solution of (6.1), (6.2) of the form

$$U(x,t) = u(\lambda;x) + \varepsilon v(x)\, e^{-\alpha t} + 0(\varepsilon^2),$$

we find, to first order in ε, that α and $v(x)$ must satisfy:

$$\begin{aligned} Lv - [\alpha + \lambda f_u(x,u)]v &= 0, && x \in D, \\ Bv &= 0, && x \in \partial D. \end{aligned} \tag{6.3}$$

Clearly, non-trivial solutions $v \not\equiv 0$ exist if and only if α is an eigenvalue of (6.3) and $v = v(\alpha;x)$ is the corresponding eigenfunction. If the eigenfunctions of (6.3) are complete in some sense, then for some coefficients a_n,

$$V(x) = \sum_n a_n v(\alpha_n;x)$$

and the solution, to first order in ε, of (6.1), (6.2) is

$$U(x,t) = u(\lambda;x) + \varepsilon \sum_n a_n v(\alpha_n;x)e^{-\alpha_n t} + 0(\varepsilon^2).$$

Thus, we are motivated to adopt the following

Definitions. A solution $u(\lambda;x)$ of (3.1) is called stable if the principal eigenvalue $\alpha \equiv \alpha_1$ of (6.3) is positive, unstable if α_1 is negative, and neutrally stable if $\alpha_1 = 0$. For any set of solutions of (3.1), that solution with the largest principal eigenvalue in (6.3) is called relatively more stable.

It should be noted that we have assumed $f(x,u)$ to be continuously differentiable with respect to u. We maintain this assumption throughout this section.

Theorem 6.1. Let $f(x,\phi)$ satisfy H-0,1,2' and be such that Λ is either the open interval $(0,\lambda^*)$ or the half-open interval $(0,\lambda^*]$. Then the minimal positive solutions of (3.1) are not unstable in $0 < \lambda < \lambda^*$. If in addition, $f(x,u)$ is convex, the minimal positive solution is relatively more stable than any other positive solution with the same values of λ. Furthermore, if $f(x,u)$ is concave (or convex), the relative stability of the set of minimal positive solutions on $0 < \lambda < \lambda^*$ increases (or decreases) as λ increases.

Proof. Let $u(\lambda;x)$ be some positive solution of (3.1), and denote the corresponding principal eigenvalue of (6.3) by $\alpha(\lambda)$. Then, with the usual inner product notation, the variational characterization of the principal eigenvalue yields

$$\alpha(\lambda) = \min_{\phi(x)\varepsilon M} \left[\frac{(\phi,L\phi)-\lambda(\phi,f_u(x,u(\lambda;x))\phi}{(\phi,\phi)}\right]. \qquad (6.4)$$

Now, recalling (4.4), we have for any $\phi(x)\ \varepsilon\ M$ and any λ in $0 < \lambda < \lambda^*$,

$$(\phi,L\phi) \geq \mu_1(\lambda)(\phi,f_u(x,\underline{u}(\lambda;x))\phi). \qquad (6.5)$$

Thus, if $\underline{\alpha}(\lambda)$ is the eigenvalue corresponding to the minimal positive solution, $\underline{u}(\lambda;x)$, we obtain from (6.4) and (6.5) that

$$\underline{\alpha}(\lambda) \geq \min \left[(\mu_1(\lambda)-\lambda)\frac{(\phi,f_u(x,\underline{u}(\lambda;x))\phi)}{(\phi,\phi)}\right].$$

By Theorem 4.1 we have $\mu_1(\lambda)-\lambda \geq 0$ and by H-2' and $\underline{u} > 0$ on D we have $f_u(x,\underline{u}) > 0$ on D. It follows, since $\phi(x) > 0$ on D, that $\underline{\alpha}(\lambda) \geq 0$, and thus, the minimal positive solutions are not unstable in $0 < \lambda < \lambda^*$.

Now, let f(x,u) be convex. Then, since any positive solution $u(\lambda;x)$ which is not minimal satisfies $u(\lambda;x) \geq \underline{u}(\lambda;x)$ on D, we must have $f_u(x,\underline{u}) \leq f_u(x,u)$ on D. The variational characterization (6.4) then implies that $\underline{\alpha}(\lambda) \geq \alpha(\lambda)$ which establishes that the minimal positive solution is relatively more stable than any other positive solution.

Finally, Corollary 3.3.1 asserts that $\underline{u}(\lambda;x)$

increases as λ increases for each $x \in D$. Thus, if f is convex, $f_u(x,\underline{u})$ increases as λ increases. The variational principle (6.4) then implies that $\underline{\alpha}(\lambda)$ decreases as $f_u(x,\underline{u})$ increases, thus concluding the proof of the fact that if f is convex, the stability of the minimal positive solution decreases as λ increases. The opposite result obviously holds for f concave. Q.E.D.

Clearly, we have the following interpretation of the above theorem in terms of the nonlinear heat conduction problems mentioned in the introduction: In the cases where the steady state solutions are not unique, namely for convex f, the "cooler" positive steady states are more stable. Perhaps a somewhat surprising result is that for concave f, although the stability of the <u>unique</u> positive solution on $0 < \lambda < \lambda^*$ increases as the current, λ, increases, no positive solution exists when $\lambda > \lambda^*$. If, as we conjecture for convex f, the limit $\lambda^* = \mu_1(\lambda^*)$ then it is not difficult to show that $\underline{\alpha}(\lambda^*) = 0$, so that the limiting minimal positive solution has neutral stability. This has been demonstrated for a special case in [6].

References

1. M. A. Krasnosel'skii, Positive Solutions of Operator Equations, P. Noordhoff Ltd., Gronigen, The Netherlands, 1964.

2. H. H. Schaefer, Some nonlinear eigenvalue problems, Symposium on Nonlinear Problems, edited by R.E.Langer, University of Wisconsin Press, 1963.

3. R. Courant and D. Hilbert, Methods of Mathematical Physics, vol. II, Interscience, New York, 1962.

4. N. Aronszajn and K. Smith, Characterization of positive reproducing kernels. Applications to Green's functions, Amer. J. Math., 79(1957) 611-622.

5. R. Bellman, On the non-negativity of Green's functions, Boll d'Unione Mate., 12 (1957) 411-413.

6. D. D. Joseph, Non-linear heat generation and stability of the temperature distribution in conducting solids, Int. J. Heat Mass Transfer, 8(1965) 281-288.

7. R. E. Bellman and R. E. Kalaba, Quasilinearization and Nonlinear Boundary Value Problems, American Elsevier Publishing Co., Inc., New York, 1965.

8. R. E. Kalaba, On nonlinear differential equations, the maximum operation, and monotone convergence, J. Math. Mech., 8 (1959) 519-574.

9. B. Wendroff, Theoretical Numerical Analysis, Academic Press, New York, 1966.

10. H. B. Keller and D. S. Cohen, Some Positone Problems Suggested by Nonlinear Heat Generation, to appear in J. Math. Mech.

11. D. S. Cohen, Positive Solutions of a Class of Nonlinear Eigenvalue Problems, to appear in J. Math. Mech.

IX. Bifurcation Phenomena in Surface Wave Theory

J.J. Stoker

1. General formulation of the boundary value problem

We consider the two-dimensional flow of a perfect, incompressible, heavy fluid in a channel of constant depth h. The coordinate system we use is shown in Figure 1. The free surface is given by the equation

$$y = \eta(x,t) \tag{1.1}$$

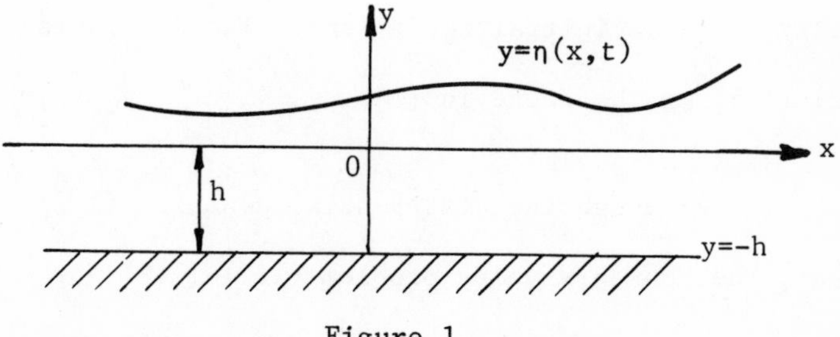

Figure 1

The motion is governed by the following boundary value problem for the velocity potential $\Phi(x,y,t)$ and the surface elevation $\eta(x,t)$:

$$\Phi_{xx} + \Phi_{yy} = 0, \ -\infty < x < \infty, \ -h < y < \eta(x,t) \qquad (1.2)$$

$$\Phi_x \eta_x - \Phi_y + \eta_t = 0 \ , \quad y = \eta(x,t) \qquad (1.3)$$

$$g\eta + \Phi_t + \frac{1}{2}(\Phi_x^2 + \Phi_y^2) + p/\rho = U^2/2, \ y = \eta(x,t) \qquad (1.4)$$

$$\Phi_y = 0 \ , \qquad y = -h \ . \qquad (1.5)$$

Here g is the acceleration of gravity, ρ is the fluid density, $p = p(x,\eta(x,t),t)$ is the prescribed surface pressure, and U is a constant. The x- and y- components of velocity, u and v, are obtained from Φ by the relations $u = \Phi_x$, $v = \Phi_y$. Equation (1.3) is the kinematic restriction that material particles on the free surface remain there, (1.4) is Bernoulli's law for the free surface, and (1.5) is the requirement that there be no vertical velocity component at the bottom of the channel. We must also specify suitable initial conditions. The derivation of (1.2)-(1.5) may be found in [1].

Although the differential equation (1.2) is linear, the boundary value problem (1.2)-(1.5) for Φ and η

is intractable because the domain of the differential equation (1.2) (which depends on η) is unknown in advance and because the boundary conditions (1.3) and (1.4) are nonlinear. We therefore resort to approximate theories based on the availability of a small dimensionless parameter. In the remainder of this lecture we shall examine the implications of two such widely used theories.

2. Linear small amplitude theory

If the pressure p on the free surface is zero, the boundary value problem (1.2)-(1.5) possesses the exact solution

$$\Phi_o = Ux \quad , \qquad \eta_o = 0 \tag{2.1}$$

which corresponds to a uniform flow with velocity U in the positive x-direction. To treat small disturbances from this state, we introduce the small parameter ε and set

$$\Phi = \Phi(x,y,t,\varepsilon) = Ux + \varepsilon\Phi^{(1)}(x,y,t) + \varepsilon^2\Phi^{(2)}(x,y,t) + \ldots \tag{2.2}$$

$$\eta = \eta(x,t,\varepsilon) = \varepsilon\eta^{(1)}(x,t) + \varepsilon^2\eta^{(2)}(x,t) + \ldots \quad .$$

Note that on the free surface,

$$\Phi=\Phi(x,\eta(x,t,\varepsilon),t,\varepsilon)=Ux + \varepsilon\Phi^{(1)}(x,0,t)+\varepsilon^2[\Phi^{(2)}(x,0,t) + \Phi_y^{(1)}(x,0,t)\eta^{(1)}(x,t)]+\ldots \tag{2.3}$$

The substitution of (2.2) and (2.3) into (1.2)-(1.5) and the equating of coefficients of like powers of ε yields the following sequence of linear problems for $\Phi^{(k)}$ and $\eta^{(k)}$:

$$\Phi_{xx}^{(k)} + \Phi_{yy}^{(k)} = 0, \quad -\infty < x < \infty, \quad -h < y < 0, \tag{2.4}$$

$$\Phi_{y}^{(k)} - U\,\eta_{x}^{(k)} - \eta_{t}^{(k)} = F^{(k)}, \quad y = 0, \tag{2.5}$$

$$g\eta^{(k)} + \Phi_{t}^{(k)} + U\Phi_{x}^{(k)} = G^{(k)}, \quad y = 0, \tag{2.6}$$

$$\Phi_{y}^{(k)} = 0, \quad y = -h;\ k = 1,2,\ldots . \tag{2.7}$$

Here $F^{(1)}=G^{(1)}=0$, and for $k > 1$, $F^{(k)}$ and $G^{(k)}$ depend on $\Phi^{(j)}$ and $\eta^{(j)}$ with $j < k$. As a consequence of the expansions (2.2) and (2.3), the domain of the differential equations (2.4) is prescribed and the free surface conditions (2.5) and (2.6) are specified on the fixed surface $y = 0$. Thus we have effected a considerable simplification of our original problem.

We first treat the case in which $U = 0$. If we eliminate $\eta^{(1)}$ from (2.5) and (2.6) for $k = 1$ by differentiation, we get the following boundary value problem for the first perturbation $\Phi^{(1)}$:

$$\Phi_{xx}^{(1)} + \Phi_{yy}^{(1)} = 0, \quad -\infty < x < \infty, \quad -h < y < 0 \tag{2.8}$$

$$\Phi_{tt}^{(1)} + g\Phi_{y}^{(1)} = 0, \quad y = 0 \tag{2.9}$$

$$\Phi_y^{(1)} = 0 \quad , \qquad y = -h \quad . \tag{2.10}$$

We seek solutions simply harmonic in time; hence we set

$$\Phi^{(1)} = e^{i\sigma t}\phi(x,y) \quad . \tag{2.11}$$

Then (2.8)-(2.10) become

$$\phi_{xx} + \phi_{yy} = 0 \quad , \qquad -h < y < 0 \ . \tag{2.12}$$

$$g\phi_y - \sigma^2\phi = 0 \quad , \qquad y = 0, \tag{2.13}$$

$$\phi_y = 0 \quad , \qquad y = h. \tag{2.14}$$

We further require that ϕ and ϕ_y be bounded for $x = \pm\infty$.

The solutions of this problem are

$$\phi \equiv 0 \tag{2.15}$$

$$\phi = A \cosh m(y+h) \begin{cases} \cos mx \\ \sin mx \end{cases} , \text{ A arbitrary,} \tag{2.16}$$

with

$$\sigma^2 = gm \tanh(mh) \ . \tag{2.17}$$

Equation (2.17) is a consequence of (2.13). The solutions $\Phi^{(1)} = e^{i\sigma t}\phi$ are standing waves with wave number m, wave length $\lambda = 2\pi/m$, and frequency σ. A. Weinstein [2] proved that (2.15) and (2.16) are the only solutions of (2.12)-(2.14) that are bounded for $x = \pm\infty$. Consequently, if $\phi \to 0$ as $x \to \pm\infty$, then $\phi \equiv 0$.

By taking linear combinations of these standing

waves we can construct progressing waves of the form

$$\Phi^{(1)} = A \cosh m(y+h) \cos (mx \pm \sigma t + \alpha) \quad , \tag{2.18}$$

where A and α are arbitrary constants. The phase speed of these waves is $c = \sigma/m$ and the wave length is again $\lambda = 2\pi/m$. From (2.17) we have that

$$c^2 = \frac{g\lambda}{2\pi} \tanh \frac{2\pi k}{\lambda} \quad . \tag{2.19}$$

Since c depends on λ, these waves are, by definition, dispersive. There are two limit cases of interest:

If U/λ is very large , $c^2 \sim g\lambda/2\pi$; (2.20)

if h/λ is very small, $c^2 \sim gh$. (2.21)

$c = c(\lambda)$ is a monotonically increasing function of λ such that as $\lambda \to \infty$, $c \to \sqrt{gh}$. This is the <u>critical wave speed</u>.

By establishing the convergence of the power series for Φ in terms of ε, T. Levi-Civita [3] and D. J. Struik [4] (cf. Appendix of [1]) proved that there exist periodic progressing waves for all values of λ and for all c such that

$$0 < c^2/gh < 1 \quad , \tag{2.22}$$

provided ε is sufficiently small. Since the progressing waves (2.18) are the lowest order terms in the development with respect to amplitude, bifurcations do occur for all c satisfying (2.22). Cf. Figure 2.

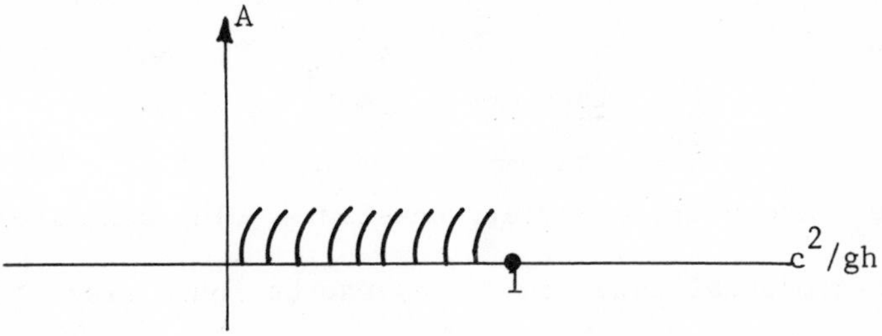

Figure 2

A denotes amplitude.

These results do not apply for $c^2 = gh$. From higher order terms it can be shown that c increases with A; this is indicated in Figure 2.

We now examine the case when $U \neq 0$. We seek steady state solutions, i.e. solutions for which the velocity (and thus the velocity potential) does not depend explicitly on the time t. The free surface condition for this case, obtained by eliminating η from (2.5) and (2.6) and by setting all t-derivatives equal to zero, is

$$g\Phi_y^{(1)} + U^2\Phi_{xx}^{(1)} = 0 \qquad \text{on } y = 0 . \tag{2.23}$$

All solutions of the boundary value problem (2.4), (2.23), and (2.7) (other than the uniform flows) can be shown to have the form (cf.[5])

$$\Phi^{(1)}(x,y) = A \cosh m(y+h)\cos(mx+\alpha) \tag{2.24}$$

with

$$\frac{U^2}{gh} = \frac{\tanh mh}{mh} \quad . \tag{2.25}$$

Here A and α are arbitrary constants. The solutions of the transcendental equation (2.25) can be found from Figure 3.

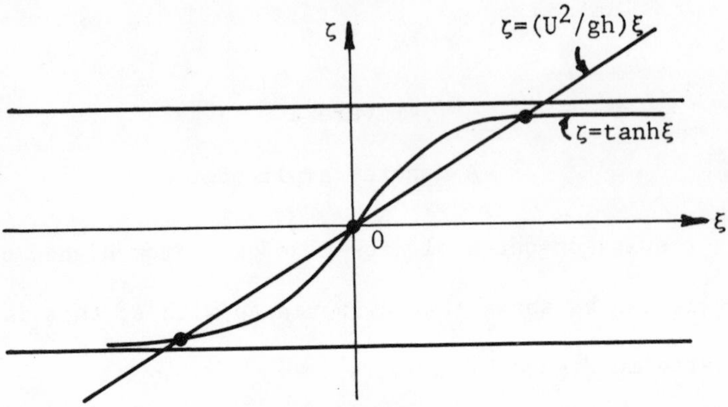

Figure 3

We see that m = 0 is always a root of (2.25) corresponding to the undisturbed state Φ_1 = const. Moreover,

i) if $U^2/gh < 1$, there are two non zero real roots;

ii) if $U^2/gh > 1$, there are no other real roots;

iii) if $U^2/gh = 1$, 0 is a triple root.

$U = \sqrt{gh}$ is called the <u>critical velocity</u>. It is an upper bound on the propagation speeds of sinusoidal waves (2.24). It is approached as $\lambda \to \infty$. (Note that the propagation speed for the medium is infinite because of incompressibility.)

Thus we have bifurcations for $0 < U^2/gh < 1$. Again we can say nothing about the behavior at the critical velocity. The resulting graph of amplitude vs. U^2/gh is like Figure 2.

We now turn to problems in which the free surface pressure is not zero. This renders the problem nonhomogeneous. For the steady state problem, if $U^2/gh < 1$, then there is no uniqueness since a solution of the homogeneous problem can always be added, whereas if $U^2/gh \geq 1$, the solution is unique because the homogeneous problem possesses only trivial solutions. If a unique solution is desired when $U^2/gh < 1$, we must impose a radiation condition: the disturbance decays upstream. (The need for a radiation condition is a rather remarkable situation for a steady-state problem.) Clearly, no such restriction is necessary when $U^2/gh \geq 1$. However for $U^2/gh = 1$, the steady flow solution for $\Phi^{(1)}$ becomes unbounded at infinity.

A typical problem for nonsteady flow in which a pressure pulse is applied to the fluid at $x = 0$, $y = 0$, $t = 0$ was solved by Stoker [6] by means of Fourier transforms. (Cf. Figure 4)

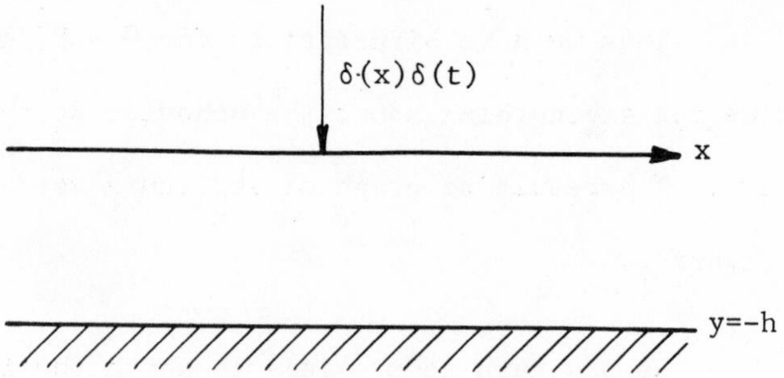

Figure 4

It was found that the solution exists and is bounded for any finite time t. For $t \to \infty$ the following results were obtained:

i) If $U^2/gh < 1$, the disturbance dies out upstream and behaves downstream like the sinusoidal waves found when $p = 0$ on the free surface.

ii) If $U^2/gh > 1$, the disturbance decays exponentially upstream and downstream.

iii) If $U^2/gh = 1$, $\Phi_t^{(1)} \sim t^{2/3}$, $\Phi_x^{(1)} \sim t^{1/3}$ for all x.

This last result indicates that the flow is infinitesimally unstable at the critical speed. It is well known that such instability does not necessarily predict an instability in the large. This shortcoming of the infinitesimal stability criterion is strikingly illustrated in this problem by the experimentally verifiable existence at the critical speed of the highly stable solitary wave predicted by the nonlinear theory. The uniqueness theory for these linear problems shows that a perturbation approach does not yield the solitary wave because a solution that dies out at infinity must be the uniform solution. Cnoidal waves also exist at the critical speed. We shall discuss these nonlinear phenomena in the next section.

As a final application of this linear theory we discuss steady flows in layered media. Since a flow in a two-layered medium is illustrated in Figure 5.

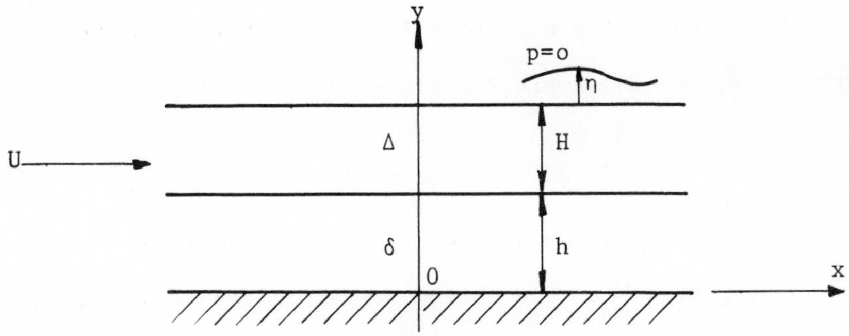

Figure 5
(Notice new coordinates.)

We use capitals to indicate variables for the upper layer, lower case symbols for the lower layer. Δ and δ denote densities. We set

$$r = H/h \quad , \qquad \rho = \Delta/\delta < 1 \quad . \tag{2.26}$$

It is convenient for this type of problem to describe the motion in terms of a stream function rather than the velocity potential. (If ψ is a stream function, then the velocity components are obtained from the relations $u = \psi_y$, $v = -\psi_x$.) When the free surface conditions and appropriate interfacial conditions are satisfied, it can be shown [7] that the motion is uniquely given by stream functions of the form

$$f = a \sin(mx+\alpha)\sinh my, \qquad \text{in lower layer}$$

$$\begin{aligned} F = A \sin(mx+\alpha)[&m \sinh my - m(1-\rho)\sinh m \cosh m(1-y) \\ &+ (gh/U^2)(1-\rho)\sinh m \sinh m(1-y)], \quad \text{in upper layer,} \end{aligned} \tag{2.27}$$

provided m satisfies a certain transcendental equation. Here a, A, and α are arbitrary constants.

It is found that for each $\lambda = 2\pi/m$, there are two types of solutions characterized by propagation speeds U_1 and U_2, $U_1 > U_2$. The motion corresponding to U_1 has its maximum amplitude on the free surface and that corresponding to U_2 has its maximum amplitude at the interface. (This latter motion is called an internal wave.) As $\lambda \to \infty$,

$$\begin{aligned} U_1 &\to C_1 \text{ where } 2C_1^2/gh = 1 + r + \sqrt{(1-r)^2+4\rho r}\ , \\ U_2 &\to C_2 \text{ where } 2C_2^2/gh = 1 + r - \sqrt{(1-r)^2+4\rho r}\ . \end{aligned} \tag{2.28}$$

Thus we have two bifurcation diagrams (Figure 6a)

corresponding to the two possible modes.

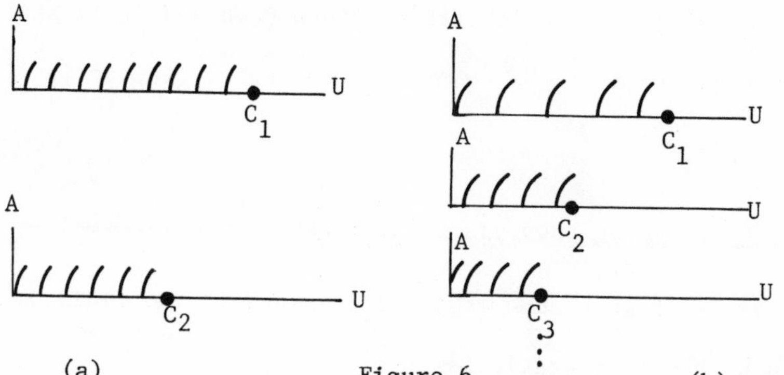

Figure 6

C_1 and C_2 are the critical speeds and they play the same role as the critical speed in the single layer case already discussed. In particular, the inadequacy of this small amplitude theory is similarly manifested at these critical speeds because the theory cannot account for stable solitary waves.

We could also consider the steady flow of a fluid with a continuously varying density. For a density that decreases exponentially with y, it is found that there are a countably infinite number of solutions modes with propagation speeds U_k and critical speeds C_k, with $C_k \sim C_1/k$. (Figure 6b). Thus there are a countably infinite set of bifurcation diagrams. The solution corresponding to U_1 has its maximum amplitude on the free surface and solutions corresponding to other modes have internal maxima. For fluids of infinite height (modeling the atmosphere) the calculations break down and it is still an open question of how to obtain meaningful results for such a case.

3. Shallow water theory: Solitary and cnoidal waves.

If we assume that the pressure in the fluid is given by the hydrostatic law

$$p = \rho g(\eta - y) \tag{3.1}$$

(in terms of the coordinates of Figure 1) then it is easy to show (cf [1]) that the motion is governed by the equations of the <u>shallow water</u> or <u>long wave theory</u>:

$$u_t + uu_x = -g\eta_x \tag{3.2}$$

$$[(\eta + h)u]_x = -\eta_t \quad . \tag{3.3}$$

This is a first order hyperbolic system having a direct analogy with the equations of one-dimensional gas dynamics. These equations do not yield the solitary wave. To obtain such waves we employ a systematic development due to K.O. Friedrichs [8] of the general hydrodynamical equations with respect to a suitable parameter. The first order terms of this theory yield (3.2) and (3.3). The choice of the expansion parameter explains why (3.2) and (3.3) are called the equations of shallow water or long wave theory. This development was employed by J. B. Keller [9] to obtain solitary waves, by Friedrichs and Hyers [10] to prove existence of the solitary wave by showing that the perturbation scheme converged, and by W. Littmann [11] to prove existence of cnoidal waves.

We obtain this theory for the two-layered fluid of Figure 7. We restrict ourselves to steady flows. (Cf. [7].)

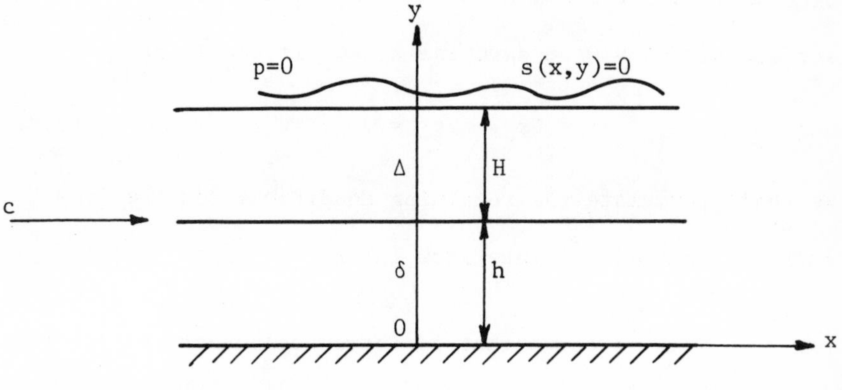

Figure 7

Quantities characterizing the upper layer are capitalized, those for the lower layer are in lower case. The velocity at infinity is now denoted c. We set $r = H/h$, $\rho = \Delta/\delta$.

In the lower layer the Euler equations of motion are

$$\delta(uu_x + vu_y) = -p_x \quad , \tag{3.4}$$

$$\delta(uv_x + vv_y) = -\delta g - p_y , \tag{3.5}$$

the continuity equation is

$$u_x + v_y = 0 \ , \tag{3.6}$$

and the irrotationality condition is given by the vanishing of the vorticity

$$v_x - u_y = 0 \ . \tag{3.7}$$

The equations for the upper layer are obtained by substituting capitals for lower case in these equations. On the free surface $s(x,y) = 0$ we have the kinematic condition

$$Us_x + Vs_y = 0 \ . \tag{3.8}$$

We shall formulate the remaining conditions for the free surface, bottom, and interface later.

It is convenient to introduce the stream function $\psi(x,y)$ for which

$$u = \psi_y \ , \qquad v = -\psi_x \ . \tag{3.9}$$

The stream lines are given by

$$\psi(x,y) = \gamma = \text{const.} \tag{3.10}$$

We choose γ such that

$$\begin{aligned} \gamma &= \psi(x,0) = 0 && \text{on the bottom,} \\ \gamma &= ch && \text{at the interface,} \end{aligned} \tag{3.11}$$

and $\gamma = c(h+H) = ch\ (1+r)$ on the free surface.

We now assume that all the stream lines have a 1-1 projection on the x-axis. Thus (3.11) can be inverted to yield

$$y = \bar{f}(x,\gamma) \qquad \text{in lower layer} \tag{3.12}$$

$$y = \bar{F}(x,\gamma) \qquad \text{in upper layer .} \tag{3.13}$$

$\bar{f}$ and $\bar{F}$ are called the <u>streamline functions</u>. We take x and γ as new independent variables and set

$$u(x,y) = u(x,\bar{f}(x,\gamma)) = \bar{u}(x,\gamma)\ , \text{ etc. in lower layer.} \tag{3.14}$$

Similar notation is used for the upper layer. Thus

$$u_x = \bar{u}_x + \bar{u}_\gamma \gamma_x = \bar{u}_x + \bar{u}_\gamma \psi_x = \bar{u}_x - \bar{v}u_\gamma\ , \text{ etc.} \tag{3.15}$$

Equations (3.4)-(3.7) become

$$\delta\overline{uu}_x = -\bar{p}_x + \overline{vp}_\gamma \quad , \tag{3.16}$$

$$\delta\overline{uv}_x = -\delta g - \overline{up}_\gamma \quad , \tag{3.17}$$

$$\bar{u}_x - \overline{vu}_\gamma + \overline{uv}_\gamma = 0 \ , \tag{3.18}$$

$$\bar{v}_x - \overline{vv}_\gamma - \overline{uu}_\gamma = 0 \quad . \tag{3.19}$$

Equations for the upper layer are analogous. The free surface condition (3.8) becomes

$$\bar{u}(\bar{s}_x - \overline{vs}_\gamma) + \bar{v}\ \bar{u}\ \bar{s}_\gamma \equiv \bar{u}\ \bar{s}_x = 0 \tag{3.20}$$

which is identically satisfied since the free surface is

given by $\bar{s}(x,c(h+H)) = 0$.

The advantage of these new variables is that the equations (16)-(19) are to be solved in the fixed strip: $-\infty < x < \infty$, $0 < \gamma < ch$, and similarly the equations for the upper layer are to be solved for $-\infty < x < \infty$, $ch < \gamma < c(h+H)$.

It is convenient to use $\bar{u}, \bar{f}$ (or $\bar{F}$), and $\bar{p}$ as dependent variables, rather than $\bar{u}, \bar{v}$, and $\bar{p}$. Then

$$\bar{f}_\gamma = 1/\psi_y = 1/\bar{u}, \quad \bar{f}_x = -\psi_x/\psi_y = \bar{v}/\bar{u} \; . \tag{3.21}$$

(We assume $\bar{u} \neq 0$.) Then the continuity equation (3.18) is identically satisfied (which is not surprising in view of the relationship between $\bar{f}$ and the stream function ψ). (3.16) and (3.17) become

$$\begin{aligned} \delta\bar{u}_x &= -\bar{f}_\gamma \bar{p}_x + \bar{f}_x \bar{p}_\gamma \\ \delta(\bar{u}\bar{f}_{xx} + \bar{u}_x \bar{f}_x) &= -\delta g \bar{f}_\gamma - \bar{p}_\gamma \; . \end{aligned} \tag{3.23}$$

The continuity equation (3.18) is replaced by the first equation in (3.21):

$$\bar{u}\,\bar{f}_\gamma = 1 \; . \tag{3.24}$$

The irrotationality condition (19) becomes

$$(\bar{f}_x/\bar{f}_\gamma)_x - \tfrac{1}{2}[(1 + \bar{f}_x^2)/\bar{f}_\gamma^2]_\gamma = 0 \; . \tag{3.25}$$

We now introduce the small dimensionless parameter ε. Frequently ε is chosen to be the ratio of a typical depth to a typical horizontal length. This choice of ε explains why the shallow water or long wave theory is so named. For the purpose of obtaining solitary and cnoidal waves, we want an expansion in the neighborhood of a uniform flow at a given speed. Consequently, we choose

$$\varepsilon = \ell - gh/c^2 \tag{3.26}$$

where ℓ is a number characterizing the uniform flow. We introduce the following new dimensionless variables in which the horizontal variable is stretched:

$$\begin{aligned} &\sigma = \sqrt{\varepsilon}x/h \quad, \eta = \gamma/ch \;, u^* = \bar{u}/c \;, U^* = \bar{U}/c \\ &v^* = \bar{v}/c, \quad V^* = \bar{V}/c \;, p^* = \bar{p}/\delta c^2, P^* = \bar{P}/\Delta c^2 \\ &f^* = \bar{f}/h \;, \quad F^* = \bar{F}/h \;, r = H/h \;, \rho = \Delta/\delta \;. \end{aligned} \tag{3.27}$$

We now drop the asterisks. Our governing equations become

$$\left.\begin{aligned} &u_\sigma = -f_\eta p_\sigma + f_\sigma p_\eta \;, \\ &\varepsilon(uf_{\sigma\sigma} + u_\sigma f_\sigma) = \varepsilon f_\eta - \ell f_\eta - p_\eta, \\ &uf_\eta = 1, \qquad\qquad 0 < \eta < 1, \\ &f_{\eta\eta} + \varepsilon[f_\sigma^2 f_{\eta\eta} + f_\eta^2 f_{\sigma\sigma} - 2f_\sigma f_\eta f_{\sigma\eta}] = 0, \end{aligned}\right. \tag{3.28}$$

$$\left.\begin{aligned} &U_\sigma = -F_\eta P_\sigma + F_\sigma P_\eta \;, \\ &\varepsilon(UF_{\sigma\sigma} + U_\sigma F_\sigma) = \varepsilon F_\eta - \ell F_\eta - P_\eta \;, \\ &UF_\eta = 1 \;, \qquad\qquad 0 < \eta < 1+r \\ &F_{\eta\eta} + \varepsilon[F_\sigma^2 F_{\eta\eta} + F_\eta^2 F_{\sigma\sigma} - 2F_\sigma F_\eta F_{\sigma\eta}] = 0 \;. \end{aligned}\right. \tag{3.29}$$

The boundary conditions are

$$\begin{aligned} f(\sigma,0) &= 0, \\ f(\sigma,1) &= F(\sigma,1) \\ p(\sigma,1) &= P(\sigma,1), \\ P(\sigma,1+r) &= 0 \quad . \end{aligned} \tag{3.30}$$

The first two equations of (3.30) ensure that the fluid particles along bottom and on the interface neither separate from nor penetrate into the adjacent medium, the third equation is the condition that the pressure be continuous across the interface, and the fourth equation is the condition that the free surface pressure be zero.

We now assume that all the variables entering into the boundary value problem (3.28), (3.29), (3.30), have expansions in integral powers of ε of the form

$$f=f(\sigma,\eta,\varepsilon)=\sum_{k=o}^{\infty} f^{(k)}(\sigma,\eta)\varepsilon^k, \quad F=F(\sigma,\eta,\varepsilon)=\sum_{k=o}^{\infty} F^{(k)}(\sigma,\eta)\varepsilon^k, \text{ etc.} \tag{3.31}$$

That expansions in integral powers are adequate was essentially proved in [10]. Since some of the highest order derivatives appearing in (3.28) and (3.29) have the coefficient ε, these equations are a singular perturbation of the equations for $\varepsilon = 0$ and we cannot expect anything better than asymptotic results.

If we substitute the expansions (3.31) into (3.28), (3.29), and (3.30), and equate coefficients of like powers of ε, we obtain a sequence of boundary value problems.

If we assume that $u^{(o)}(-\infty,\eta) = U^{(o)}(-\infty,\eta) = 1$, the solution of the equations of the zero-th order approximation is readily shown to be

$$\begin{aligned} u^{(o)} &= 1 & U^{(o)} &= 1 \\ f^{(o)} &= \eta & F^{(o)} &= \eta \\ p^{(o)} &= \ell(1 + pr - \eta) & P^{(o)} &= \ell(1 + r - \eta). \end{aligned} \tag{3.32}$$

This represents a parallel flow with velocity c in both layers.

The boundary value problem for the first order theory is the linear system

$$\begin{aligned} &u_\sigma^{(1)} + \ell f_\sigma^{(1)} + p_\sigma^{(1)} = 0 & & U_\sigma^{(1)} + \ell F_\sigma^{(1)} + P_\sigma^{(1)} = 0 \\ &\ell f_\eta^{(1)} + p_\eta^{(1)} = 1 & 0 < \eta < 1 \quad & \ell F_\eta^{(1)} + P_\eta^{(1)} = 1 & 1 < \eta < 1+r \\ &f_\eta^{(1)} + u^{(1)} = 0 & & F_\eta^{(1)} + U^{(1)} = 0 \\ &f_{\eta\eta}^{(1)} = 0 & & F_{\eta\eta}^{(1)} = 0 \end{aligned} \tag{3.33}$$

$$f^{(1)}(\sigma,0)=0,\ f^{(1)}(\sigma,1)=F^{(1)}(\sigma,1),\ p^{(1)}(\sigma,1)=\rho P^{(1)}(\sigma,1),$$
$$P^{(1)}(\sigma,1 + r) = 0.$$

The solution of (3.33) is given by

$$u^{(1)} = -a_1(\sigma) \qquad U^{(1)} = A_1(\sigma)(\eta-1)+a_1(\sigma)$$

$$f^{(1)} = a_1(\sigma)\eta \qquad F^{(1)} = -A_1(\sigma) \tag{3.34}$$

$$p^{(1)} = -\ell a_1(\sigma)+a_1(\sigma)+(\eta-1-\rho r)+k_1, \quad P^{(1)} = -\ell A_1(\sigma)(\eta-1)-\ell a_1(\sigma) +A_1(\sigma)+(\eta-1-r)+ K_1$$

where k_1 and K_1 are constants. Due to the pressure boundary conditions, $a_1(\sigma)$ and $A_1(\sigma)$ must satisfy

$$(1 - \ell+\rho\ell)\ a_1'(\sigma) - \rho A_1'(\sigma) = 0, \tag{3.35}$$
$$\ell a_1'(\sigma) + (\ell r-1)A_1'(\sigma) = 0\ .$$

If a_1' and A_1' are not to vanish identically (and thus yield the uniform flow), the determinant of coefficients of (3.35) must equal zero, from which it follows that

$$\ell = \frac{1 + r\pm[(1-r)^2 + 4r\rho]^{1/2}}{2r(1-\rho)}\ . \tag{3.36}$$

This is the same result as that given in (2.28) which was based on the linear small amplitude theory. Thus bifurcation occurs at the critical speeds. Cf. Figure 8.

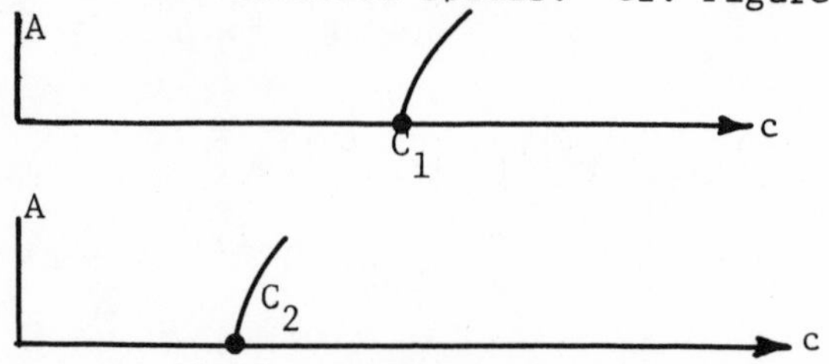

Figure 8

To find the amplitudes a_1 and A_1 we must go to the second order approximation.

$$u_\sigma^{(2)} = a_1'(\sigma)\eta - a_1(\sigma)a_1'(\sigma) - \ell f_\sigma^{(2)} - p_\sigma^{(2)}, \quad 0 < \eta < 1$$

$$U_\sigma^{(2)} = A_1'(\sigma)(\eta-1) + a_1'(\sigma) - A_1(\sigma)A_1'(\sigma) - \ell F_\sigma^{(2)} - P_\sigma^{(2)}, \quad 1 < \eta < 1+r .$$

The solution of this system involves new functions $a_2(\sigma)$ and $A_2(\sigma)$ which must satisfy the following two ordinary differential equations obtained from the pressure boundary conditions:

$$(1-\ell+\rho\ell)a_2'(\sigma) - \rho A_2'(\sigma) = I \quad , \tag{3.38}$$

$$\ell a_2'(\sigma) + (\ell r-1)A_2'(\sigma) = J \; ,$$

where

$$I = \frac{1}{6}(3-\ell+\rho\ell)a_1'''(\sigma) + (\rho-1)a_1'(\sigma) + 3a_1(\sigma)a_1'(\sigma) - 3\rho A_1(\sigma)A_1'(\sigma),$$

$$J = \frac{1}{6}(\ell-6r+3\ell r^2)a_1'''(\sigma) + \frac{1}{6}(\ell r^3-3r^2)A_1'''(\sigma) + a_1'(\sigma) + rA_1'(\sigma) - 3A_1'(\sigma)A_1'(\sigma).$$

Since the determinant of coefficients of (3.38) vanishes, I and J must be related by

$$(\ell r-1)I + \rho J = 0 \quad . \tag{3.39}$$

Using (3.35), we can simplify (39) to obtain

$$m_0 a_1'''(\sigma) = m_1 a_1(\sigma)a_1'(\sigma) + m_2 a_1'(\sigma) \quad . \tag{3.40a}$$

The constants m_0, m_1, m_2, depending on r,ρ,ℓ,K_1, are given by

$$
\begin{aligned}
3m_o &= r(r+1)\ell - (r^2+1+3\rho r) \\
m_1 &= -3[\ell^2(r^2-1) + \ell(1-2r) + 1]/(\ell r-1) \\
m_2 &= -[2\ell r(\rho-1)+r+1] + 3(1-\ell)K_1/(\ell r-1).
\end{aligned} \tag{3.40b}
$$

The general solution of (3.40) can be expressed in terms of Jacobi elliptic functions. These solutions lead to cnoidal waves. The solitary wave may be considered a limit case of cnoidal waves or it may be found directly by the integration of (3.40) subject to the decay conditions. This yields the solution

$$a_1(\sigma) = \frac{-3m_2}{m_1} \operatorname{sech}^2 \frac{\sigma}{2}(m_2/m_o)^{1/2} \tag{3.41}$$

$$A_1(\sigma) = \frac{\ell a_1(\sigma)}{1-\ell r} \quad . \tag{3.42}$$

If $H = 0$, the solution reduces to that of [9] for a single layer.

There are two types of behavior of solitary waves in a two-layered fluid:

i) At the higher critical speed, all streamlines go above the corresponding lines of the uniform flow. The ratio of the amplitude of the wave at the free surface to that at the interface is $1/(1-\ell_2 r)$. If $\delta \simeq \Delta$, then this ratio approximately equals 1+r. If $\delta = \Delta$ and $h = H$, then this ratio is 2.

ii) At the lower critical speed, various cases occur. In general, though, the amplitude at the free surface tends to be small compared with that at the interface. For certain parameter ranges, the wave at the interface may be a wave of elevation or a wave of depression. The wave at the free surface has the opposite behavior.

The problem for fluid with a density that decreases exponentially with y is treated in [7].

Bibliography

[1] J.J. Stoker. Water Waves. Interscience, N.Y. 1957.

[2] A. Weinstein, Sur un problème aux limites dans une bande indéfinie, Inst. France, Acad. Sci. C.R., 184, 1927, p. 497 ff.

[3] T. Levi-Civita, Détermination rigoreuse des ondes permanentes d'ampleur finie, Math. Ann. 93, 1925, pp. 264-314.

[4] D.J. Struik, Détermination rigoureuse des ondes irrotationelles périodiques dans un canal à profondeur finie, Math. Ann. 95, 1926, pp. 595-634.

[5] A.S. Peters. Unpublished manuscript.

[6] J.J. Stoker, Unsteady waves on a running stream. C.P.A.M., 6, 1953, pp. 471-481.

[7] A.S. Peters & J.J. Stoker, Solitary Waves in Liquids Having Non-Constant Density, C.P.A.M. 13, 1960, pp. 115-164.

[8] K.O. Friedrichs, On the derivation of the shallow water theory, Appendix to J.J. Stoker, The formation of breakers and bores. C.P.A.M., 1, 1948, pp. 81-87.

[9] J.B. Keller, The solitary wave and periodic waves in shallow water, C.P.A.M., 1, 1948, pp. 323-339

[10] K.O. Friedrichs & D.H. Hyers, The existence of solitary waves, C.P.A.M., 7, 1954, pp. 517-550.

[11] W. Littmann, On the existence of periodic waves near critical speed, C.P.A.M., 10, 1957, pp. 241-269.

X. Perturbation Theory of Quasiperiodic Solutions of Differential Equations.

J. Moser

1. Introduction.

The theory of nonlinear oscillations has largely been restricted to the study of periodic solutions of differential equations. In this lecture we discuss some extensions of these results to the theory of almost periodic solutions and we examine some of the subtle difficulties involved in this generalization.

Definition. A function $f(t)$ is called quasiperiodic if it can be represented in the form

$$f(t) = F(\omega_1 t, \ldots, \omega_n t) \tag{1.1}$$

where $F(x_1,\ldots,x_n)$ is a continuous function of period 2π in $x_1,\ldots,x_n$.

Such a function has a Fourier representation

$$f = \sum_j c_j e^{it(j,\omega)} \tag{1.2}$$

where $j = (j_1,\ldots,j_n)$ is an n-vector of integers and

$$(j,\omega) = \sum_{\nu=1}^{n} j_\nu \omega_\nu . \tag{1.3}$$

We assume that $\omega_1,\ldots,\omega_n$ are rationally independent, i.e. if $(j,\omega) = 0$ then $j = 0$. This assumption causes no loss of generality since the set of ω's can always be reduced to a rationally independent set. We call the ω's the basic frequencies.

From (1.2) we see that the class of quasiperiodic functions is closed under addition and multiplication. Quasiperiodic functions are almost periodic functions with a finite base. A periodic function is a quasiperiodic function with just one basic frequency. We observe that the set of numbers of the form (j,ω) (the spectrum of f) is dense on the real line if $n > 1$. For simplicity we assume that all functions appearing in this lecture are real analytic.

2. Periodic Solutions*.

Before discussing the question of quasiperiodic solutions of ordinary differential equations, we recall some of the characteristic difficulties associated with periodic solutions. We can expect these difficulties to be magnified in the quasiperiodic case. As a typical example we treat the Duffing equation

$$x_{tt} + \alpha^2 x + \beta x^3 = \varepsilon f(t). \tag{2.1}$$

Here ε is a small parameter and $f(t)$ has period 2π in t. Equation (2.1) represents a perturbation of the autonomous equation

$$x_{tt} + \alpha^2 x + \beta x^3 = 0. \tag{2.2}$$

Equation (2.2) has the integral

$$x_t^2 + \alpha^2 x^2 + \beta x^4/2 = E(\text{const}), \tag{2.3}$$

which for β positive is the equation of a family of closed curves C_E, parametrized by E, in the phase plane (Fig. 2.1).

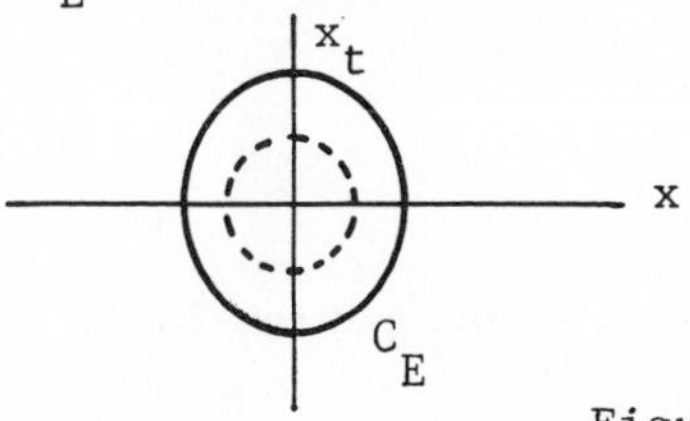

Figure 1

*The concepts discussed in this section are treated in the standard texts on ordinary differential equations and non-linear oscillations .

For each E, the parameters α and β can be so chosen that any solution of (2.2) having initial values on C_E has period 2π. But by the method of Poincaré, it can be shown that there are only two initial points on C_E from which a solution of period 2π of the perturbed system (2.1) bifurcates. Thus if $x(t,\varepsilon)$ denotes the set of solutions of (2.1) of period 2π, than $\lim_{\varepsilon \to o} x(t,\varepsilon)$ does not constitute the set of solutions of (2.2) of period 2π with initial values on C_E. These same remarks hold if we make the change of variables $x = \varepsilon^{1/3} z$ which reduces (2.2) to the form

$$z_{tt} + \alpha^2 z = \varepsilon^{2/3}(f-\beta z^3). \tag{2.4}$$

(Equation (2.4) is a perturbation of a linear system.) Thus the permanence of periodic solutions under a perturbation may require the imposition of certain subsidiary conditions on the parameters appearing in the problem.

We note that a general non-autonomous periodic system

$$y_t = f(y,t) = F(y,\omega t) \tag{2.5}$$

where f has period $2\pi/\omega$ in t and F has period 2π in ωt is equivalent to the autonomous system

$$\begin{aligned} x_t &= \omega \\ y_t &= F(y,x) \end{aligned} \tag{2.6}$$

with $x(0) = 0$. We can therefore treat periodic solutions of nonautonomous systems by studying the augmented autonomous system (2.6). We recall the standard perturbation theory for such systems:

Consider the autonomous system

$$z_t = h(z,\varepsilon). \tag{2.7}$$

For $\varepsilon = 0$, let (2.7) have the solution $z_o(t)$ with period 2π. Then for sufficiently small $\varepsilon > 0$, the perturbed system (2.7) has a solution $z(t,\varepsilon)$ of period $T(\varepsilon)$ in t such that $z(t,0) = z_o(t)$ and $T(0) = 2\pi$ provided that the set of periodic solutions $\dot{z}(t)$ of period 2π of the variational equation

$$\dot{z}_t = h_z(z_o(t),0)\dot{z} \tag{2.8}$$

is one dimensional, i.e. $\dot{z}(t) = a\dot{z}_o(t)$. Thus the existence of a periodic solution of the perturbed system depends on a non-degeneracy condition in terms of the variational equations. We shall see that similar results hold for the quasiperiodic problem.

3. Typical problems for quasiperiodic motions.

We shall deal with a generalization of the system (2.6):

$$\begin{aligned} x_t &= \omega \\ y_t &= F(x,y) \end{aligned} \tag{3.1}$$

where x is an n-vector and y is an m-vector. F(x,t) has period 2π in $x_1,\ldots,x_n$ and $\omega_1,\ldots,\omega_n$ are rationally independent. We pose the question: Do quasiperiodic solutions of (3.1) persist when (3.1) is perturbed? The answer to this question is, in general, no, because small perturbations may alter the values of the ω's in such a way that the rational independence of the ω's is destroyed.

Let us examine the case n = 2. It is convenient to study this problem in the x_1, x_2-plane (Fig. 3.1) in which $F(x_1, x_2, y)$ is doubly periodic.

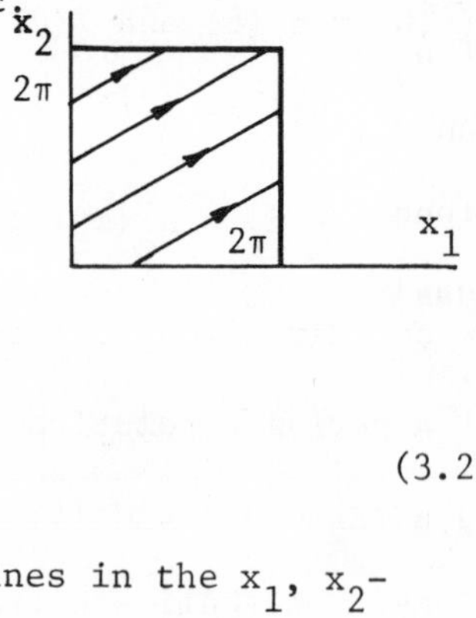

Figure 2

The equations

$$x_{1t} = \omega_1,\ x_{2t} = \omega_2 \tag{3.2}$$

correspond to a family of straight lines in the x_1, x_2-plane with the irrational slope ω_2/ω_1. (cf Fig. 3.1). By identifying the lines $x_1 = 0$ with $x_1 = 2\pi$ and $x_2 = 0$ with $x_2 = 2\pi$, we may regard x_1 and x_2 as surface coordinates of a torus. The vector field given by (3.2) is called the <u>flow</u> on the torus corresponding to (3.1). We observe that each orbit of (3.2) is dense on the torus.

A system of differential equations

$$x_t = f \tag{3.3a}$$

is called <u>structurally stable</u> if the vector field corresponding to the perturbed system

$$x_t = f + \varepsilon\psi \tag{3.3b}$$

is equivalent to that of the unperturbed system (3.3a) in the sense that under an appropriate homeomorphism the orbits of (3.3b) are mapped into those of (3.3a). For $n = 2$, Pliss [1] showed that the system of the form (3.2) is structurally stable if and only if ω_2/ω_1 is rational and if the flow has the form shown in Figure 3

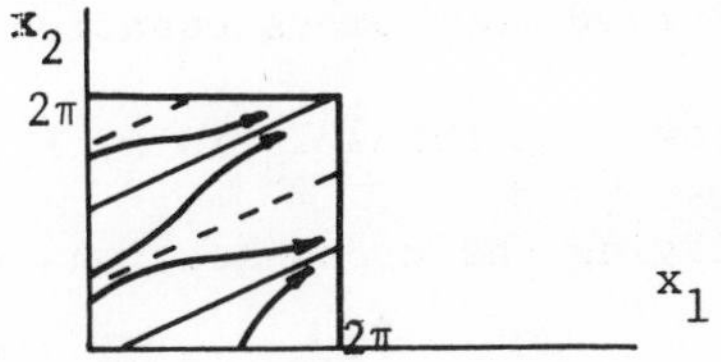

Figure 3

Here the straight solid lines correspond to stable periodic solutions and the straight dashed lines to unstable periodic solutions. Thus if ω_2/ω_1 is irrational, then under small perturbations, the structure of the flow will change and will not, in general, remain equivalent to the parallel flow. We therefore cannot expect the density of the flow on the torus to be preserved under a perturbation.

If the concept of a quasiperiodic solution is to have physical significance such solutions must persist under perturbations. In view of our preceding remarks, we can expect success in formulating conditions for the permanance of quasiperiodic motions only if we restrict the class of differential equations. For example, Kolmogorov [2], [3] and Arnol'd [4], [5] were able to establish the existence of quasiperiodic solutions of N basic frequencies for Hamiltonian systems with N degree of freedom. We exhibit some other examples of systems for which we can construct such a perturbation theory.

Example 1: Duffing's equation (2.1). The solutions of the unperturbed autonomous equation (2.2) can be described by the flow on a torus T_o in x, x_t, t-space. T_o is obtained by identifying the cross-sections t = 0 and t = 2π of

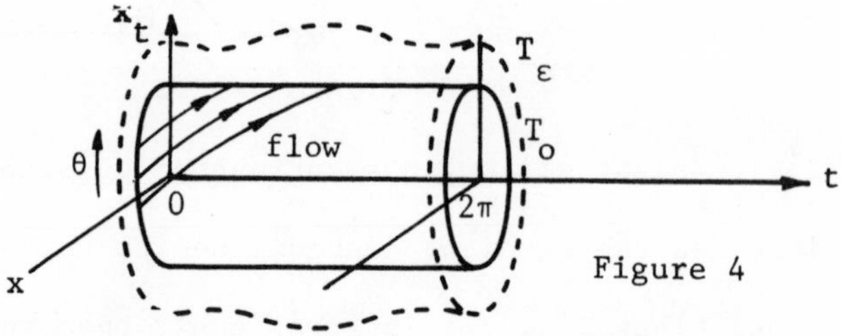

Figure 4

the cylinder with generators normal to the curve (2.3). This torus is outlined by solid lines in Figure 4. The surface coordinates for this torus are t and an angular coordinate θ that parametrizes the curve (2.3). The constant E(energy) of (2.3) may be used to parametrize these tori. The delicate proof of the boundedness of the perturbed equation (2.1) can be obtained by showing that there is a nearby torus T_ε, described by similar coordinates, on which each orbit is dense; i.e. by showing the existence of quasiperiodic solutions of (2.1) with two basic frequencies. (The torus T_ε is outlined by the dashed line in Figure 4.) The essential restriction for quasiperiodicity is that (2.2) be a conservative system. (If damping say, were present then we could not expect the existence of such tori because all solutions would tend to equibrium.)

Example 2.

$$x_t = B(x,\varepsilon), \text{ div } B = 0. \tag{3.4}$$

Here x and B are 3-vectors. This equation occurs in plasma physics. For $\varepsilon = 0$ this system possesses a one parameter family of invariant tori (magnetic surfaces). Do such magnetic surfaces exist for small perturbations? The affirmative answer to this question is a consequence of the restriction that div B = 0.

Example 3:

$$y_t = g(y,t,\varepsilon), \ g(y,-t,\varepsilon) = -g(y,t,\varepsilon). \tag{3.5}$$

y is an m-vector and g is quasiperiodic in t with basic frequencies $\omega_1,\ldots,\omega_n$.

Because of the reversibility condition on g, it can be shown that every solution of (3.5) in $|y| < 1$ for sufficiently small ε is quasiperiodic.

Example 4. Weakly coupled oscilators.

$$q_{\nu tt} + F_\nu(q_\nu) = \varepsilon G_\nu(q,q_t) \quad \nu = 1,\ldots,n. \tag{3.6}$$

For $\varepsilon = 0$, (3.6) is a system of n uncoupled oscillators. Quasiperiodic solutions of the unperturbed system can be continued if the reversibility condition

$$G(q, -q_t) = G(q,q_t) \tag{3.7}$$

is satisfied.

As a special case of (3.6) we consider

$$q_{\nu tt} + \omega_\nu^2 q_\nu = \varepsilon Q_\nu(q,q_t,\varepsilon), \quad \nu = 1,\ldots,n \tag{3.8}$$

where the ω's are rationally independent. To study this system we introduce coordinates x_ν, y_ν by the transformation

$$q_{\nu t} + i\omega_\nu q_\nu = y_\nu e^{ix_\nu} \tag{3.9}$$

which reduces (3.8) to the form

$$x_t = \omega + \varepsilon f(x,y,\varepsilon) \tag{3.10}$$

$$y_t = \varepsilon g(x,y,\varepsilon)$$

where

$$f_\nu = y_\nu^{-1} \operatorname{Im}(e^{-ix_\nu} Q_\nu), g_\nu = \operatorname{Re}(e^{-ix_\nu} Q_\nu).$$

For $\varepsilon = 0$, (3.10) has solutions

$$x = x^o + \omega t, \; y = y^o.$$

4. Formulation of the general problem.

We consider the autonomous system

$$z_t = h(z) \tag{4.1}$$

where z is a vector in n + m dimensional space. This system corresponds to the unperturbed form of a more general system. We assume that there exists an n-dimensional <u>invariant torus</u>, i.e. a torus on which the vector field is everywhere tangential. We also assume that one can introduce coordinates

$x_1,\ldots,x_n;\ y_1,\ldots,y_m$ by a nonsingular transformation

$$z = \phi(x,y)$$

near the torus in such a manner that the torus corresponds to y = 0 with $x_1,\ldots,x_n$ (mod 2π) the angle coordinates and $y_1,\ldots,y_m$ the normal coordinates (Fig. 5).

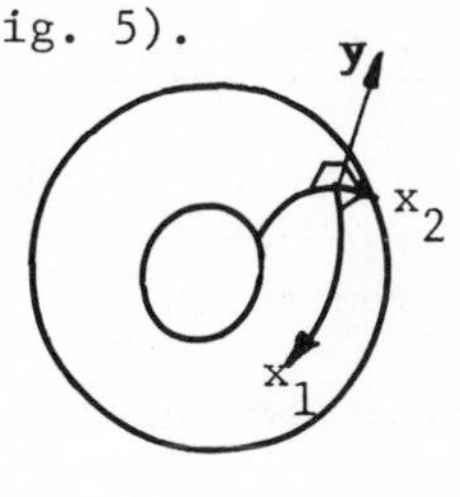

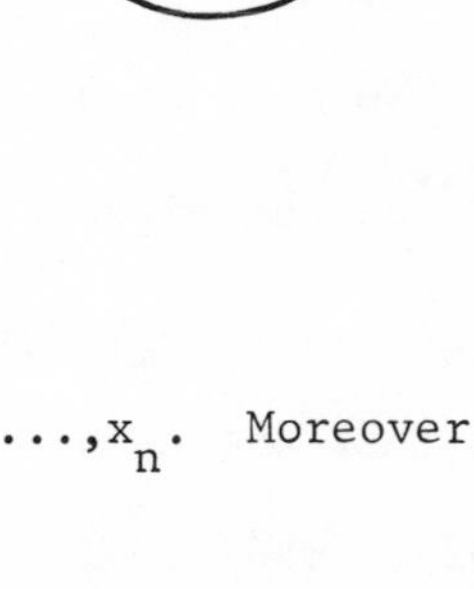

Figure 5

Thus (4.1) becomes

$$x_t = F(x,y),\ y_t = G(x,y) \tag{4.2}$$

where F and G have period 2π in $x_1,\ldots,x_n$. Moreover, we have

$$G(x,0) \equiv 0 \text{ for all } x, \tag{4.3}$$

since the torus is invariant under the vector field. The flow on the torus is given by

$$x_t = F(x,0) \tag{4.4}$$

which is a differential equation on the torus. In virtue of (4.3) and (4.4), we write (4.2) in the form

$$\begin{aligned} x_t &= F(x,0) + O(y). \\ y_t &= G_y(x,0)y + O(y^2). \end{aligned} \tag{4.5}$$

Associated with (4.5) are the linearized or variational equations

$$\begin{aligned} x_t &= F(x,0) \equiv \omega, \\ y_t &= G_y(x,0)y \equiv \Omega y. \end{aligned} \tag{4.6}$$

We now assume that the n-vector ω and the m x m matrix Ω are constant. This severe restriction is imposed since hardly anything is known otherwise. (For the periodic case, n = 1, however, the Floquet theory shows that there exists a transformation that carries (4.6) into a system of the same form having constant coefficients.)

We also assume that Ω can be diagonalized. Let $\Omega_1,\ldots,\Omega_m$ be the eigenvalues of Ω. We call the numbers $\omega_1,\ldots,\omega_n$; $\Omega_1,\ldots,\Omega_m$, <u>characteristic numbers</u>. It can easily be shown that the numbers of the form (j,ω) and the eigenvalues of Ω (mod$(j,\omega)i$) are invariant under coordinate changes of (4.6) that preserve the constancy of ω and Ω.

We now investigate the perturbed system corresponding to (4.2):

$$x_t = F(x,y) + \varepsilon f(x,y,\varepsilon),$$

$$y_t = G_t(x,y) + \varepsilon g(x,y,\varepsilon).$$

If we set $y = \sqrt{\varepsilon}\, w$, then (4.7) becomes

$$\begin{aligned} x_t &= F(x,0) + O(\sqrt{\varepsilon}\,) = \omega + O(\sqrt{\varepsilon}\,) . \\ w_t &= G_y(x,0)w + O(\sqrt{\varepsilon}\,) = \Omega w + O(\sqrt{\varepsilon}\,) . \end{aligned} \tag{4.8}$$

Thus (4.8) is a perturbation of the linearized system (4.6). We therefore treat systems of the form

$$\begin{aligned} x_t &= \omega + \varepsilon f(x,y,\varepsilon). \\ y_t &= \Omega y + \varepsilon g(x,y,\varepsilon). \end{aligned} \tag{4.9}$$

where ω is a constant vector and Ω is a constant diagonalizable matrix. Of course, f and g in (4.9) are not the same functions as in (4.7). The functions f and g are of period 2π in $x_1,\ldots,x_n$.

For $\varepsilon = 0$, (4.9) has the n-parameter family of solutions

$$x = \omega t + a, y = 0$$

which correspond to quasiperiodic solutions. They are, of course, not quasiperiodic in the sense of our previous definition, because they grow linearly, but we recall that the x's correspond to angular variables. Therefore we shall speak of quasiperiodic solutions if

$$e^{ix_\nu},\ y_\mu, \nu = 1,\ldots,n,\ \mu = 1,\ldots,m$$

are quasiperiodic in t.

We assume that $\omega_1,\ldots,\omega_n$ are rationally independent and moreover that there exist positive constants γ and $\tau > n - 1$ such that

$$\begin{aligned} &|(j,\omega)| \geq \gamma|j|^{-\tau} \\ &|(j,\omega)i-\Omega_\mu| \geq \gamma|j|^{-\tau} \\ &|(j,\omega)i-\Omega_\mu + \Omega_{\mu'}| \geq \gamma|j|^{-\tau}, \mu, \mu' = 1,2,\ldots,m \end{aligned} \tag{4.11}$$

for all integers $j_1,\ldots,j_n$ with $|j| = |j_1| + \cdots + |j_n| > 0$.

5. Main theorem.

In this section we shall apply various transformations to the coordinates of the system (4.9). We call a set of coordinates normal if the linearized equations in the form (4.6) have constant coefficients. Since the coefficients of the linearized equations corresponding to the perturbed system (4.9) are not constant, the coordinates x, y are not normal.

We pose the problem: Find a quasiperiodic solution of (4.9) with the same characteristic numbers $\omega_1,\ldots,\omega_n$, $\Omega_1,\ldots,\Omega_m$ as for the solution of the unperturbed system ($\varepsilon = 0$). This is a stringent requirement and even in the periodic case (n = 1) one cannot expect that ω_1, $\Omega_1,\ldots,\Omega_m$ remain constant. We must therefore modify (4.9) by introducing a number of parameters in such a manner that quasiperiodic solutions can be obtained. We consider the modified system:

$$\begin{aligned} x_t &= \omega + \varepsilon f(x,y,\varepsilon) + \lambda \\ y_t &= \Omega y + \varepsilon g(x,y,\varepsilon) + \mu + My \end{aligned} \tag{5.1}$$

where λ is a constant n-vector, μ a constant m-vector, and M a constant m x m matrix. For reasons that will become clear, we require that

$$\Omega^* \mu = 0, \quad \Omega^* M = M\Omega^* . \tag{5.2}$$

(Ω^* is the adjoint operator (transposed conjugate) of Ω.)

Our main result is that for given f, g, there exist modifying terms λ,μ,M, which are analytic in ε, vanish for $\varepsilon = 0$, and satisfy (5.2) such that the modified system (5.1) has quasiperiodic solutions depending analytically on ε and possessing the <u>same</u> characteristic numbers for all ε.

To formulate this result more precisely we recall that the characteristic numbers $\omega_1,\ldots,\omega_n,\Omega_1,\ldots,\Omega_m$ are only defined with respect to normal coordinates. Therefore the above statement requires the determination of normal coordinates for the perturbed system. These normal coordinates

ξ, η will be related to x, y by a coordinate transformation

$$x = \xi + u(\xi,\varepsilon)$$
$$y = \eta + v(\xi,\varepsilon) + V(\xi,\varepsilon)\eta \tag{5.3}$$

where u, v, and V have period 2π in $\xi_1,\ldots,\xi_m$ and vanish for $\varepsilon = 0$. The first equation in (5.3) represents a reparametrization of the coordinates on the torus, $v(\xi,\varepsilon)$ represents a relocation of the position of the torus and the matrix $V(\xi,\varepsilon)$ accounts for a change of direction of the y-coordinates.

We can now give a precise statement of our result:

Theorem: *Consider system* (4.9) *where* ω *and* Ω *satisfy* (4.11). *There exist unique analytic power series* $\lambda(\varepsilon)$, $\mu(\varepsilon)$, $M(\varepsilon)$ *satisfying* (5.2) *such that the modified system* (5.1) *possesses quasi-periodic solutions with the same characteristic numbers as the unperturbed solution. In fact, there exists a coordinate transformation of the form* (5.3) *analytic in* ξ, η, ε *which transforms* (5.1) *into a system of the form*

$$\xi_t = \omega + O(\eta)$$
$$\eta_t = \Omega\eta + O(\eta^2). \tag{5.4}$$

The quasi-periodic solutions are then obtained by inserting

$$\xi = \omega t + \xi^o , \quad \eta = 0 \tag{5.5}$$

into (5.3).

For this conclusion to hold for the original system (4.9) we must examine the circumstances under which

$$\lambda = \mu = M = 0. \tag{5.6}$$

These are the bifurcation equations. Note that these equations involve other parameters natural to the problem. For there to be a sufficient number of parameters available to satisfy (5.6), the special restrictions in the examples are needed.

We do not present the full proof of this theorem but just show that one can determine formal power series in ε for λ, μ, M and u, v, V which satisfy the requirements of the theorem. The main burden of the proof is the proof of convergence which is given in [6].

We expand the eight quantities $\lambda(\varepsilon)$, $\mu(\varepsilon)$, $M(\varepsilon)$, $u(\xi,\varepsilon)$, $v(\xi,\varepsilon)$, $V(\xi,\varepsilon)$, $f(x,y,\varepsilon)$, $g(x,y,\varepsilon)$ into series of the form

$$\lambda(\varepsilon) = \lambda^{(1)}\varepsilon + \lambda^{(2)}\varepsilon^2 + \cdots, \text{ etc.}, \tag{5.7}$$

and substitute these expressions into (5.3). We determine the coefficients by equating coefficients of like powers of ε. We concentrate on the coefficient of ε; the higher powers are treated similarly. From (5.3) and (5.4), for $\eta = 0$, we obtain

$$x_t = (1 + \varepsilon u_\xi^{(1)})\xi_t + O(\varepsilon^2) = (1 + \varepsilon u_\xi^{(1)})\omega + O(\varepsilon^2), \qquad (5.8)$$

whereas from (5.1), for $\eta = 0$, we get

$$x_t = \omega + \lambda^{(1)}\varepsilon + \varepsilon f^{(1)}(\xi,0) + O(\varepsilon^2). \qquad (5.9)$$

The comparison of (5.8) and (5.9) gives

$$u_\xi^{(1)}\omega - \lambda^{(1)} = f^{(1)}(\xi,0). \qquad (5.10)$$

A similar treatment of the y-equation and its η-derivative yields for $\eta = 0$ the following results:

$$v_\xi^{(1)}\omega - \Omega v^{(1)} - \mu^{(1)} = g^{(1)}(\xi,0), \qquad (5.11)$$

$$V_\xi^{(1)}\omega - (\Omega V^{(1)} - V^{(1)}\Omega) - M^{(1)} = g_y^{(1)}(\xi,0). \qquad (5.12)$$

For higher order expansions we obtain equations differing from (5.10), (5.11), (5.12) only in that the right-hand sides contain additional functions depending upon lower order coefficients.

We must show that the partial differential equations (5.10)-(5.12) admit a solution periodic in ξ for any choice of the right-hand side. By means of Fourier expansions of these equations (cf. (1.2)) it can be shown that such a solution exists. The conditions (4.11) and (5.2) are just the conditions for the solvability of these equations. The details of these straightforward calculations can be found in [7]. We treat this question from a different viewpoint in the next section.

6. Bifurcation equations.

The results discussed in Section 5 can be treated more effectively and elegantly by the introduction of some notions from differential geometry. Such an approach furnishes a compact and clear description of the necessary parameter range (described by (5.2)) and shows when such parameters are actually available in a particular example.

With a differential equation

$$x_t = F(x,y), \quad y_t = G(x,y) \tag{6.1}$$

we associate the differential operator

$$F \frac{\partial}{\partial x} + G \frac{\partial}{\partial y} \equiv \sum_{\nu=1}^{n} F_\nu(x,y) \frac{\partial}{\partial x_\nu} + \sum_{\mu=1}^{m} G_\mu(x,y) \frac{\partial}{\partial y_\mu} \tag{6.2}$$

whose characteristics are the solutions of (6.1). Similarly with the linearized equations corresponding to (6.1) we associate the operator

$$F(x,0) \frac{\partial}{\partial x} + [G(x,0) + G_y(x,0)y] \frac{\partial}{\partial y} \ . \tag{6.3}$$

If we introduce the operators

$$\begin{aligned} D &= \omega \frac{\partial}{\partial \xi} + \Omega\eta \frac{\partial}{\partial \eta} \\ N &= \lambda \frac{\partial}{\partial \xi} + (\mu + M\eta) \frac{\partial}{\partial \eta} \\ F &= f^{(1)}(\xi,0)\frac{\partial}{\partial \xi} + [g^{(1)}(\xi,0)+g_y^{(1)}(\xi,0)\eta]\frac{\partial}{\partial \eta} \\ U &= u^{(1)}(\xi)\frac{\partial}{\partial \xi} + [v^{(1)}(\xi) + V^{(1)}(\xi)\eta]\frac{\partial}{\partial \eta} \end{aligned} \tag{6.4}$$

then equations (5.10), (5.11), (5.12) take the form

$$[D,U] - N = F \tag{6.5}$$

where $[D,U] \equiv DU-UD$ is the commutator of D with U. The condition (5.2) and the constancy of λ, μ, and M imply that

$$[D^*,N] = 0 \tag{6.6}$$

where

$$D^* = -\omega \frac{\partial}{\partial \xi} + \Omega^* \eta \frac{\partial}{\partial \eta} \tag{6.7}$$

is the adjoint of D. Thus the allowable parameter range for λ, μ, M can be characterized by those operators N satisfying (6.6).

We now show that (6.5) can be solved for arbitrary F. Let X be an operator of the form (6.2). Consider the linear operator

$$\Theta : X \to [D,X].$$

The orthogonal complement of the range of Θ consists of all Y such that

$$[D^*,Y] = 0.$$

(This result is a consequence of the definition of the inner product of two matrices A, B as tr AB^*.) Thus N is in the orthogonal complement of range of Θ.

We require the following

Lemma: Consider the operator

$$Y = a(\xi)\frac{\partial}{\partial\xi} + (b(\xi) + B(\xi)\eta)\frac{\partial}{\partial\eta} \tag{6.8}$$

<u>where</u> a, b, B <u>have period</u> 2π <u>in</u> $\xi_1,\ldots,\xi_n$. <u>If</u> $[D^*,Y] = 0$ <u>and if</u> (4.11) <u>is satisfied then</u> a, b, B <u>are constants and</u> $\Omega^* b = 0$, $\Omega^* B - B\Omega^* = 0$. The proof of this result follows from a Fourier expansion of the variables of the equation $[D^*,Y] = 0$.

For (6.5) to be solvable, N + F must be in the range of Θ. We write F in the form $F = F_1 + F_2$ where F_1 is in the range of Θ and F_2 is in the orthogonal complement. Since F_2 has the form (6.8), it follows from the lemma that F_2 has constant coefficients satisfying $\Omega^* b = \Omega^* B - B\Omega^* = 0$. Thus we can ensure that N + F is in the range of Θ by taking $N = -F_2$. Hence equations of the form (6.5) can be solved. Moreover, we now have relations between λ, μ, M and certain parameters natural to the problem, namely those parameters that appear in F_2. Thus the bifurcation equations

$$\lambda = 0, \quad \mu = 0, \quad M = 0 \tag{6.9}$$

are a set of restrictions on the parameters of the problem (4.9) that must be satisfied in order for (4.9) to have quasi-periodic solutions with the same characteristic numbers as the unperturbed system.

For the application of this method to a given differential equation it is important to discuss how one can solve the bifurcation equation. In general, if Ω is a matrix with m distinct eigenvalues different from zero, one has from equation (5.2) that $\mu = 0$ and M has m free parameters. Therefore the bifurcation equation consists of $n + m$ equations in that case. If on the other hand $\Omega = 0$, then all components of μ, M are unrestricted and one has $n + m + m^2$ equations.

In general, one cannot expect that one has sufficiently many parameters available to satisfy all these equations. However, if the class of differential equations has some symmetry properties or belongs to a smaller Lie algebra then the number of bifurcation equations can be reduced and satisfied by parameters entering in the equations. In this manner the results of Section 3 can be obtained.

Instead of discussing this part of the theory in full we illustrate it merely for the example 3 of Section 3. The equations can be written in the form

$$x_t = \omega; \; y_t = \varepsilon g(y,x,\varepsilon) \text{ where } g(y,-x,\varepsilon) = -g(y,x,\varepsilon). \tag{6.10}$$

We observe that the first equation is not perturbed at all and $\Omega = 0$. Therefore we set

$$\begin{aligned} D &= \omega \frac{\partial}{\partial \xi} \\ F &= (g(0,\xi) + g_y(0,\xi)y) \frac{\partial}{\partial \eta} \end{aligned} \tag{6.11}$$

where the coefficients of F are odd under the transformation $\xi \to -\xi$. Also we find that transformations (5.3) can be restricted by setting $u \equiv 0$, since the x-equation has not been perturbed. Furthermore, the coefficients $v(\xi,\varepsilon), V(\xi,\varepsilon)$ can be restricted to even functions of ξ. With these remarks the procedure can be carried out within the narrower class of operators. In particular, the operator N which contains the modifying parameters λ, μ, M consists of those operators F which commute with D. From the lemma and $\Omega = 0$ it follows that N has constant coefficients, i.e. is of the form

$$N = (\mu + M) \frac{\partial}{\partial \eta} .$$

Since, moreover, the coefficients of the operators considered are odd, it follows that $\mu = 0$, $M = 0$ hence $N = 0$. Thus the bifurcation equations are automatically satisfied and we obtain quasi-periodic solutions for the given differential equations (6.10) without any modifying terms.

The considerations of this section can be interpreted from the viewpoint of the theory of Lie groups. In particular, we let $\tilde{A}$ denote the algebra of operators of the form F and let $\tilde{N}$ denote all elements of $\tilde{A}$ that commute with D. Then the restrictions on the differential equations narrows the algebra $\tilde{A}$. If $\tilde{A}$ is so small that $\tilde{N}$ contains just the zero element, as in the example above, then the bifurcation equations are automatically satisfied.

The important connection between Lie groups and Lie algebras is illustrated by the example of canonical mappings and the Hamiltonian differential equations

$$\frac{d}{dt} p_\nu = H_{q_\nu}(p,q), \quad \frac{d}{dt} q_\nu = -H_{p_\nu}(p,q), \quad \nu = 1,\ldots,N.$$

The canonical transformations, i.e., transformations which preserve $\sum_\nu dp_\nu dq_\nu$, form a group under composition. It is well known that the infinitesimal canonical transformations can be viewed as Hamiltonian differential equations, and, conversely, that the flow generated by a Hamiltonian system is a canonical transformation. Moreover, if one subjects a Hamiltonian system to a canonical transformation it is transformed again into a Hamiltonian system.

In this example the canonical transformations form a Lie group and the Hamiltonian system the corresponding Lie algebra. More generally, one associates with every group of transformations

$$z \to z' = \Phi(z)$$

of the Euclidean space into itself the Lie algebra of the infinitesimal transformations. These can be given in the form of differential equations

$$\frac{dz}{dt} = \Phi(z)$$

or the associated partial differential operator

$$X = \Phi(z) \frac{\partial}{\partial z} .$$

The fact that the composition of two transformations does not lead out of the group leads to the consequence that also the commutator XY-YX of two elements in the Lie algebra belongs to it.

In the case of Hamiltonian differential equations our bifurcation equations reduce to n equations, if x as well as y have n components. If one has n additional parameters available - as one generally does- then our result leads to an existence proof of quasiperiodic solutions for Hamiltonian systems. For the details we refer to the papers [6] and [7].

This lecture is based in part on [6] and [7] where further details, examples, and references may be found.

BIBLIOGRAPHY

[1] Pliss, V.A. Structural Stability of Differential Equations on a Torus. Vestnik Leningrad University, Ser. Math. Mech. & Astronomy, 1960, No. 13, 15-23.

[2] Kolmogorov, A. On conservation of conditionally periodic motions for a small change in Hamilton's function,

Dokl. Akad. Nauk, SSR 98 (1954), 527-530.

[3] Kolmogorov, General theory of dynamical systems and classical mechanics, Proceedings of International Congress of Mathematics, Noordhoff, Amsterdam, 1957, vol. 1, pp. 315-333.

[4] Arnol'd, V.I., Small divisor and stability problems in classical and celestial mechanics, Uspehi Mat. Nauk, 18 (114) (1963), pp. 81-92.

[5] Arnol'd, V.I., Proof of A. N. Kolmogorov's theorem on the preservation of quasiperiodic motions under small perturbations of the Hamiltonian, Ibid., 18 (113) (1963), pp. 13-40.

[6] Moser, J. Convergent Series Expansions for Quasiperiodic Motions. Math. Ann. 169, 1967, 136-176.

[7] Moser, J. On the Theory of Quasiperiodic Motions, SIAM Rev. 8, 1966, 145-172.

XI. Some Buckling Problems in Nonlinear Elasticity

C. Sensenig

1. Introduction.

Using the exact three-dimensional theory of non-linear elasticity, we treat two problems in the buckling of a circular cylinder.

Problem 1: The cylinder is squeezed in a lubricated cylindrical vise. Thus the curved lateral surface of the undeformed cylinder remains cylindrical in the deformed configuration. Moreover, the shear force on the lateral surface is zero and the tractions applied to the initially flat end faces are also zero. (Cf. Fig.1.).

Problem 2: The cylinder is compressed between two lubricated parallel plates so that the end faces of the cylinder remain parallel. Thus the ends have zero shear and the lateral surface has zero traction. (Cf. Fig. 2.).

Fig.1

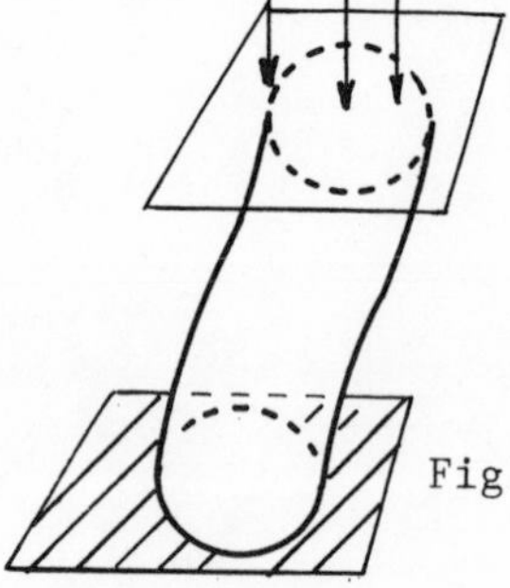

Fig.2

In each problem we assume that the body force is zero. We note that by specifying displacements rather than the corresponding tractions on parts of the boundary of the cylinder we are able to prescribe the deformed shape of those parts of the boundary. This considerably simplifies the problem.

When the loading corresponding to the enforced displacement is sufficiently large the cylinder buckles. For problem 1 we define buckling to occur when the end faces lose their planarity and for problem 2, when the lateral surface loses its cylindricity. The first buckling modes for problems 1 and 2 are illustrated in Figs. 1 and 2.

In problem 1 we seek the critical radius and in problem 2, the critical length at which buckling occurs.

Our development is carried out for an arbitrary homogeneous isotropic material having a strain energy density function (i.e., a hyperelastic material). We then specialize our results by selecting a particular form for the strain energy density. Throughout, we make no assumptions on the relative dimensions of the cylinder.

2. Formulation of the Boundary Value Problem.

We formulate our problems in terms of the cylindrical coordinates $(\theta^1,\theta^2,\theta^3) = (r,\theta,z)$. All components of tensors exhibited in this section are understood to be referred to this coordinate system. The covariant components of the metric tensor are

$$(g_{ij}) = \begin{pmatrix} 1 & 0 & 0 \\ 0 & r^2 & 0 \\ 0 & 0 & 1 \end{pmatrix} \tag{2.1a}$$

and the contravariant components are

$$(g^{ij}) = \begin{pmatrix} 1 & 0 & 0 \\ 0 & 1/r^2 & 0 \\ 0 & 0 & 1 \end{pmatrix} \quad . \tag{2.1b}$$

The various components of a tensor with covariant components T_{ij} are related by

$$T_{ij} = g_{ik}T^{k}{}_{j} = g_{jk}T_{i}{}^{k} = g_{ik}g_{j\ell}T^{k\ell} \tag{2.2}$$

where the summation convention holds.

The location of the material particle originally at (r,θ,z) is given by the position vector with components $u^i(r,\theta,z)$. The deformation is described by the gradient of the position vector which is a tensor having components

$$(P^i{}_j) = \begin{pmatrix} \partial u^1/\partial r & \partial u^1/\partial\theta - ru^2 & \partial u^1/\partial z \\ \partial u^2/\partial r + u^2/r & \partial u^2/\partial\theta + u^1/r & \partial u^2/\partial z \\ \partial u^3/\partial r & \partial u^3/\partial\theta & \partial u^3/\partial z \end{pmatrix} \tag{2.3}$$

For zero body force the equilibrium equations are

$$\frac{\partial Q^{11}}{\partial r} + \frac{\partial Q^{12}}{\partial\theta} + \frac{\partial Q^{13}}{\partial z} + \frac{Q^{11}}{r} - rQ^{22} = 0. \tag{2.4}$$

$$\frac{\partial Q^{21}}{\partial r} + \frac{\partial Q^{22}}{\partial\theta} + \frac{\partial Q^{23}}{\partial z} + \frac{1}{r}(Q^{12} + 2Q^{21}) = 0,$$

$$\frac{\partial Q^{31}}{\partial r} + \frac{\partial Q^{32}}{\partial\theta} + \frac{\partial Q^{33}}{\partial z} + \frac{Q^{31}}{r} = 0,$$

where Q^{ij} are the components of the Kirchhoff Stress tensor (whose physical components measure force per unit <u>undeformed</u> area.). Q^{ij} must satisfy

$$Q^{ik}P^j{}_k = Q^{jk}P^i{}_k\,. \tag{2.5}$$

(We observe that (2.5) has just three independent equations). Equation (2.4) is a consequence of the balance of forces, (2.5) is a consequence of the balance of moments. Note that Q^{ij} are not the components of a symmetric tensor.

We introduce the symmetric tensor $H^i_{.j}$, which measures strain, by defining $H^i_{.j} + \delta^i_{.j}$ (where $\delta^i_{.j}$ is the Kronecker delta) to be the unique positive definite square root of the tensor with components $P_{.j}^{\ i} P^j_{\ k}$, i.e.

$$(H^i_{.j} + \delta^i_{.j})(H^j_k + \delta^j_k) = P_{.j}^{\ i} P^j_{\ k} \tag{2.6}$$

$$(H^i_{.j} + \delta^i_{.j}) a_i a^j > 0 \text{ for all nonzero vectors } a_i .$$

We define the following invariants of $H^i_{.j}$:

$$s_1 = H^i_i , \; s_2 = H^i_j H^j_i , \; s_3 = H^i_j H^j_k H^k_i . \tag{2.7}$$

We also define the rotation tensor with components $C^i_{\ .j}$ by the relations

$$H^i_{.j} + \delta^i_{.j} = C_k^{\ i} P^k_{\ .j} , \; C_k^{\ i} C^k_{\ j} = \delta^i_{.j} , \; \det\,(C^i_{\ .j}) = 1. \tag{2.8}$$

The response of the material is characterized by a strain energy density function $W = W(s_1, s_2, s_3)$ in terms of which the stress-strain laws are

$$Q^i{}_j = (W_1 - 2W_2 + 3W_3)C^i{}_j + 2(W_2 - 3W_3)P^i{}_j + 3W_3 P^i{}_k C_\ell{}^k P^\ell{}_j \tag{2.9}$$

where

$$W_i \equiv \partial W/\partial s_i, \quad i = 1,2,3. \tag{2.10}$$

Equation (2.9) gives the most general stress-strain law for a homogeneous, isotropic elastic medium for which no dissipation occurs during a deformation. It is a nonlinear generalization of Hooke's law.

Note that (2.9) is consistent with (2.5). Our governing equations are the determinate system (2.3), (2.4), (2.9) of 21 equations for the 21 unknown components $u^i, Q^i{}_j, P^i{}_j$. Alternatively we may regard (2.4) as a determinate system of three equations for the three unknown u^i once the appropriate substitutions are made. Note that the strain energy density function W is regarded as a prescribed function of its arguments s_1, s_2, s_3. We now formulate boundary conditions for our problem.

For problem 1 we assume that the undeformed cylinder occupies the region $0 \leq r \leq R$, $|z| \leq h$. We seek solutions having axial symmetry, i.e. solutions for which u^i are independent of θ, $u^2 = 0$, and $u^1 = 0$ for $r = 0$.

These restrictions lead to certain simplifications in the boundary conditions, which are

$$u^1 = aR\ , \quad 0 < a < 1, \quad \text{for } r = R \tag{2.11a}$$

$$Q^2{}_1 = Q^3{}_1 = 0\ , \quad \text{for } r = R \tag{2.11b}$$

$$Q^1{}_3 = Q^2{}_3 = Q^3{}_3 = 0, \quad \text{for } z = \pm h\ . \tag{2.11c}$$

Condition (2.11a) implies that the radial displacement is prescribed for the lateral surface, (2.11b), that the shear on the lateral surface is zero, and (2.11c) that the tractions on the ends are zero.

For problem 2 we assume that the undeformed cylinder occupies the region $0 \le r \le R$, $0 \le z \le L$. The boundary conditions for this problem are

$$u^3 = 0 \quad \text{for } z = 0 \tag{2.12a}$$

$$u^3 = bL,\ 0 < b < 1, \quad \text{for } z = L \tag{2.12b}$$

$$Q^1{}_3 = Q^2{}_3 = 0 \quad \text{for } z = 0, L \tag{2.12c}$$

$$Q^1{}_1 = Q^2{}_1 = Q^3{}_1 = 0 \quad \text{for } r = R\ . \tag{2.12d}$$

We do not assume axial symmetry here. Further details on the formulation of these problems can be found in [7].

3. A Special Solution

We expect

$$u^1 = ar\ , \quad u^2 = 0\ , \quad u^3 = bz \tag{3.1}$$

to be a special solution to both our problems where

$0 < a < 1$ for problem 1 and $0 < b < 1$ for problem 2. From (2.3)

$$(P^i{}_j) = \begin{pmatrix} a & 0 & 0 \\ 0 & a & 0 \\ 0 & 0 & b \end{pmatrix} \qquad (3.2)$$

$$C^i{}_j = \delta^i_j \qquad (3.3)$$

Let

$$\varepsilon = a-1 \quad , \qquad \delta = b-1 \quad . \qquad (3.4)$$

Then (2.9) gives

$$(Q^i{}_j) = \begin{pmatrix} A_1 & 0 & 0 \\ 0 & A_1 & 0 \\ 0 & 0 & A_2 \end{pmatrix}, \quad (Q^{ij}) = \begin{pmatrix} A_1 & 0 & 0 \\ 0 & A_1/r^2 & 0 \\ 0 & 0 & A_2 \end{pmatrix} \qquad (3.5)$$

$$A_1 = W_1 + 2\varepsilon W_2 + 3\varepsilon^2 W_3$$
$$A_2 = W_1 + 2\delta W_2 + 3\delta^2 W_3$$

where W_1, W_2, W_3 are evaluated at the special solution and hence are functions of ε and δ only.

The substitution of Q^{ij} from (3.5) into (2.4) shows that the equilibrium equations are satisfied by (3.1). From (2.11) we see that the boundary conditions of problem 1 are satisfied if $A_2 = 0$, and from (2.12), the boundary conditions of problem 2 are satisfied if $A_1 = 0$. Hence we assume W has the property that for each ε in some interval $\varepsilon_0 < \varepsilon < 0$(i.e. for each a in the interval $\varepsilon_0 + 1 < a < 1$) there is a δ such that $A_2 = 0$, and for each δ in some interval $\delta_0 < \delta < 0$ (i.e. for each b in the interval $\delta_0 + 1 < b < 1$) there is an ε such that $A_1 = 0$. Then (3.1) does give a special solution to both our problems.

4. The Perturbed Problem

We now assume the existence of a family of solutions to each problem depending on a parameter ω such that the solutions are not of the form (3.1) for $\omega > 0$ but are of that form for $\omega = 0$. We also assume that u^i has a right hand derivative with respect to ω at $\omega = 0$. We let

$$\overset{o}{u}{}^i = u^i\big|_{\omega=0} \text{ and } \dot{u}^i = \frac{\partial u^i}{\partial\omega}\Big|_{\omega=0} .$$

This notation is used for other functions as well. Then the values of a and b for the special solution corresponding to $\omega = 0$ are the values for which buckling can start.

Defining $W_{ij} \equiv \partial^2 W/\partial s_i \partial s_j$ and using the results of the last two sections, we find that

$$
\begin{aligned}
\dot{C}^{12} &= (\dot{P}^{12} - \dot{P}^{21})/2a \\
\dot{C}^{13} &= (\dot{P}^{13} - P^{31})/(a+b) \\
\dot{C}^{23} &= (\dot{P}^{23} - P^{32})/(a+b) \\
\dot{C}^{ij} &= -\dot{C}^{ji} \qquad\qquad (4.1) \\
\dot{s}_1 &= \dot{P}^1{}_1 + \dot{P}^2{}_2 + \dot{P}^3{}_3 \\
\dot{s}_2 &= 2\varepsilon(\dot{P}^1{}_1 + \dot{P}^2{}_2) + 2\delta\dot{P}^3{}_3 \\
\dot{s}_3 &= 3\varepsilon^2(\dot{P}^1{}_1 + \dot{P}^2{}_2) + 3\delta^2\dot{P}^3{}_3 \\
\dot{Q}^i{}_j &= (\overset{o}{W}_1 - 2\overset{o}{W}_2 + 3\overset{o}{W}_3)\,\dot{C}^i{}_j + 2(\overset{o}{W}_2 - 3\overset{o}{W}_3)\dot{P}^i{}_j \\
&\quad + 3\overset{o}{W}_3(\dot{P}^i{}_r \overset{o}{C}{}^r{}_s \overset{o}{P}{}^s{}_j + \overset{o}{P}{}^i{}_r \dot{C}^r{}_s \overset{o}{P}{}^s{}_j + \overset{o}{P}{}^i{}_r \overset{o}{C}{}^r{}_s \dot{P}^s{}_j) \\
&\quad + [(\overset{o}{W}_{1k} - 2\overset{o}{W}_{2k} + 3\overset{o}{W}_{3k})\overset{o}{C}{}^i{}_j + 2(\overset{o}{W}_{2k} - 3\overset{o}{W}_{3k})\overset{o}{P}{}^i{}_j \\
&\quad + 3\overset{o}{W}_{3k}\overset{o}{P}{}^i{}_r \overset{o}{C}{}^r{}_s \overset{o}{P}{}^s{}_j]\dot{s}_k
\end{aligned}
$$

From this we obtain

$$
\begin{aligned}
\dot{Q}^1{}_1 &= (A_3 + A_4)\dot{P}^1{}_1 + A_4\dot{P}^2{}_2 + A_5\dot{P}^3{}_3 \\
\dot{Q}^2{}_2 &= A_4\dot{P}^1{}_1 + (A_3 + A_4)\dot{P}^2{}_2 + A_5\dot{P}^3{}_3 \\
\dot{Q}^3{}_3 &= A_5(\dot{P}^1{}_1 + \dot{P}^2{}_2) + (A_6 + A_7)\dot{P}^3{}_3 \\
\dot{Q}^1{}_2 &= (A_3 + \frac{1}{2a} A_8)\dot{P}^1{}_2 - \frac{1}{2a} A_8\dot{P}_2{}^1 \\
\dot{Q}^1{}_3 &= (A_9 + \frac{1}{a+b} A_{10})\dot{P}^1{}_3 - \frac{1}{a+b}A_{10}\dot{P}^3{}_1 \qquad\qquad (4.2) \\
\dot{Q}^2{}_3 &= (A_9 + \frac{1}{a+b}A_{10})\dot{P}^2{}_3 - \frac{1}{a+b}A_{10}\dot{P}^{32} \\
\dot{Q}^2{}_1 &= (A_3 + \frac{1}{2a} A_8)\dot{P}^2{}_1 - \frac{1}{2a} A_8\dot{P}^{12} \\
\dot{Q}^3{}_1 &= (A_9 + \frac{1}{a+b} A_{10})\dot{P}^3{}_1 - \frac{1}{a+b}A_{10}\dot{P}^1{}_3 \\
\dot{Q}^3{}_2 &= (A_9 + \frac{1}{a+b} A_{10})\dot{P}^3{}_2 - \frac{1}{a+b}A_{10}\dot{P}_2{}^3
\end{aligned}
$$

where

$$
\begin{aligned}
A_1 &= \overset{o}{W}_1 + 2\varepsilon\overset{o}{W}_2 + 3\varepsilon^2\overset{o}{W}_3 \\
A_2 &= \overset{o}{W}_1 + 2\delta\overset{o}{W}_2 + 3\delta^2\overset{o}{W}_3 \\
A_3 &= 2\overset{o}{W}_2 + 6\varepsilon\overset{o}{W}_3 \\
A_4 &= \overset{o}{W}_{11} + 4\varepsilon\overset{o}{W}_{12} + 6\varepsilon^2\overset{o}{W}_{13} + 4\varepsilon^2\overset{o}{W}_{22} + 12\varepsilon^3\overset{o}{W}_{23} + 9\varepsilon^4\overset{o}{W}_{33} \\
A_5 &= \overset{o}{W}_{11} + 2(\varepsilon+\delta)\overset{o}{W}_{12} + 3(\varepsilon^2+\delta^2)\overset{o}{W}_{13} + 4\varepsilon\delta\overset{o}{W}_{22} \\
&\quad + 6\varepsilon\delta(\varepsilon+\delta)\overset{o}{W}_{23} + 9\varepsilon^2\delta^2\overset{o}{W}_{33} \\
A_6 &= \overset{o}{W}_{11} + 4\delta\overset{o}{W}_{12} + 6\delta^2\overset{o}{W}_{13} + 4\delta^2\overset{o}{W}_{22} + 12\delta^3\overset{o}{W}_{23} + 9\delta^4\overset{o}{W}_{33} \\
A_7 &= 2\overset{o}{W}_2 + 6\delta\overset{o}{W}_3 \\
A_8 &= \overset{o}{W}_1 - 2\overset{o}{W}_2 - 3\varepsilon(\varepsilon+2)\overset{o}{W}_3 \\
A_9 &= 2\overset{o}{W}_2 + 3(\varepsilon+\delta)\overset{o}{W}_3 \\
A_{10} &= \overset{o}{W}_1 - 2\overset{o}{W}_2 - 3(\varepsilon+\delta+\varepsilon\delta)\overset{o}{W}_3
\end{aligned}
\tag{4.3}
$$

The perturbed equilibrium equations are obtained by putting a dot over each variable in (2.4) and substituting (4.2) into these equations. (Note that we must raise the lower index of $Q^i{}_j$.) For problem 1 we have $\dot{u}^2 \equiv 0$ and $\dot{u}^1$ and $\dot{u}^3$ are independent of θ. Moreover $A_2 = 0$; hence (4.3) implies that $A_{10} = -bA_9$. Thus the perturbed equilibrium equations for problem 1 reduce to the form

$$
\begin{aligned}
&(A_3+A_4)\left(\frac{\partial^2\dot{u}^1}{\partial r^2} + \frac{1}{r}\frac{\partial\dot{u}^1}{\partial r} - \frac{\dot{u}^1}{r^2}\right) + \frac{aA_9}{a+b}\frac{\partial^2\dot{u}^1}{\partial z^2} + \left(A_5 + \frac{bA_9}{a+b}\right)\frac{\partial^2\dot{u}^3}{\partial r\partial z} = 0 \\
&\frac{aA_9}{a+b}\left(\frac{\partial^2\dot{u}^3}{\partial r^2} + \frac{1}{r}\frac{\partial\dot{u}^3}{\partial r}\right) + (A_6 + A_7)\frac{\partial^2\dot{u}^3}{\partial z^2} + \left(A_5 + \frac{bA_9}{a+b}\right)\left(\frac{\partial^2\dot{u}^1}{\partial r\partial z} + \frac{1}{r}\frac{\partial\dot{u}^1}{\partial z}\right) = 0.
\end{aligned}
\tag{4.4}
$$

For problem 2, $A_1 = 0$. Hence (4.3) implies that $A_8 = -aA_3$ and $A_{10} = -aA_9$. Thus the perturbed equilibrium equations for this problem are

$$(A_3+A_4)\left(\frac{\partial^2\dot{u}^1}{\partial r^2} + \frac{1}{r}\frac{\partial\dot{u}^1}{\partial r} - \frac{\dot{u}^1}{r}\right) + \frac{A_3}{2r^2}\frac{\partial^2\dot{u}^1}{\partial\theta^2} + \frac{bA_9}{a+b}\frac{\partial^2\dot{u}^1}{\partial z^2} \tag{4.5}$$

$$+ (A_4+A_3/2)\frac{\partial^2\dot{u}^2}{\partial r\partial\theta} - \frac{A_3}{r}\frac{\partial\dot{u}^2}{\partial\theta} + \left(A_5 + \frac{aA_9}{a+b}\right)\frac{\partial^2\dot{u}^3}{\partial r\partial z} = 0$$

$$\frac{A_3}{2}\left(\frac{\partial^2\dot{u}^2}{\partial r^2} + \frac{3}{r}\frac{\partial\dot{u}^2}{\partial r}\right) + \frac{(A_3+A_4)}{r^2}\frac{\partial^2\dot{u}^2}{\partial\theta^2} + \frac{bA_9}{a+b}\frac{\partial^2\dot{u}^2}{\partial z^2}$$

$$+\frac{(A_4+A_3/2)}{r^2}\frac{\partial^2\dot{u}^1}{\partial r\partial\theta} + \frac{(3A_3/2+A_4)}{r^3}\frac{\partial\dot{u}^1}{\partial\theta}$$

$$+\left(A_5+\frac{aA_9}{a+b}\right)\frac{1}{r^2}\frac{\partial^2\dot{u}^3}{\partial\theta\partial z} = 0$$

$$\frac{bA_9}{a+b}\left(\frac{\partial^2\dot{u}^3}{\partial r^2} + \frac{1}{r}\frac{\partial\dot{u}^3}{\partial r} + \frac{1}{r^2}\frac{\partial^2\dot{u}^3}{\partial\theta^2}\right) + (A_6+A_7)\frac{\partial^2\dot{u}^3}{\partial z^2}$$

$$+ \left(A_5+\frac{aA_9}{a+b}\right)\left(\frac{\partial^2\dot{u}^1}{\partial r\partial z} + \frac{1}{r}\frac{\partial\dot{u}^1}{\partial z} + \frac{\partial^2\dot{u}^2}{\partial\theta\partial z}\right) = 0$$

The perturbed boundary conditions are obtained by dotting the boundary conditions (2.11) and (2.12). Since a and b appear in the boundary conditions, we must also let a and b depend on ω. Then a,b,ε,δ should each have a superposed zero in (4.1), (4.2), (4.3), (4.4), (4.5).

Nevertheless for typographical convenience we suppress this symbol for the remainder of this work. Using the same relations as used in obtaining (4.4) and (4.5), we get

$$\dot{u}^1 = \dot{a}R \text{ for } r = R$$

$$\dot{Q}^3{}_1 = \frac{A_9}{a+b}\left(a\,\frac{\partial \dot{u}^3}{\partial r} + b\,\frac{\partial \dot{u}^1}{\partial z}\right) = 0 \text{ for } r = R$$

$$\dot{Q}^1{}_3 = \frac{A_9}{a+b}\left(a\,\frac{\partial \dot{u}^1}{\partial z} + b\,\frac{\partial \dot{u}^3}{\partial r}\right) = 0 \text{ for } z = \pm h \qquad (4.6)$$

$$\dot{Q}^3{}_3 = A_5\left(\frac{\partial \dot{u}^1}{\partial r} + \frac{1}{r}\,\dot{u}^1\right)+(A_6+A_7)\frac{\partial \dot{u}^3}{\partial z} = 0 \text{ for } z = \pm h$$

for the perturbed boundary conditions of problem 1, and

$$\dot{u}^3 = 0 \text{ for } z = 0$$

$$\dot{u}^3 = \dot{b}L \text{ for } z = L$$

$$\dot{Q}^1{}_3 = \frac{A_9}{a+b}\left(\frac{\partial \dot{u}^1}{\partial z} + a\,\frac{\partial \dot{u}^3}{\partial r}\right) = 0 \text{ for } z = 0,L$$

$$\dot{Q}^2{}_3 = \frac{A_9}{a+b}\left(b\,\frac{\partial \dot{u}^2}{\partial z} + a\,\frac{1}{r2}\,\frac{\partial \dot{u}^3}{\partial \theta}\right) = 0 \text{ for } z = 0,L$$

$$\dot{Q}^1{}_1 = (A_3+A_4)\frac{\partial \dot{u}^1}{\partial r} + A_4\left(\frac{\partial \dot{u}^2}{\partial \theta} + \frac{1}{r}\,\dot{u}^1\right)+ A_5\frac{\partial \dot{u}^3}{\partial z} = 0 \text{ for } r=R.$$

$$\dot{Q}^2{}_1 = \frac{1}{2}\,A_3\left(\frac{\partial \dot{u}^2}{\partial r} + \frac{1}{r^2}\,\frac{\partial \dot{u}^1}{\partial \theta}\right) = 0 \text{ for } r = R \qquad (4.7)$$

$$\dot{Q}^3{}_1 = \frac{A_9}{a+b}\left(b\,\frac{\partial \dot{u}^3}{\partial r} + a\,\frac{\partial \dot{u}^1}{\partial z}\right) = 0 \text{ for } r = R$$

for the perturbed boundary conditions of problem 2.

5. Solutions of problem 1.

We express $\dot{u}^1$ and $\dot{u}^3$ in the form

$$\dot{u}^1 = \dot{a}\, r + \sum_{n=1}^{\infty} f_n(z)\alpha_n(r)$$
$$\dot{u}^3 = \dot{b}\, z + \sum_{n=1}^{\infty} g_n(z)\beta_n(r) \qquad (5.1)$$

and attempt to choose α_n and β_n so that variables separate in (4.4) and (4.6). This is accomplished if we let $\alpha_n(r) = J_1(k_n r)$ and $\beta_n(r) = J_0(k_n r)$ where J_0 and J_1 are Bessel functions of the first kind, and the numbers k_n will be chosen later. Then the differential equations and recursion relations for Bessel's functions give

$$\alpha_n = J_1(k_n r)$$
$$\beta_n = J_0(k_n r)$$
$$\alpha_n' + \frac{1}{r}\alpha_n = k_n\beta_n \qquad (5.2)$$

$$\beta_n' = -k_n\alpha_n$$
$$\alpha_n'' + \frac{1}{r}\alpha_n' - \frac{1}{r^2}\alpha_n = -k_n^2\alpha_n$$
$$\beta_n'' + \frac{1}{r}\beta_n' = -k_n^2\beta_n$$

Substituting (5.1) and (5.2) into (4.4) and (4.6) we obtain

$$-(A_3 + A_4)k_n^2 f_n + \frac{a}{a+b} A_9 f_n'' - (A_5 + \frac{b}{a+b} A_9)k_n g_n' = 0 \quad n=1,2,..$$
$$-\frac{a}{a+b} A_9 k_n^2 g_n + (A_6 + A_7)g_n'' + (A_5 + \frac{b}{a+b} A_9)k_n f_n' = 0 \qquad (5.3)$$

$$(-ak_n g_n + bf_n')\alpha_n = 0 \text{ for } r = R$$

$$f_n \alpha_n = 0 \text{ for } r = R$$

$$af_n' - bk_n g_n = 0 \text{ for } z = \pm h \tag{5.4}$$

$$A_5 k_n f_n + (A_6 + A_7) g_n' = 0 \text{ for } z = \pm h$$

The first two equations of (5.4) indicate that k_n should be chosen so that $k_n R$ is the nth zero of J_1. Doing this, we are left with the homogeneous differential equations (5.3) and the homogeneous boundary conditions in the last two lines of (5.4). Requiring that a non-zero solution exists determines the values of a,b,ε, and δ at which the nth mode of buckling can start. Although this calculation could be carried out for any strain energy density function W, here we present results for only the special function given by

$$W = \frac{\lambda}{2} s_1 + \mu s_2 \tag{5.5}$$

where λ and μ are the usual Lamé constants.

If we let ε_n be the value of ε at which the nth buckled mode can start we obtain

$$\varepsilon_n = \frac{2(\lambda+\mu)\left(1 - \dfrac{\sinh 2k_n h}{2k_n h}\right)}{\lambda + (5\lambda+4\mu)\dfrac{\sin 2k_n h}{2k_n h}} \tag{5.6}$$

As $n \to \infty$, $\varepsilon_n \to -\frac{2(\lambda+\mu)}{5\lambda+4\mu}$ so that all buckled modes can start before the deformed radius becomes as small as $\frac{3\lambda+2\mu}{5\lambda+4\mu}R = \frac{1+\sigma}{2+\sigma}R$ where σ is Poisson's ratio. In particular all buckled modes can start before the deformed radius if $\frac{1}{2}$ R.

The value for ε_n given by (5.6) agrees to lowest order terms in $k_n h$ with the value obtained with a thin plate theory. From (5.6) we see that ε_n is a function of $4k_n^2h^2$ and Poisson's ratio σ. Figure 3 shows the graph of $(-\varepsilon_n)$ versus $4k_n^2h^2$ for $\sigma = .3$. The straight line is the corresponding graph obtained from the thin plate theory and is the tangent line to the curve at the origin.

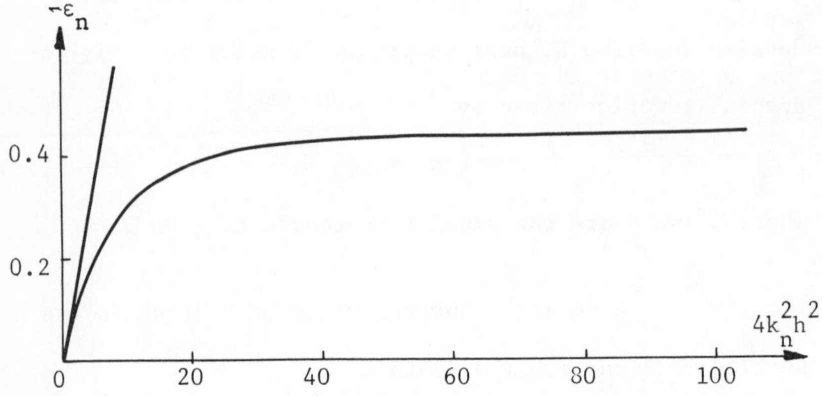

Fig. 3

6. Solutions of problem 2.

For simplicity we look for solutions in which the undeformed axis of the cylinder goes into a plane curve. Then we can assume without loss of generality that the axis goes into a curve starting at the origin in the plane $\theta = 0$. We expect u^1 to be an even function of θ, u^2 to be an odd function of θ, and u^3 to be an even function of θ. We also expect that u^1, u^2, and u^3 could be extended smoothly below the plane $z = 0$ so that u^1 would be an even function of z, u^2 would be an even function of z, and u^3 would be an odd function of z. Therefore we write the following expansions of $\dot{u}^1$, $\dot{u}^2$, and $\dot{u}^3$.

$$\dot{u}^1 = \dot{a}\, r + \sum_{m=o}^{\infty} \sum_{n=o}^{\infty} a_{mn}(r) \cos m\theta \cos k_n z$$

$$\dot{u}^2 = \sum_{m=o}^{\infty} \sum_{n=o}^{\infty} b_{mn}(r) \sin m\theta \cos k_n z$$

$$\dot{u}^3 = \dot{b}\, z + \sum_{m=o}^{\infty} \sum_{n=o}^{\infty} c_{mn}(r) \cos m\theta \sin k_n z \tag{6.1}$$

$$k_n = \frac{\Pi n}{L}$$

Substituting from (6.1) into (4.5) and (4.7), we find that variables separate. From (4.5) we obtain

$$(A_3+A_4)(a''_{mn} + \frac{1}{r} a'_{mn} - \frac{1}{r^2} a_{mn}) - \frac{1}{2}A_3 \frac{m^2}{r^2} a_{mn} - \frac{b}{a+b} A_9 k_n^2 a_{mn}$$

$$+ (A_4 + \frac{1}{2} A_3)\, m\, b'_{mn} - A_3 \frac{m}{r} b_{mn} + (A_5 + \frac{a}{a+b} A_9) k_n c'_{mn} = 0$$

$$\frac{1}{2} A_3(b''_{mn} + \frac{3}{r} b'_{mn}) - (A_3+A_4)\frac{m^2}{r^2} b_{mn} - \frac{b}{a+b} A_9 k_n^2 b_{mn} \tag{6.2}$$

$$- (A_4 + \frac{1}{2}A_3)\frac{m}{r^2} a'_{mn} - (\frac{3}{2} A_3+A_4)\frac{m}{r^3} a_{mn} - (A_5 + \frac{a}{a+b} A_9)\frac{mk_n}{r^2} c_{mn} = 0$$

$$\frac{b}{a+b} A_9 (c''_{mn} + \frac{1}{r} c'_{mn} - \frac{m^2}{r^2} c_{mn}) - (A_6 + A_7) k_n^2 c_{mn}$$

$$- (A_5 + \frac{a}{a+b} A_9) k_n (a'_{mn} + \frac{1}{r} a_{mn} + mb_{mn}) = 0$$

From the nontrivial boundary conditions of (4.7) we get

$$(A_3 + A_4) a'_{mn} + A_4 (mb_{mn} + \frac{1}{r} a_{mn}) + A_5 k_n c_{mn} = 0 \text{ for } r = R,$$

$$b'_{mn} - \frac{m}{r^2} a_{mn} = 0 \text{ for } r = R,$$

$$bc'_{mn} - ak_n a_{mn} = 0 \text{ for } r = R. \tag{6.3}$$

Requiring that there exist a non-zero solution to the homogeneous equations (6.2) with homogeneous boundary conditions (6.3) determines the values of $a, b, \varepsilon, \delta$ at which the mn-th buckled mode can start. Although it is clear that this procedure can be carried out for any strain energy density function we again give results only for the special strain energy density given by (5.5). In this case we discover that non-zero solutions exist only if $m = 1$ and $n \neq 0$. The condition that a non-zero solution exist is that

$$\begin{vmatrix} a_{11} & a_{12} & a_{13} & \\ a_{21} & a_{22} & a_{23} & = \quad 0 \\ a_{31} & a_{32} & a_{33} & \end{vmatrix}$$

where

$$a_{11} = -\frac{1}{r_n^*}[I_1'(r_n^*) - \frac{1}{r_n^*} I_1(r_n^*)]$$

$$a_{12} = -(\frac{3A+2B}{2B} \frac{1}{\bar{r}_n} + \frac{A}{2B} \bar{r}_n) I_1'(\bar{r}_n) + (\frac{A+2B}{2B} + \frac{\lambda}{2\mu} + \frac{3A+2B}{2B} \frac{1}{\bar{r}_n^2}) I_1(\bar{r}_n)$$

$$a_{13} = -\frac{A}{B} I_1''(\bar{r}_n)$$

$$a_{21} = -\frac{1}{r_n^*} I_1'(r_n^*) + (\frac{1}{r_n^{*2}} + \frac{1}{2}) I_1(r_n^*)$$

$$a_{22} = -\frac{3A+2B}{2B} \frac{1}{\bar{r}_n}[I_1'(\bar{r}_n) - \frac{1}{\bar{r}_n} I_1(\bar{r}_n)] + \frac{A}{2B} I_1(\bar{r}_n) \tag{6.5}$$

$$a_{23} = \frac{A}{B} \frac{1}{\bar{r}_n} [I_1'(\bar{r}_n) - \frac{1}{\bar{r}_n} I_1(\bar{r}_n)]$$

$$a_{31} = -\frac{a}{b} \frac{1}{\bar{r}_n} I_1(r_n{}^*)$$

$$a_{32} = \frac{\lambda+2\mu}{\mu} \frac{a}{b} I_1'(\bar{r}_n)$$

$$a_{33} = \frac{2A}{B} I_1'(\bar{r}_n)$$

where

$$A = \lambda + \frac{2\mu a}{a+b}$$

$$B = \frac{2\mu b}{a+b}$$

$$\bar{r}_n = k_n r$$

$$r_n^* = \sqrt{\frac{B}{\mu}}\, \bar{r}_n$$

and I_o and I_1 are modified Bessel functions of the first kind. Again the $a, b, \varepsilon, \delta$ appearing in (6.5) and (6.6) should have a superposed zero. Letting δ_n be the value of $\overset{o}{\delta}$ determined by (6.4), we can solve numerically for δ_n. In figure 4 we give the graph of $(-\delta_n)$ versus $(\frac{\Pi nR}{L})^2$ for several values of σ. The straight line graph is the value of $(-\delta_n)$ given by the usual thin column theory. The $(-\delta_n)$ from the thin column theory is independent of σ and is tangent at the origin to the curve of the exact theory for each value of σ.

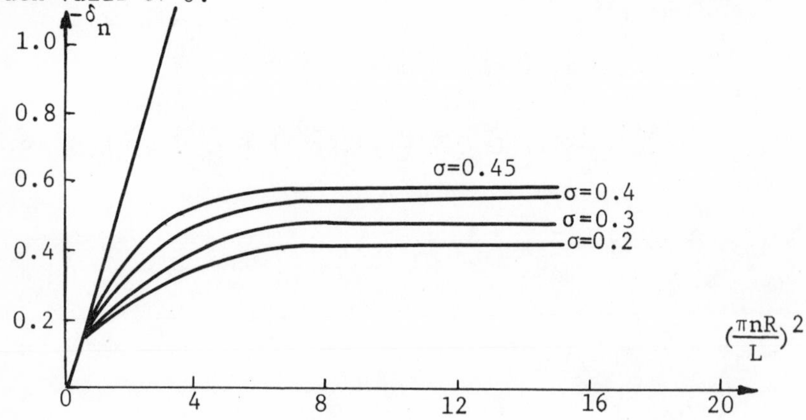

Figure 4

7. Conclusion

The results given here are based in part on [7]. Other papers treating similar problems with the exact theory are listed in the Bibliography.

Bibliography

[1] Biot, M. A., Exact Theory of Buckling of a Thick Slab, Appl. Sci. Res., Vol. 12, Section A, pp. 183-198, 1963.

[2] John, F., Plane Strain Problems for a Perfectly Elastic Material of Harmonic Type, Comm. Pure Appl. Math., Vol. 13, 1960, pp. 230-296.

[3] Lubkin, S., Determination of Buckling Criteria by Minemization of Total Energy, N.Y.U., CIMS, Res. Rep. IMM-NYU 241, 1957.

[4] Lur'e, A. I., Bifurcation of Equilibrium of a Perfectly Elastic Body, Jour. App. Math. Mech., Vol. 30, 1966, pp. 855-869.

[5] Read, H. E., On the Stability of Equilibrium of Thick and thick-Walled Isotropic Elastic Solids, Ph.D. Thesis, University of Delaware, 1964.

[6] Sensenig, C. B., The Buckling of a Thick Circular Plate using a Non-Linear Theory, N.Y.U., C.I.M.S., Res. Rep. IMM-NYU., 262, 1959.

[7] Sensenig, C. B., Instability of Thick Elastic Solids, Comm. Pure Appl. Math., Vol. 17, 1964, pp. 451-491.

[8] Wilks, E. W., On the Stability of a Circular Tube und under End Thrust, Quart. J. Mech. and Appl. Math., Vol 8, 1955, pp. 88-100.

XII. Equilibrium States of Nonlinearly Elastic Rods

Stuart Antman

1. Introduction.

The Euler-Bernoulli theory of the plane bending of inextensible elasticae is characterized by the constitutive relation

$$M = \text{const.}(k-K) \tag{1.1}$$

Here k is the curvature of the deformed rod, K is the curvature of the undeformed rod, and M is the bending moment. For problems in which the undeformed shape of the rod is circular and the rod is subject to a hydrostatic pressure (Cf. Fig. 1), it is known that the solution of the governing equations can be found by quadratures leading to representations in terms of elliptic functions of Jacobi or Weierstrass type. (Cf. Lectures I and IV.)

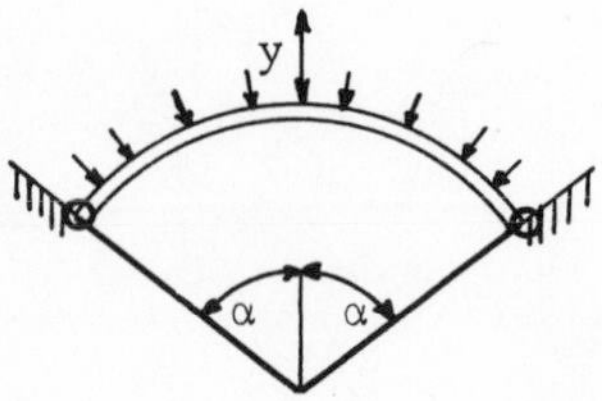

Figure 1

To fix ideas, let us consider the problem in which the ends of the arch are hinged as in Figure 1. In this case there is a trivial solution and nontrivial solutions bifurcate from it at the eigenvalues of the linear problem. If we now wish to incorporate the effect of extensibility in this problem, the analysis becomes more difficult since there is no trivial solution except for zero load. To study such problems, it would be convenient if their solutions could be obtained by quadratures. This is not the case, however, if we supplement (1.1) by the constitutive relation

$$N = \text{const.}\ \varepsilon \qquad (1.2)$$

where N is the axial stress resultant and ε is either the extension (change of length per unit length) or the material strain of the reference curve characterizing the rod.

We therefore pose the questions:

i) Is there a simple form of the constitutive equations that leads to problems that are integrable by quadratures?

ii) Are there constitutive equations that can be regarded as the natural analog of the equations of three-dimensional nonlinear elasticity?

The answer to these questions is affirmative as is shown in [1] and [2]. Indeed, the same equations suffice for both questions (i) and (ii). If we let τ be the arc length of the undeformed rod, $s(\tau)$ the arc length of the deformed rod, $\Phi(\tau)$ the tangent angle to the undeformed rod, and $\phi(\tau)$ the tangent angle to the deformed rod, then these constitutive equations are

$$M = \frac{\partial W}{\partial \mu}\ , \ N = \frac{\partial W}{\partial \delta}\ , \ W = W(\mu,\delta,\tau) \tag{1.3}$$

with

$$\delta = s'-1,\ \mu = s'k-K = (1+\delta)k-K = -(\phi-\Phi)' \tag{1.4}$$

where the prime denotes differentiation with respect to τ.

δ is called the extension and μ, the bending. We observe that for a uniform extension of a circular arc into another circular arc of different radius, the quantity k-K changes but μ remains zero. Hence the strain measure μ isolates the effect of bending.

To ensure physically reasonable behavior, we require that M be a monotonically increasing function of μ for fixed δ, N be a monotonically increasing function of δ for fixed μ, and (1.3) be invertible to yield μ and δ as functions of M and N. These properties are guaranteed by requiring that the Hessian matrix

$$\begin{pmatrix} W_{\mu\mu} & W_{\mu\delta} \\ W_{\mu\delta} & W_{\delta\delta} \end{pmatrix}$$

for the strain energy function W be positive definite.

It can be shown [1] that (1.1) and (1.2) furnish a good approximation to equations of the form (1.3) when the extension is small.

2. Formulation of the governing equations.

The equilibrium equations can be obtained from Fig. 2, the free body diagram of a differential element of the rod. Here Q denotes the shear resultant and q, the normal load.

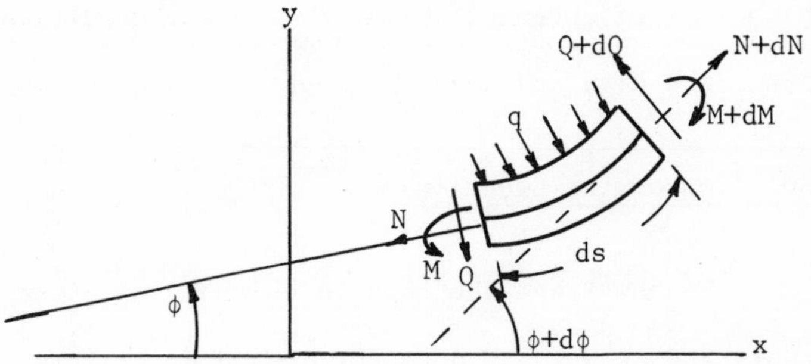

Figure 2

We assume there is neither a tangential load nor a distributed moment applied to the body. If we eliminate Q from the three resulting equilibrium equations and write remaining two equations in terms of the undeformed arc length τ, we obtain

$$\left(\frac{M'}{1+\delta}\right)' - (\mu+K)N - q(1+\delta) = 0, \tag{2.1}$$

$$(\mu+K)M' + (1+\delta)N' = 0 \quad . \tag{2.2}$$

To these we add the constitutive equations

$$M = W_\mu \quad , \qquad N = W_\delta \tag{2.3}$$

and the goemetric relations

$$\phi' = \mu+K \tag{2.4}$$

$$x' = (1+\delta)\cos\phi \ , \ y' = (1+\delta)\sin\phi \quad . \tag{2.5}$$

The sign convention for these quantities is indicated in Figure 2. Equations (2.1)-(2.5) form a determinate system to which must be appended suitable boundary conditions. The functions $K(\tau)$ and $q(\tau)$ are regarded as prescribed.

3. Solution of the equations.

We now treat the case in which K and q are constants and in which W does not depend explicitly on τ. We seek a general representation for the solution of the system (2.1)-(2.5).

Multiplying (2.1) by $M'/(1+\delta)$ and integrating the resulting expression we obtain

$$M'^2 + (1+\delta)^2N^2 - 2qM(1+\delta)^2 = a(1+\delta)^2 \tag{3.1}$$

where a is an arbitrary integration constant. This equation is valid for any constitutive assumption. The substitution of (2.3) into (2.1) yields

$$W'^2_\mu = a(1+\delta)^2 + 2q(1+\delta)^2W_\mu-(1+\delta)^2W_\delta^2 \tag{3.2}$$

and the substitution of (2.3) into (2.2) yields

$$(\mu+K)W'_\mu + (1+\delta)W'_\delta = 0 \quad . \tag{3.3}$$

Since K is constant(3.3) can be written as

$$[(\mu+K)W_\mu]'+[(1+\delta)W_\delta]'-W_\mu\mu'-W_\delta\delta' = 0 \tag{3.4}$$

and since W does not depend explicitly on τ,

$$W' = W_\mu\mu' + W_\delta\delta' \quad . \tag{3.5}$$

Thus (3.4) can be integrated to yield

$$(\mu+K)W_\mu + (1+\delta)W_\delta - W = b \tag{3.6}$$

where b is an arbitrary constant of integration. Equation (3.6) is just an algebraic relation between μ and δ.

We now simplify (3.2) We first write (3.3) in the form

$$(\mu+K)[W_{\mu\mu}\mu'+W_{\mu\delta}\delta'] + (1+\delta)[W_{\delta\mu}\mu'+W_{\delta\delta}\delta'] = 0. \tag{3.7}$$

Assuming that

$$(\mu+K)W_{\mu\delta}+(1+\delta)W_{\delta\delta} \neq 0, \tag{3.8}$$

we obtain from (3.7) that

$$-\delta' = \frac{(\mu+K)W_{\mu\mu}+(1+\delta)W_{\delta\mu}}{(\mu+K)W_{\mu\delta}+(1+\delta)W_{\delta\delta}}\,\mu' \tag{3.9}$$

and therefore

$$W_\mu' = W_{\mu\mu}\mu' + W_{\mu\delta}\delta' = \frac{(1+\delta)[W_{\mu\mu}W_{\delta\delta}-W_{\mu\delta}^2]}{(\mu+K)W_{\mu\delta}+(1+\delta)W_{\delta\delta}}\,\mu' \tag{3.10}$$

Hence (2) becomes

$$\mu'^2 = (a+2qW_\mu-W_\delta^2)\left[\frac{(\mu+K)W_{\mu\delta}+(1+\delta)W_{\delta\delta}}{W_{\mu\mu}W_{\delta\delta}-W_{\mu\delta}^2}\right]^2 \tag{3.11}$$

The denominator on the right hand side of (3.11) does not vanish in virtue of the positive definiteness of the Hessian of W. If we solve (3.6) for δ as a function of μ, which is possible if (3.8) holds, then the right hand side of (3.11) may be regarded as a function of μ only and thus (3.11) furnishes the equations of the phase plane trajectories of μ. Furthermore, if we denote the right-hand side of (3.11) by $f(\mu)$, then (3.11) has the integral

$$\tau = \pm \int f^{-1/2} d\mu + \text{const} \tag{3.12}$$

which is an implicit equation for μ as a function of τ. Once this is known δ can be found from (3.6) and $\phi(\tau)$, $x(\tau)$, $y(\tau)$ can be obtained by further integrations.

In case (3.8) is violated, we may assume that the numerator of (3.9) does not vanish. We can then carry analogous operations that lead to the following phase plane equation for δ:

$$\delta'^2 = (a + 2q\, W_\mu - W_\delta) \left[\frac{(\mu+K)W_{\mu\mu} + (1+\delta)W_{\mu\delta}}{W_{\mu\mu}\, W_{\delta\delta} - W_{\mu\delta}^2} \right]^2 . \tag{3.13}$$

The right hand side of this equation is now regarded as a function of δ.

In the next section we show how the availability of equations of the form (3.11) or (3.13) enables us to obtain important qualitative information for a typical boundary value problem.

4. Example. We take $W = EI\mu^2/2 + EA\delta^2/2$ where EI and EA are prescribed constants. Then the constitutive equations are linear in the strain measures μ and δ: $M = EI\mu$, $N = EA\delta$. Since $s' = 1 + \delta > 0$ (--this is a continuity condition--), (3.6) may be written as

$$1 + \delta = [B - (\mu + K)^2 I/A]^{1/2}, \tag{4.1}$$

where B is an arbitrary constant. Then (3.11) becomes

$$(EI\mu')^2 = [B-(\mu+K)^2 I/A] \cdot \{a+2EIq\mu - (EA)^2[(B-(\mu+K)^2 I/A)^{1/2} - 1]^2\} \tag{4.2}$$

The change of variables $\mu + K = (AB/I)^{1/2} \sin \psi$, $w = \tan(\psi/2)$ converts (4.2) to a form which can be integrated by Weierstrass elliptic integrals, but such a result does not seem to promote either numerical convenience or physical interpretation. We therefore proceed by studying a specific boundary value problem and employing an approach that readily lends itself to generalization. We treat the problem corresponding to Fig. 1. We let 2α

be the angle subtended by the underformed arc so that $-\alpha/K \leq \tau \leq \alpha/K$. The ends of the rod are smoothly hinged so that no moment can be applied there; hence we have the boundary condition:

$$M(\pm\ \alpha/K) = 0$$

which implies that

$$\mu(\pm\ \alpha/K) = 0. \tag{4.3}$$

Moreover we have the geometric restriction that the ends are fixed which yields the conditions

$$x(\alpha/K) - x(-\alpha/K) = 2 \sin \alpha/K, \tag{4.4}$$

$$y(\alpha/K) - y(-\alpha/K) = 0.$$

By means of (2.5) the conditions (4.4) can be written as certain integral expressions in ϕ.

Introducing the new dimensionless variables

$$\zeta = (\mu+K)\ \alpha/K,\ t = K\tau/\alpha,\ \beta^2 = K^2 I/\alpha^2 A,\ p = \alpha^3 q/K^3 EI, \tag{4.5}$$

we can write (4.1), (4.2), (4.3) in the form:

$$1 + \delta = (\gamma^2 - \beta^2\zeta^2)^{1/2}, \tag{4.6}$$

$$(d\zeta/dt)^2 = (1+\delta)^2[a_o + 2p(\zeta - \alpha) - \delta^2/\beta^4]$$

$$=(\gamma^2 - \beta^2\zeta^2)\ a_o + 2p(\zeta - a) - [(\gamma^2 - \beta^2\zeta^2)^{1/2} - 1]^2/\beta^4 \tag{4.7}$$

$$\equiv h(\zeta), \quad -1 \leq t \leq 1,$$

$$\zeta(\pm\ 1) = \alpha, \tag{4.8}$$

where γ^2 and a_o are arbitrary constants. From (4.6) and (4.8) we see that the extension at $t = \pm 1$ is the same; denoting this by δ_o we find from (4.6) that

$$\gamma^2 = (1+\delta_o)^2 + \beta^2\alpha^2. \tag{4.9}$$

The original system of differential equations corresponding to (2.1) - (2.5) admits constant solutions. But by means of these equations one can easily show that the constant solution $\zeta = \alpha$ satisfying (4.8) is trivial because it can satisfy the remaining boundary conditions (4.4) only if $k = K$, $\delta = 0$ and $p = 0$. (For some other systems of boundary conditions, however, there are non-trivial constant solutions.)

We now examine the restrictions that the boundary conditions (4.8) impose on the nature of solutions of our system by studying $h(\zeta)$ defined in (4.7). From (4.7) we have that

$$h(\alpha) = (1 + \delta_o)^2(a_o - \delta_o^2/\beta^4) \tag{4.10}$$

Eq (4.7) then implies that $h(\alpha) > 0$ for a nontrivial solution. Moreover, (4.7) shows that $h(\zeta)$ has zeros at $\zeta = \pm \gamma/\beta$. Now since ζ must have the same value α at each end of the rod, Rolle's theorem implies that there is a value $t = T$ in the open interval $(-1, 1)$ for which $d\zeta/dt = 0$ but $d^2\zeta/dt^2 \neq 0$. (If $d^2\zeta/dt^2$ did equal zero here, then the uniqueness theory for the second order equation corresponding to (2.1) would make the solution trivial.) If the requirement that $1 + \delta > 0$ is not to be violated, these conditions imply that $h(\zeta)$ has a simple zero at $\zeta(T)$ with $|\zeta(T)| < \gamma/\beta$. If we let ζ_1 be the greatest zero of $h(\zeta)$ less than α at which $h(\zeta)$ changes sign and let ζ_2 be the least zero of $h(\zeta)$ greater than α at which $h(\zeta)$ changes sign, then at least one of the zeros ζ_1 and ζ_2 lies in the open interval $(-\gamma/\beta, \gamma/\beta)$ of the ζ-axis and $h(\zeta)$ has the form shown in Fig. 3.

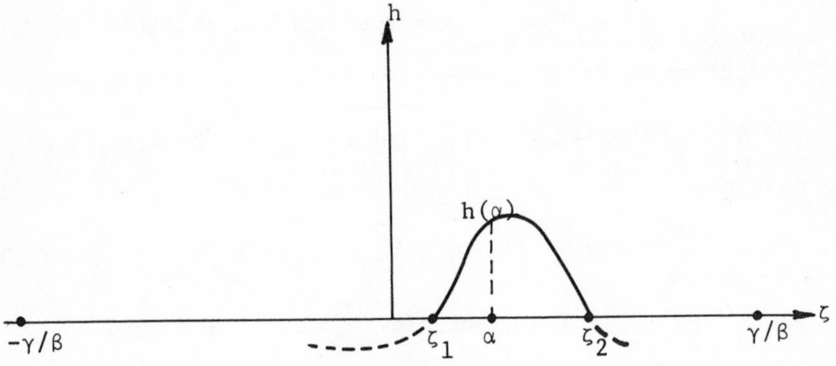

Fig. 3

When $h(\zeta)$ has this form the qualitative nature of the solution function $\zeta(t)$ is well known (from a phase plane analysis, e.g.). In particular $\zeta(t)$ is periodic with half period $\omega = \int_{\zeta_1}^{\zeta_2} h(\zeta)^{-1/2} d\zeta$, is bounded in the strip $\zeta_1 \leq \zeta \leq \zeta_2$, and is symmetric about its points of tangency to the lines $\zeta = \zeta_1$ and $\zeta = \zeta_2$. These properties are illustrated in Fig. 4.

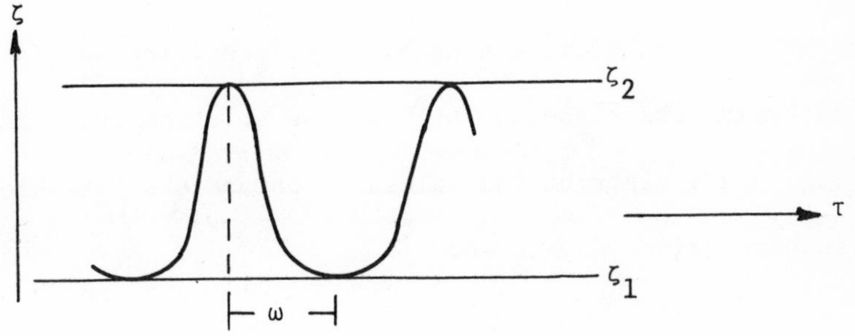

Fig. 4

We therefore deduce from the imposition of condition (4.8) that for each value of n, n = 0, 1, 2,..., there can be one symmetric solution with

$$2/(2n + 1) \leq \omega < 1/n,$$

one symmetric solution with

$$1/(n+1) < \omega \leq 2/(2n + 1),$$

and two asymmetric solutions, (mirror images of each other)

with

$$\omega = 1/(n+1).$$

If one of the zeros ζ_1 and ζ_2, say ζ_2, should have absolute value greater than γ/β, then any solution $\zeta = \zeta(t)$ that touches the line $\zeta = \zeta_2$ must be discarded because it violates the restriction that $1 + \delta > 0$. (We have already shown that both zeros cannot simultaneously exceed γ/β in absolute value.)

The additional subsidiary conditions of (4.4) determine the shape and size of the solution curve in Fig. 4 and restrict the values of parameters for which such solutions may arise.

We observe that this analysis holds for any strain energy function W for which Fig. 4 is valid. We remark that the constitutive equations for the material of this example are somewhat artificial since the axial force N approaches the finite limit $-$ EA as $\delta \to -1$.

Although we have exhibited representations for the solutions of the problem of Section 3, we have not demonstrated that these solutions can accommodate boundary conditions consistent with equilibrium, i.e. we have not shown that the transcendental equations for the boundary conditions can be solved for the integration constants. In the next two sections, we address ourselves to this question of existence from a more abstract viewpoint. Moreover we remove the restrictions that K = const. q = const. and W not depend explicitly on t.

5. Existence theory for inextensible rods.

We generalize some of the results of Lecture IV to treat inextensible rods having the constitutive relation

$$M = W_\mu \ , \ W = W(\mu,\tau) \tag{5.1}$$

and the material constraint of inextensibility

$$\delta = 0 \iff s' = 1. \tag{5.2}$$

We impose the following physically reasonable restrictions on W:

$$W_{\mu\mu} > 0, \tag{5.3}$$

$$W(\mu,\tau) \geq K|\mu|^\alpha + \gamma(\tau) \ , \ K > 0, \ \alpha > 1, \tag{5.4}$$

where K and α are constants and $\gamma(\tau)$ is an integrable function. The significance of (5.3) was discussed at the end of Section 1; (5.4) is a condition on W for large bending.

We let ℓ be the length of the rod so that $0 \leq \tau \leq \ell$. We assume, for simplicity, that the ends are either hinged or built in. For a hinged end

$$\phi' \text{ is prescribed;} \tag{5.5a}$$

for a built-in end

$$\phi \text{ is prescribed.} \tag{5.5b}$$

Moreover, we assume that the end points are fixed. Thus

$$\int_0^\ell \cos \phi(\tau)d\tau = \Delta, \quad \int_0^\ell \sin \phi(\tau)d\tau = 0 \tag{5.6}$$

where $\Delta < \ell$ is a given number.

We set

$$\psi = -(\phi - \Phi), \text{ so that } \mu = \psi'. \tag{5.7}$$

Then the potential energy functional for such rods which are subject to a hydrostatic pressure q is given by

$$V[\psi] = V_1 + qV_2 \tag{5.8a}$$

where

$$V_1 = \int_0^\ell W(\psi'(\tau), \tau)d\tau \tag{5.8b}$$

$$V_2 = \frac{1}{2}\int_0^\ell (xy' - yx')d\tau = \frac{1}{2}\int_0^\ell\int_0^\tau \sin[\phi(\tau)-\phi(\xi)]d\xi d\tau. \tag{5.8c}$$

The second equality in (5.8c) is a consequence of (2.5) and (5.2). V_2 is, to within an additive constant, proportional to the signed area "enclosed" by the closed curve formed by the rod in its undeformed and deformed states. (This curve need not be simple.)

The governing equations for this problem can be shown by the method of Lecture IV to be the Euler equations for the functional V subject to (5.4). We now prove several existence theorems for problems of this nature by using some functional analytic machinery similar to that described in Lecture IV.

We employ the Sobolev space

$$W_\alpha^{(1)}(0,\ell) \equiv \{\psi : \psi,\ \psi' \varepsilon\ L_\alpha(0,\ \ell)\}\ ,\ \alpha > 1 \qquad (5.9)$$

(where derivatives are taken in the distributional sense) which is a reflexive Banach space with norm

$$||\psi|| = \{\int_0^\ell [|\psi|^\alpha + |\psi'|^\alpha]\ d\tau\}^{\frac{1}{\alpha}} \quad . \qquad (5.10)$$

Let S be the Banach space consisting of those elements of $W_\alpha^{(1)}(0,\ell)$ satisfying boundary conditions of the form (5.5) and let E_o consist of those elements of S that satisfy (5.6). These spaces may be constructed by completion.

We need the following theorems.

Theorem A. A weakly lower semi-continuous functional on a

bounded, weakly closed, nonempty set of a reflexive Banach space assumes its minimum there.

Theorem B. If $F = F(\underset{\sim}{u}, \tau)$, $\underset{\sim}{u} = (u_1, \ldots, u_N)$, and the Hessian matrix $F_{\underset{\sim}{u}\underset{\sim}{u}}$ is positive definite, then the functional $\int_0^\ell F(\underset{\sim}{u}, \tau)dt$ is weakly lower semi-continuous in

$$W_\alpha^{(1)}(0, \ell).$$

Theorem C (Sobolev): $W_\alpha^{(1)}(0, \ell)$ can be compactly imbedded in the Banach space $C(0, \ell)$ of continuous functions having the maximum norm.

Theorem D: If $x_n \to x$ weakly in a Banach space B_1 and B_1 is compactly imbedded in a Banach space B_2, then $x_n \to x$ strongly in B_2.

Proof of these theorems may be found in [3] and [4].

We now state and prove some preliminary lemmas.

Lemma 1: $V_1 \to \infty$ as $||\psi|| \to \infty$.
The proof is an immediate consequence of (5.4).

Lemma 2: V_1 is a weakly lower semi-continuous functional.

This follows from (5.3) and Theorem B.

Lemma 3: The functionals V_2, $\int_0^\ell \cos\phi(\tau)d\tau$, $\int_0^\ell \sin\phi(\tau)d\tau$

are weakly continuous on S.

The proof of this lemma was furnished in Lecture IV and depends upon Theorems C and D.

Lemma 4: $M = \sup_{\psi \epsilon E_o} V_2[\psi]$ and $m = \inf_{\psi \epsilon E_o} V_2[\psi]$ are finite numbers.

This result is just a consequence of the classical isoperimetric problem.

We define the manifold

$$E_2(R) \equiv \{\psi : V_2[\psi] = R,\ m < R < M\}. \tag{5.11}$$

Lemma 5: The sets E_o and $E_o \cap E_2$ are non empty.

The proof of this lemma follows by constructing an element for each set. This is possible since $\Delta < \ell$. We omit such a construction.

We now can prove the following existence theorems.

Theorem 1: For arbitrary fixed q, there exists an element ψ_o of E_o that furnishes $V[\psi]$ with an absolute minimum on E_o.

Proof: Lemmas 1 and 4 imply that $V \to \infty$ as $||\psi|| \to \infty$. Hence we need only seek a minimum for V on some bounded subset of E_o. Lemmas 2 and 3 imply that V is weakly lower semi-continuous on E_o. Lemma 3 implies that E_o is weakly closed and Lemma 5 asserts that E_o is non-empty. Thus the hypotheses of Theorem A are met and this theorem is proved.

Theorem 2: For each R, $m < R < M$, there exists an element ψ_2 of $E_o \cap E_2$ that furnishes $V_1[\psi]$ with an absolute minimum on $E_o \cap E_2$.

This proof is analogous to the proof of Theorem 1 and is omitted.

We also have the following regularity theorem:

Theorem 3: If in addition to (5.3) and (5.4), the function $W(\mu,\delta)$ satisfies

$$|W_\mu| < \text{const } (|\mu|^\alpha + 1), \tag{5.12}$$

then the minimizing functions ψ_o and ψ_2 of Theorems 1 and 2 are twice continuously differentiable on $[0,\ell]$ and are classical solutions of the Euler equations.

Proof: Theorems C and D imply that ψ_o and ψ_2 are continuous. This fact, coupled with conditions (5.3), (5.4), and (5.12) enables us to apply the Tonelli theory of the Calculus of Variations which ensures the conclusion of the theorem.

We now turn to the extensible case.

6. Existence theory for extensible rods.

In analogy to (5.3) and (5.4) we require that the matrix

$$\begin{bmatrix} W_{\mu\mu} & W_{\mu\delta} \\ W_{\delta\mu} & W_{\delta\delta} \end{bmatrix} \text{ be positive definite} \tag{6.1}$$

and that

$$W(\mu,\delta,\tau) \geq K(|\mu|^{\alpha} + |\delta|^{\beta}) + \gamma(\tau), K>0, \ \alpha>1, \ \beta>1 \tag{6.2}$$

where K, α, and β, are constants and $\gamma(\tau)$ is an integrable function. Using the notation of (5.7) we require that

$$\psi \text{ or } \psi' \text{ be prescribed at each end.} \tag{6.3}$$

Corresponding to (5.6), we have

$$\int_0^{\ell} [1+\delta(\tau)]\cos \phi(\tau)d\tau = \Delta \ , \ \int_0^{\ell} [1+\delta(\tau)]\sin \phi(\tau)d\tau = 0 \tag{6.4}$$

with $\Delta<\ell$ a given number. We set

$$\sigma' = \delta = s' - 1 \tag{6.5}$$

and require that

$$\sigma(0) = \delta(0) = 0. \tag{6.6}$$

The potential energy functional for the extensible rod subject to a hydrostatic pressure q is given by

$$U[\psi, \sigma] = U_1[\psi, \sigma] + q\, U_2[\psi, \sigma] \tag{6.7a}$$

where

$$U_1 = \int_0^{\ell} W(\psi', \sigma', \tau)dt \tag{6.7b}$$

$$U_2 = \frac{1}{2}\int_0^{\ell}[1+\sigma'(\tau)]\int_0^{\tau}[1+\sigma'(\xi)]\sin[\phi(\tau)-\phi(\xi)]\,d\xi\, d\tau \tag{6.7c}$$

The Euler equations for U subject to (6.3) and (6.4) are the governing equations discussed in Section 2.

Let S be the Banach space of pairs (ψ,σ) with $\psi \,\varepsilon W_{\alpha}^{(1)}(0,\ell)$, $\sigma\ \varepsilon\ W_{\beta}^{(1)}(0,\ell)$ and with ψ satisfying (6.3) and σ satisfying (6.6). Let E_o consist of those elements of S that satisfy (6.4).

Equation (6.2) implies

Lemma 5: $U_1 \to \infty$ as $||\psi|| + ||\sigma|| \to \infty$.

Here and in the sequel $||\psi||$ and $||\sigma||$ denote the norms of ψ and σ in their respective Sobolev spaces.

Relation(6.1)and theorem B imply

Lemma 6: U_1 is a weakly lower semi-continuous functional.

Lemma 7: The functionals U_2, $\int_0^{\ell}[1 + \sigma'(\tau)]\cos[\psi(\tau)-\Phi(\tau)]d\tau$, and $\int_0^{\ell}[1 + \sigma'(\tau)]\sin[\psi(\tau)-\Phi(\tau)]d\tau$ are weakly continuous on S.

Proof: We just treat the functional

$$F[\psi,\sigma] = \int_0^\ell [1 + \sigma'(\tau)]\sin[\psi(\tau) - \Phi(\tau)]d\tau;$$

the proof for the other two functionals is analogous.

Let $(\psi_n,\sigma_n) \to (\psi,\sigma)$ weakly. In view of the Riesz Representation Theorem, this means that

$$\int_0^\ell [\psi_n\eta + \psi_n'\eta']d\tau \to \int_0^\ell [\psi\eta + \psi'\eta']d\tau \tag{6.8}$$

$$\int_0^\ell [\sigma_n\zeta + \sigma_n'\zeta']d\tau \to \int_0^\ell [\sigma\zeta + \sigma'\zeta']d\tau \tag{6.9}$$

for arbitrary $\eta\varepsilon W_{\alpha'}^{(1)}(0,\ell)$ and for arbitrary $\zeta\varepsilon W_{\alpha'}^{(1)}(0,\ell)$ where $\frac{1}{\alpha} + \frac{1}{\alpha'} = 1$ and $\frac{1}{\beta} + \frac{1}{\beta'} = 1$.

Now

$$F[\psi,\sigma] - F[\psi_n,\sigma_n]$$

$$= \int_0^\ell \sin[\psi(\tau) - \Phi(\tau)] \cdot [\sigma'(\tau) - \sigma_n'(\tau)]d\tau \tag{6.10}$$

$$+ \int_0^\ell [1 + \sigma_n']\{\sin[\psi(\tau) - \Phi(\tau)]-\sin[\psi_n(\tau)-\Phi(\tau)]\}d\tau.$$

We examine the second integral of (6.10). The absolute value of this integral is less than

$$2\int_0^\ell 1+\sigma_n'(\tau)\left|\left|\sin\tfrac{1}{2}(\psi(\tau)-\psi_n(\tau)\right|\right|\cos\tfrac{1}{2}(\psi(\tau)+\psi_n(\tau)-2\Phi(\tau)\right|d\tau$$

$$\leq \int_0^{\ell} |1+\sigma_n'(\tau)|\,|\psi(\tau)-\psi_n(\tau)|\,d\tau \leq \ell \max|1+\sigma_n'(\tau)|\max_{\tau}|\psi(\tau)-\psi_n(\tau)|. \tag{6.11}$$

By Theorems C and D, the last term of (6.11) approaches zero.

We now treat the first integral of (6.10). Let us choose the ζ of eq (6.9) to have the property that

$$\int_0^{\ell} \zeta(\tau)d\tau = 0 . \tag{6.12}$$

Then integrating (6.9) by parts, we have

$$\int_0^{\ell} [\sigma'(\tau) - \sigma_n'(\tau)]\ [\zeta'(\tau) - \int_0^{\tau} \zeta(\xi)d\xi]\ dt \to 0. \tag{6.13}$$

By choosing $\zeta(\tau)$ to be any smooth solution of the linear equation

$$\zeta''(\tau) - \zeta(\tau) = \frac{d}{d\tau} \sin[\ \psi(\tau) - \phi(\tau)] \tag{6.14}$$

subject to condition (6.12), we can identify (6.13) with the first integral of (6.10). Thus the first integral of (6.10) also approaches zero as $n \to \infty$. Thus F is weakly continuous. Q.E.D.

<u>Theorem</u> 4: <u>Let</u> $\beta > 2$. (β <u>is defined in</u> (2).) <u>Then for arbitrary fixed</u> q, <u>there exists an element</u> (ψ_o, σ_o) <u>of</u> E_o <u>that furnishes</u> $U[\psi, \sigma]$ <u>with an absolute minimum on</u> E_o.

Proof: This condition on β ensures that $U \to \infty$ as

$||\psi|| + ||\sigma|| \to 0$. Since E_o is readily shown to be nonempty, the remainder of the proof follows that of Theorem 1.

Theorem 5: *Let*

$$E_2(R) = \{(\psi, \sigma) : U_2[\psi, \sigma] = R\} . \qquad (6.15)$$

Then for each number R, *there exists an element* (ψ_2, σ_2) *of* $E_o \cap E_2$ *that furnishes* $V_1[\psi, \sigma]$ *with an absolute minimum on* $E_o \cap E_2$.

Proof: From simple geometric considerations, the set $E_o \cap E_2$ can be shown to be nonempty. The rest of the proof follows that of Theorem 1.

Theorem 6: *If in addition to* (6.1) *and* (6.2), *the function* $W(\mu, \delta, \tau)$ *satisfies the inequality.*

$$||W_\mu| + |W_\delta| \leq \text{const} \; (|\mu|^\alpha + |\delta|^\beta + 1), \qquad (6.16)$$

then the minimizing functions (ψ_o, σ_o) *and* (ψ_2, σ_2) *of Theorems* 4 *and* 5 *are twice continuously differentiable on* $[0,\ell]$ *and are classical solutions to the Euler equations.*

The proof follows that of Theorem 3 and is omitted.

In theorem 4 we required that β be greater than 2 whereas in theorem 5 no such restriction was necessary. The need for this assumption has a simple physical significance that is best explained by example. Consider the inflation of a circular ring by an internal pressure $q > 0$. We assume that W is independent of τ and that $W_\mu(0,\delta) = 0, W_\delta(\mu, 0) = 0$. Let the undeformed radius be 1. We seek conditions under which the ring can be in equilibrium in the shape of a circular ring of radius $R > 1$. It is readily seen that the

$$\psi = 0,\ M = 0,\ \delta = R - 1,\ N = qR \tag{6.17}$$

satisfies (2.1), (2.2), the first equation of (2.3), and the periodicity conditions. If (6.17) is to be a solution, then the second equation of (2.3) must be satisfied:

$$q\,R = W_\delta\ (0,\ R - 1). \tag{6.18}$$

If we plot the left hand side of (6.18) as a function of $R - 1$, then we obtain a family of straight lines intercepting the $(R - 1)$ - axis at $(R - 1) = -1$ which is parametrized by the slope q. The plot of the right hand side of (6.18) as a function of $R - 1$ yields a single curve that behaves like $(R - 1)^{\beta - 1}$ for large R. Clearly, if $\beta \leq 2$, then there is some value q^* such that the curve $N = W_\delta(0,\ R - 1)$ will not intersect the curves $N = q\ R$ for

$q > q^*$. On the other hand, we see that for any R there is a q given by (6.18) for which (6.17) is a solution. Thus the ring can stay in equilibrium for arbitrarily large internal pressure only if the material is sufficiently "hard" in extension. Thus two different stress-strain laws that may be regarded as essentially equivalent for small deformations (e.g., N is proportional to δ: $N = f(\mu)\delta$ and N is proportional to the material strain: $N = \frac{1}{2}f(\mu)\,[\,(\delta+1)^2-1\,]$ produce strikingly different results for large deformation. Such results are also found for membranes. (Cf. [5]). This mechanism may be expected to operate for boundary conditions (6.3) and (6.4).

We note in passing that this same graphical analysis holds for a ring subject to external pressure if we let q assume negative values. In this case, if (6.17) is to be a solution for all negative q, then $W_\delta(\mu,\sigma')$ must approach $-\infty$ as δ approaches -1.

7. Conclusion.

The theorems of Section 6 and 7 ensure the existence of 'preferred' solutions. These are the simplest such theorems. More sophisticated results can be obtained by using techniques discussed in Lectures VI and VII and in the bibliographic references there. The bifurcation question can be treated by the methods of Lectures VI and VII or by the Poincaré procedure used in Lectures II and IV coupled with the methods of Lecture XI. For those problems in which a "trivial" solution can be identified, the methods of Lecture IV can be used to prove the existence of nontrivial solutions.

This lecture is based in part on [1] and [6].

Bibliography

[1] S. Antman, General solutions for plane extensible elasticae having nonlinear stress-strain laws, Quart. Appl. Math., 26, 35-47, (1968)

[2] I. Tadjbakhsh, The variational theory of the plane motion of the extensible elastica, Int. J. of Eng. Sci. 4, 433-450, (1966).

[3] Vainberg, Variational Methods for the Study of Nonlinear Operators, (transl) Holden-Day, San Francisco, 1964.

[4] Sobolev, S. L., Applications of Functional Analysis in Mathematical Physics, (transl) A.M.S. Providence, 1961.

[5] A. E. Green and J. E. Adkins, Large Elastic Deformations, Oxford, 1960.

[6] S. Antman, Equilibrium States of Nonlinearly Elastic Rods, J. Math. Anal. and Appl., to appear.

XIII.1. Nonuniqueness of Rectangular Solutions of the Bénard Problem

Paul H. Rabinowitz

1. Introduction.

In this lecture we study the Bénard problem which is a relatively simple convection problem. We want a mathematical description of the following idealized experiment: An infinite horizontal layer of viscous fluid initially at rest lies between two rigid perfectly conducting walls. A constant temperature gradient is maintained between the walls, the lower wall being hotter. If the temperature gradient is small, the fluid remains at rest and heat is transported through the fluid only by conduction. However when the temperature gradient is increased beyond a certain critical value, the fluid undergoes time independent motions called convection currents. Heat is now transported through the fluid by convection as well as conduction. In actual experiments, the fluid arranges itself in a regular cellular pattern and motions take place only within the cells [1], [2]. The shape of the cells seems to depend strongly on the shape of the container [2].

One can give a simple qualitative explanation of the above phenomena. The bottom portion of the fluid expands because of the heating and becomes less dense. It therefore tends to rise. However the fluid being viscous resists this buoyancy force. If the temperature gradient is small the viscous forces are dominant and the fluid remains at rest, heat being transported only by conduction. When the critical temperature gradient is exceeded, the buoyancy force becomes large enough to overcome the viscosity of the fluid and convection begins.

Bénard conducted the original experiments in this area. His fluid had a free upper surface and he found the cells to be in the shape of hexagons [2]. However this effect was later shown [3] to be due primarily to surface tension which plays a negligible role in the problem we consider here.

We seek to show that the above convective phenomena can be obtained mathematically from the equations of motion of the fluid. The conduction solution is easily obtained and exists for all values of the temperature gradient. Thus the problem mathematically becomes one of non-uniqueness. We must show that on exceeding a critical temperature gradient, new solutions of the equations of motion corresponding to convection branch or bifurcate from the conduction solution.

Our main result will be the existence of such new convection solutions corresponding physically to rectangular cells. The reason for looking for rectangular cellular solutions is that this is the simplest problem to pose mathematically. In §2 the problem is so formulated. The linearized equations are studied in §3. It is shown there that the smallest eigenvalue of the linearized equations is simple. This is crucial for our method.

An iteration scheme to solve the nonlinear problem is introduced in §4 and its convergence is established in §5. Rather than give a cryptic explanation now, we postpone a discussion of our method until §4 at which point the necessary preliminaries will have been developed.

There is a large literature devoted to the Bénard problem. Much work deals with the linearized theory. In particular we mention the book of Chandrasekhar [4] where there is a large bibliography. Several people have attacked the full nonlinear problem using numerical techniques or formal methods. In this regard we mention Malkus and Veronis [5], Busse [6], and Krishnamurti [1], who use formal expansion methods and to whose work our method is somewhat related. A somewhat different formal method is used in Segel [8]. Of the numerical treatments we mention the thesis of Chorin [9]. Joseph [10] has shown for the full nonlinear equations the uniqueness of the conduction solutions for subcritical temperature gradients. However to the best of our knowledge there has been no rigorous existence result for the nonlinear problem.

This work is partly inspired by the striking results of Velte [11], [12], who treated the viscous flow through a pipe heated from below (a problem similar to the Bénard problem) and the Taylor problem of viscous flow between rotating cylinders. He demonstrated the bifurcation of solutions by use of topological degree of mapping arguments. Iudovich [13] has used similar methods to treat a problem in viscous flow.

In this lecture we employ more constructive methods to obtain results analogous to those of Velte. Our approach furnishes a more precise description of the bifurcation.

2. Mathematical Formulation of the Problem.

In appropriate dimensionless coordinates, the Boussinesq approximation of the Navier-Stokes equations leads to the formulation of the Bénard problem as the following boundary value problem for the velocity $\underline{u} = (u,v,w)$, temperature θ, and pressure p:

$$\Delta \underline{u} - \nabla p + R\theta \underline{e} = (\underline{u} \cdot \nabla)\underline{u}, \qquad \underline{e} = (0,0,1) \quad , \tag{2.1a}$$

$$\Delta\theta + w = P(\underline{u} \cdot \nabla)\theta \quad , \tag{2.1b}$$

$$\nabla \cdot \underline{u} = 0 \quad , \tag{2.1c}$$

for $-\infty < x < \infty$, $-\infty < y < \infty$, $-1 < z < 1$.

The boundary conditions are

$$\underline{u} = 0 \quad , \qquad \theta = 0 \qquad \text{at } z = \pm 1 \quad . \tag{2.2}$$

Note that (2.1c) and (2.2) imply that

$$w_z = 0 \qquad \text{at } z = \pm 1 \quad . \tag{2.3}$$

Here R is the Rayleigh number and P is the Prandtl number, which are prescribed dimensionless constants incorporating physical, geometrical, and thermodynamic parameters.

The trivial solution $\underline{u} = 0$, $\theta = 0$, $p = 0$ of (2.1) and (2.2) corresponds to the conductive solution (For details on the derivation of (2.1), see [4]).

We look for solutions corresponding to rectangular cells. Thus we want solutions that are periodic in the x and y directions with periods $\frac{2\pi}{a}$ and $\frac{2\pi}{b}$ respectively. This does not yet introduce the cellular nature of the solution. Experimentally one finds that fluid motions only take place within the cells and no heat is transported across cell walls. That the cell walls are effectively thermal insulators suggests that we seek a solution which is even as well as periodic in x and y. An examination of the effect of this form on (2.1) leads us to the ansatz for the solution:

$$u = \sum_{j,k=0}^{\infty} A_{jk}(z) \sin jax \cos kby$$

$$v = \sum_{j,k=0}^{\infty} B_{jk}(z) \cos jax \sin kby$$

$$w = \sum_{j,k=0}^{\infty} C_{jk}(z) \cos jax \cos kby$$

$$\theta = \sum_{j,k=0}^{\infty} D_{jk}(z) \cos jax \cos kby$$

$$p = \sum_{j,k=0}^{\infty} E_{jk}(z) \cos jax \cos kby$$

with boundary conditions (2.2) and (2.3). For the moment a and b are left free.

3. The Linearized Equations.

We already have one solution to (2.1) and (2.2), namely

$$\underline{u} = 0, \ \theta = p = 0. \tag{3.1}$$

It has been shown by Joseph [10] that the full nonlinear equations possess a unique solution for $R \leq R_c$, where R_c is the smallest eigenvalue of the linearized equations, linearized about the trivial solution (3.1). (Henceforth we refer to these as the linearized equations.) Thus the solution (3.1) is the only solution to (2.1) and (2.2) for $R \leq R_c$.

It is natural to seek a solution to (2.1) near $R = R_c$, $\underline{u} = 0$, $\theta = p = 0$. Before so doing, however, it is necessary to make a closer study of the linearized equations. These are:

$$\begin{aligned} &\Delta\underline{u} - \nabla p + R\theta\underline{e} = 0 \\ &\Delta\theta + w = 0 \\ &\nabla \cdot \underline{u} = 0 \end{aligned} \tag{3.2}$$

where $\underline{u}$, θ, p are to have the form (2.4) with (2.2) as boundary conditions.

In (3.2) the Rayleigh number R appears as an

eigenvalue parameter. We seek those values of R for which there exist nontrivial solutions to (3.2). We can settle this question quickly by noting that our equations (3.2) can be interpreted as the Euler equation of a variational problem. To make this precise, let us denote a cell by $\mathcal{C}$: $-1 \leq z \leq 1$, $0 \leq x \leq \frac{2\pi}{a}$, $0 \leq y \leq \frac{2\pi}{b}$ and write $d\underline{x}$ for dxdydz. Let

$$I[u,v,w] \equiv I[\underline{u}] = \frac{\int_{\mathcal{C}} |\nabla\underline{u}|^2 d\underline{x}}{\int_{\mathcal{C}} |\nabla\theta|^2 d\underline{x}} \tag{3.3}$$

where $|\nabla\underline{u}|^2 = |\nabla u|^2 + |\nabla v|^2 + |\nabla w|^2$.

Lemma 1: The equations (3.2) are the Euler equations of the variational problem

$$I[\underline{u}] = \text{minimum} \tag{3.4}$$

subject to the side conditions $\nabla \cdot \underline{u} = 0$, $\Delta\theta + w = 0$, and boundary conditions (2.2), $\underline{u}$ having the form (2.4).

Proof: The vanishing of the first variation gives

$$\int_{\mathcal{C}} (\nabla\underline{u} \cdot \nabla\delta\underline{u} - R_c \nabla\theta \cdot \nabla\delta\theta) d\underline{x} = 0 \tag{3.5}$$

where $\underline{u}$, θ are the minimizing functions, $R_c = I[\underline{u}]$, and $\delta\underline{u}$, $\delta\theta$ are any admissible variations, i.e. $\delta\underline{u}$ is of the form (2.4) with $\nabla \cdot \delta\underline{u} = 0$, $\Delta\delta\theta + \delta w = 0$. Integrating by parts and using the side conditions we find

$$0 = \int_{\mathcal{C}} (\Delta\underline{u} \cdot \delta\underline{u} - R_c\theta\Delta\delta\theta)d\underline{x} = \int_{\mathcal{C}} (\Delta\underline{u} \cdot \delta\underline{u} + R_c\theta\delta w)d\underline{x} \quad (3.6)$$

$$= \int_{\mathcal{C}} (\Delta\underline{u} + R_c\theta\underline{e}) \cdot \delta\underline{u}d\underline{x} \quad . \quad (3.7)$$

Thus $\underline{u} + R_c\theta\underline{e}$ is orthogonal to the space of divergence free vectors. This implies as in [14] that

$\Delta\underline{u} + R_c\theta\underline{e}$ is the gradient of a scalar, i.e.

$$\Delta\underline{u} + R_c\theta\underline{e} = \nabla p \quad (3.8)$$

which verifies our assertion.

Because of the "elliptic" nature of the above variational problem, we expect an increasing sequence of eigenvalues (R_n) with corresponding smooth eigenfunctions. Moreover each eigenvalue will be of finite multiplicity. However the method we employ to solve (2.1) and (2.2) requires that the smallest eigenvalue R_c be simple. Thus to show this we are forced to make a more detailed analysis of (3.2) using more strongly the specific form (2.4) of our solutions.

If we substitute the Fourier series for $\underline{u}$, θ, p into (3.2) and eliminate the x,y dependence, we are led to the infinite system of ordinary differential equations

$$\begin{aligned} &L_{jk}A_{jk} + jaE_{jk} = 0 \\ &L_{jk}B_{jk} + kbE_{jk} = 0 \qquad j,k = 0,1,\ldots \\ &L_{jk}C_{jk} - E'_{jk} + RD_{jk} = 0 \\ &L_{jk}D_{jk} + C_{jk} = 0 \\ &jaA_{jk} + kbB_{jk} + C'_{jk} = 0 \quad . \end{aligned} \tag{3.9}$$

Here $L_{jk} = \dfrac{d^2}{dz^2} - ((ja)^2 + (kb)^2)$ and $' = \dfrac{d}{dz}$.

As boundary conditions we have from (2.2) and (2.3):

$$A_{jk} = B_{jk} = C_{jk} = D_{jk} = 0 = C'_{jk} \quad \text{at } z = \pm 1. \tag{3.10}$$

We can use the first, second, and fifth equations of (3.9) to eliminate E'_{jk} from the third and are finally led to the system:

$$L_{jk}^2 C_{jk} = R(j^2a^2 + k^2b^2)D_{jk} \tag{3.11}$$

$$L_{jk}D_{jk} = -C_{jk}$$

$$C_{jk} = C'_{jk} = D_{jk} = 0 \quad \text{at } z = \pm 1 \tag{3.12}$$

Note that for each value of j and k we obtain a system of the same form. Letting $\omega_{jk}^2 = j^2a^2 + k^2b^2$ and dropping subscripts for brevity, we get

$$L^2C = R\omega^2 D \tag{3.13}$$

$$LD = -C$$

$$C = C' = D = 0 \qquad \text{at } z = \pm 1 \tag{3.14}$$

Remark: It is easily seen that (3.13), (3.14) can be obtained from a variational formulation, namely

$$\frac{\int_{-1}^{1} |LC|^2 dz}{\omega^2 \int_{-1}^{1} ((D')^2 + \omega^2 D^2) dz} = \text{minimum}$$

where $LD = -C$, and C, D satisfy the boundary conditions (3.14). Thus by standard theorems of the calculus of variations [15] the eigenvalues of (3.13), (3.14) are nonnegative (actually positive - see lemma 5), of finite multiplicity, and form an increasing sequence tending to infinity.

We next convert (3.13) to an integral equation which possesses a positive kernel. By an analogue of the Frobenius theory of positive matrices, the smallest eigenvalue of (3.13) is simple (for each ω). Then to construct a simple smallest eigenvalue of the partial differential equations (3.2), we appropriately choose the parameters a and b.

To begin, we note the following lemma which can be found in [16] or [17].

<u>Lemma</u> 2: Let $M = a(z)\frac{d^2}{dz^2} + b(z)\frac{d}{dz} + c(z)$ where $a(z) > 0$ and $c(z) < 0$ for $z \in [-1,1]$. If $a(z)$, $b(z)$, $c(z)$ are sufficiently smooth, e.g., four times continuously differentiable, then

(α) The Green's function $G(z,\zeta)$ of M under the boundary conditions $G(\pm 1,\zeta) = 0 = H_z(\pm 1,\zeta)$ is negative for $z,\zeta \in (-1,1)$.

(β) The Green's function $H(z,\zeta)$ of M^2 under the boundary conditions $H(\pm 1,\zeta) = 0 = H_z(\pm 1,\zeta)$ is positive for $z,\zeta \in (-1,1)$.

Since L satisfies the hypotheses of Lemma 2, L has a negative Green's function $G(z,\zeta,\omega)$ and L^2 a positive Green's function $H(z,\zeta,\omega)$. We can use these Green's functions to convert (3.13) into a system of integral equations:

$$C(z,\omega) = R\omega^2\int_{-1}^{1} H(z,\zeta,\omega)D(\zeta,\omega)d\zeta$$

$$D(z,\omega) = -\int_{-1}^{1} G(z,\zeta,\omega)C(\zeta,\omega)d\zeta. \qquad (3.15)$$

Combining these equations, we find:

$$C(z,\omega) = R\int_{-1}^{1} K(z,\zeta,\omega)C(\zeta,\omega)d\zeta \qquad (3.16)$$

where $K(z,\zeta,\omega) = \omega^2\int_{-1}^{1} H(z,\tau,\omega)G(\tau,\zeta,\omega)d\tau$.

Note that $K(z,\zeta,\omega) > 0$ if $z,\zeta\varepsilon(-1,1)$. At this point we employ a result of Krein and Rutman [18].

Lemma 3: Let A be a compact linear operator on a Banach space B. Assume A maps a cone κ of B into itself and that A has a nonzero element in its spectrum. Then A has a positive eigenvalue λ with $\lambda \geq |\mu|$ for any other μ in the spectrum of A. Moreover there is at least one eigenvector v of A in κ and at least one eigenvector ψ of A^* in κ^*.

Here A^* is defined by $A^*: B^* \to B^*$, $A^*f = f A$ where B^* is the dual of B, and $\kappa^* = \{f \in B^* | f(x) \geq 0$ for all $x \in \kappa\}$.

For the problem we are considering we take B to be the Hilbert space $L^2[-1,1]$, κ, the cone of nonnegative functions in B, and A, our integral operator which is compact and linear. R corresponds to λ^{-1}. We know A has nonzero real spectrum because of the alternate variational formulation of the equation. Thus by the result of Krein and Rutman, (3.16) possesses a positive smallest eigenvalue $\underline{R}(\omega)$ with corresponding nonnegative eigenfunction $C(z,\omega)$. That $C(z,\omega)$ is infinitely differentiable is easily shown.

Actually since $K(z,\zeta) > 0$ if $z,\zeta \varepsilon (-1,1)$, it follows that $C(z,\omega) > 0$ if $z \varepsilon (-1,1)$. The adjoint integral operator to (3.16) likewise possesses an eigenfunction which is positive in $(-1,1)$ corresponding to $\underline{R}(\omega)$.

Lemma 4: $\underline{R}(\omega)$ is a simple eigenvalue of (3.16).

Proof: For notational convenience we drop the ω's. Suppose R possesses a second eigenfunction $\phi(z)$. We first show that $|\phi(z)|$ must also be an eigenfunction of (3.16). From (3.16) we have

$$|\phi(z)| \leq \underline{R}\int_{-1}^{1} K(z,\zeta)|\phi(\zeta)|d\zeta \quad . \tag{3.17}$$

Assume that $|\phi(z)|$ were not an eigenfunction. Then (3.17) implies we have inequality at some point z_o:

$$|\phi(z_o)| < R\int_{-1}^{1} K(z_o,\zeta)|\phi(\zeta)|d\zeta \quad . \tag{3.18}$$

The adjoint equation possesses a positive solution $C^*(z)$ corresponding to $\underline{R}$:

$$C^*(z) = \underline{R}\int_{-1}^{1} K(\zeta,z)C^*(\zeta)d\zeta \quad .$$

From (3.17), (3.19) we find

$$\int_{-1}^{1} C^*(z)|\phi(z)|dz = \underline{R}\int_{-1}^{1}\int_{-1}^{1} K(\zeta,z)C^*(\zeta)|\phi(z)|d\zeta dz$$

$$= \underline{R}\int_{-1}^{1}\int_{-1}^{1} K(z,\zeta)C^*(z)|\phi(\zeta)|d\zeta dz$$

which contradicts (3.18). Thus $|\phi(z)|$ is an eigenfunction of (3.16) together with $\phi(z)$. Note that $|\phi(z)| > 0$ if $z\varepsilon(-1,1)$. Let $z_1\varepsilon(-1,1)$. By our above argument, $\left|C(z) - \frac{C(z_1)}{|\phi(z_1)|}|\phi(z)|\right|$ is an eigenfunction of (3.16) which vanishes at z_1, a contradiction. Thus $\underline{R}(\omega)$ is a simple eigenvalue.

Thus from the above lemmas, we find a simple smallest eigenvalue $\underline{R}(\omega)$ of (3.16) which is positive and the corresponding eigenfunction $C(z,\omega)$ is positive in $(-1,1)$. From (3.15) the corresponding $D(z,\omega)$ is also positive in $(-1,1)$. The functions $C(z,\omega)$, $D(z,\omega)$ are infinitely differentiable.

From (3.13), (3.14), it is seen that $C(-z,\omega)$, $D(-z,\omega)$ are solutions together with $C(z,\omega)$, $D(z,\omega)$. Since $\underline{R}(\omega)$ is a simple eigenvalue, it follows $C(z,\omega)$ and $D(z,\omega)$ are even functions of z. Returning to the system (3.9), it is easily seen that the corresponding $A(z,\omega)$, $B(z,\omega)$, $E(z,\omega)$ are odd functions of z.

Thus we have shown:

Theorem 1: The system (3.13), (3.14) possesses a simple smallest eigenvalue $\underline{R}(\omega) > 0$. The corresponding eigenfunctions $C(z,\omega)$, $D(z,\omega)$ are positive even functions of z in (-1,1) and are infinitely differentiable there.

We observe that from each solution of (3.13), (3.14) we obtain a corresponding solution to (3.9), (3.10) and to (3.2), (2.2). We obtain the totality of solutions of (3.2), (3.22) in this manner.

Although for each j and k, the smallest eigenvalue of (3.16) is simple, it need not be the case that the smallest eigenvalue of (3.2) is simple. It could happen for some ω_1, ω_2, that $\underline{R}(\omega_1) = \underline{R}(\omega_2)$. Thus we next show that a and b can be chosen so as to obtain a simple smallest eigenvalue of (3.2).

By numerical calculations it has been shown [19] that $\underline{R}(\omega)$ is a convex function of ω with a minimum of 106.8 at $\omega = 1.56$. Thus if we take $j = k = 1$, $a^2 + b^2 = (1.56)^2$, $0 \leq a, b \leq 1.56$, we obtain a one parameter family of a's and b's which give a simple smallest eigenvalue for (3.2) as well as for (3.9). The simplicity for (3.2) follows from the convexity of $\underline{R}(\omega)$. The above set of a's and b's give those rectangular shapes which could appear at the onset of convection.

Remark: The extreme cases a = 0 or b = 0 correspond to two dimensional solutions called rolls. In what follows we exclude them, i.e. we take a, b ≠ 0. We do this because this is the technically more difficult case, being a three dimensional problem. The case a = 0 or b = 0 is handled analogously but more easily since the problem is two dimensional. Physically, the rolls are the more interesting case because they are actually observed [1] whereas it is not clear whether one obtains rectangles.

Since we are unable to show theoretically that $\underline{R}(\omega)$ is a convex function of ω, we are forced to use a more cumbersome argument.

Let $\underline{R}(\omega)$ denote any eigenvalue of (3.13), (3.14).

Lemma 5: $\underline{R}(\omega) \geq \frac{1}{2}(\omega^4 + c\omega^{-2})$ where c is a constant independent of ω.

The proof is obtained by multiplying the first equation of (3.13) by C and the second by D and then by employing the Schwarz and Poincaré inequalities. We omit the details here.

Remark: The estimate of Lemma 5 holds in particular for $\underline{R}(\omega)$ and implies the minimum over ω of $\underline{R}(\omega)$ is attained in the interior of some interval $[\sigma,\tau]$ where $\sigma > 0$ and $\tau < \infty$. We show next $R_c \equiv \min_\omega R(\omega)$ is attained at only finitely many points in $[\sigma,\tau]$. For this we need the generalization of a result of Rellich due to Dunford and Schwartz [20]:

<u>Lemma</u> 6: Let $T(\mu)$ be a continuous linear operator on a Banach space, with $T(\mu)$ depending analytically on a parameter μ for $|\mu - \mu_o| < \varepsilon$. Assume $R(\mu_o)$ is a simple eigenvalue of $T(\mu_o)$. If $\mathcal{O}$ is an open set containing $R(\mu_o)$ and its closure $\bar{\mathcal{O}}$ contains no other spectra of $T(\mu_o)$, then there exists δ, $0 < \delta < \varepsilon$, such that for $|\mu - \mu_o| < \delta$, $\mathcal{O}$ contains the eigenvalue $R(\mu)$ of $T(\mu)$where $R(\mu)$ depends analytically on μ for $|\mu - \mu_o| < \delta$.

<u>Remark</u>: The result is stated much more generally in [20] but for the case of a simple eigenvalue, it reduces to Lemma 6.

<u>Lemma</u> 7: $R_c = \min_{\omega\varepsilon[\sigma,\tau]} R(\omega)$ is attained at only finitely many points in $[\sigma,\tau]$.

Proof: The Green's functions $G(z,\zeta,\omega)$, $H(z,\zeta,\omega)$ of L and L^2 with the boundary conditions (3.14) are (see [16]):

$$G(z,\zeta,\omega) = \frac{\sinh \omega(\zeta-1)\sinh \omega(z+1)}{\omega \sinh \omega} \qquad z \leq \zeta$$

$$= G(\zeta,z,\omega) \qquad z \geq \zeta$$

$$\begin{aligned} H(z,\zeta,\omega) &= -\frac{1}{h(\omega)}\{[(\sinh\ \omega + \omega\ \cosh\ \omega)\, g(\omega(\zeta-1)) \\ &\quad - f(\omega)f(\omega(\zeta-1))]g(\omega(z+1)) \\ &\quad + [g(\omega)f(\omega(\zeta-1)) + f(\omega)g(\omega(\zeta-1))]f(\omega(z+1))\} \qquad z \leq \zeta \\ &= H(\zeta,z,\omega) \qquad z \geq \zeta \end{aligned}$$

where $f(\omega) = \omega\sinh\omega$, $g(\omega) = \sinh\omega-\omega\cosh\omega$, and $h(\omega) = 2\omega(\omega^2\sinh^2\omega-\omega^4)$. Thus by inspection G and H are real analytic functions of ω in $[\sigma,\tau]$ and are therefore analytic in some complex neighborhood of $[\sigma,\tau]$. Thus the same is true of the linear integral operator of (3.16) associated with G and H. This will be the $T(\omega)$ of Lemma 6. By this lemma $\underline{R}(\omega)$ is an analytic function of ω in some complex neighborhood of $[\sigma,\tau]$. In particular for $\omega\varepsilon[\sigma,\tau]$, $\underline{R}(\omega)$ is a real analytic function which implies its minimum can be attained at only finitely many points in $[\sigma,\tau]$.

Now we are in a position to determine a and b so that (3.2) possesses a simple smallest eigenvalue. Suppose R_c is attained at $\omega = \omega_1,\ldots,\omega_n$, with ω_n the largest of the ω_i. We show for "most" values of (a,b) on the arc $a^2 + b^2 = \omega_n^2$, $a,b > 0$, that R_c is a simple eigenvalue of (3.2).

As we mentioned earlier, the points $a = 0$, $b = 0$ are excluded for convenience. Assume further $b \leq a$. To find admissible a,b, we study $\{j^2a^2 + k^2b^2 | j,k$ nonnegative integers$\}$. For $j = k = 1$, we get $a^2 + b^2 = \omega_n^2$. R_c will be simple if for no other values of j and k do we get $j^2a^2 + k^2b^2 = \omega_i^2$, $1 \leq i \leq n$. By our choice of ω_n, $j^2a^2 + k^2b^2 \geq \omega_i^2$ with equality only if $j = k = 1$ provided $j, k \geq 1$. Thus we need only consider the cases $k = 0$ or $j = 0$. For the former case, $j^2a^2 > \omega_n^2$ $j \geq 2$. Thus possibly $a^2 = \omega_i^2 = (\omega_n^2 - b^2)^{1/2}$, $1 \leq i \leq n - 1$. We exclude these n-1 values of (a,b).

Next consider the case $j = 0$. The set of possible b's lies in the interval $(0,\omega_n/\sqrt{2}]$. We may write

$$(0,\omega_n/\sqrt{2}] = \bigcup_{m=1}^{\infty} S_m$$

where $S_1 = \{b | \omega_n/\sqrt{2} \geq b > \omega_n/2\},\ldots,S_m$ $= \{b | \frac{\omega_n}{m} \geq b > \frac{\omega_n}{m+1}\},\ldots$. If $b \in S_m$, $b^2,\ldots,(mb)^2 \leq \omega_n^2$. Moreover these m functions $b^2,\ldots,(mb)^2$ have mutually disjoint range in $(0,\omega_n]$. This implies at most n points in S_m can produce a nonsimple R_c. Thus we have shown:

Theorem 2: All values of (a,b) on $a^2 + b^2 = \omega_n^2$, $a,b > 0$ produce a simple smallest eigenvalue of (3.2) aside from an exceptional set which is countable and consists only of isolated points.

We denote the eigenfunction corresponding to R_c by $\underline{u}_c$, θ_c, p_c. We impose the normalization

$$\int_{\mathcal{C}} (|\nabla u_c|^2 + R_c|\nabla\theta_c|^2)d\underline{x} = 1 \tag{3.20}$$

Consider next the inhomogeneous linear equations:

$$\begin{aligned} &\Delta\underline{u} - \nabla p + R_c\theta\underline{e} = \underline{f} \\ &\Delta\theta + w = \phi \\ &\nabla \cdot \underline{u} = 0 \end{aligned} \tag{3.21}$$

where $\underline{f} = (f,g,h)$ and ϕ are of the form (2.4). We take (2.2) as boundary conditions and seek a solution also of the form (2.4). To be able to do this, $(\underline{f},\phi)$ must be orthogonal to the solutions of the adjoint homogeneous equations. These can be written as

$$\begin{aligned} &\Delta\underline{U} - \nabla P + \Theta\underline{e} = 0 \\ &\Delta\Theta + R_c W = 0 \\ &\nabla \cdot \underline{U} = 0 \end{aligned} \tag{3.22}$$

where $\underline{U}$, Θ, P also have the form (2.4) and satisfy the boundary conditions (2.2). By inspection we see we can take $\underline{U} = \underline{u}_c$, $\Theta = R_c\theta_c$, $P = p_c$. Thus the necessary condition f,ϕ must satisfy is

$$\int_{\mathcal{C}} (u_{\underline{c}} \cdot \underline{f} + R_c\theta_c\phi)d\underline{x} = 0 \quad . \tag{3.23}$$

This condition is also sufficient as the next theorem shows. To state the theorem we introduce some notation. Let H_m denote the completion of continuous infinitely differentiable functions in x,y,z which are $\frac{2\pi}{a}$ periodic in x, $\frac{2\pi}{b}$ periodic in y, with respect to the inner product

$$(p,q)_m = \sum_{|\sigma|=m} \int_{\mathcal{C}} D^\sigma p D^\sigma q d\underline{x} + \int_{\mathcal{C}} pq d\underline{x} \quad .$$

Here $|\sigma| = \sigma_1 + \sigma_2 + \sigma_3$, with $\sigma_1, \sigma_2, \sigma_3 \geq 0$, and $D^\sigma = \frac{\partial^{|\sigma|}}{\partial x^{\sigma_1} \partial y^{\sigma_2} \partial z^{\sigma_3}}$. We denote the norm in H_m by $|| \; ||_m$. It is not difficult to show that $|| \; ||_m$ is equivalent (for functions which have one of the forms of (2.4)) to $| \; |_m$ where

$$|p|_m^2 = \sum_{j,k=o}^{\infty} [\int_{-1}^{1} |p_{jk}^{(m)}(z)|^2 dz + (j^2a^2+k^2b^2)^m \int_{-1}^{1} p(z)^2 dz] \quad (3.24)$$

Here $p_{jk}^{(m)}$ denotes $\frac{d^m}{dz^m} p_{jk}$ and p_{jk} is the j,k Fourier coefficient of p. We omit the details.

Theorem 3: If $\underline{f}$, $\phi \in H_m$ are of the form (2.4) and satisfy the orthogonality condition (3.23) the inhomogeneous system (3.21) possesses a unique solution $\underline{u}$, θ, p of the form (2.4) satisfying the boundary conditions (2.2). $\underline{u}$, θ is orthogonal (in the sense of $(\; , \;)_o$) to $\underline{u}_c$, θ_c. Moreover $\underline{u}$, $\theta \in H_{m+2}$, $p \in H_{m+1}$, and

$$|\underline{u}|_{m+2} + |\theta|_{m+2} + |p|_{m+1} \leq \alpha(|\underline{f}|_m + |\phi|_m) \quad (3.25)$$

where α is a constant. (As earlier, by $|\underline{u}|$ we mean the sum of the norms of its components).

This theorem may be obtained from a more general theorem of Douglis and Nirenberg [23] or alternatively by substituting (3.14) into (3.21), reducing it to an infinite system of ordinary differential equations, obtaining existence and estimates there, and then synthesizing these to obtain the proof. For details see [24].

4. An Iteration Scheme.

In this section we show how to construct a solution to (3.21). The convergence of the scheme will be established in §5.

We know the equations (2.1) possess only the trivial zero solution for $R \leq R_c$. Thus we are motivated to seek a solution near this one for $R > R_c$, $R - R_c$ small. Let $\underline{x} = (x,y,z)$. We attempt to find a solution of the form:

$$\underline{u}(\underline{x},\varepsilon) = \varepsilon \underline{u}_c(x) + \varepsilon^2 \delta u(\underline{x},\varepsilon)$$

$$\theta(\underline{x},\varepsilon) = \varepsilon\theta_c(\underline{x}) + \varepsilon^2\delta\theta(\underline{x},\varepsilon)$$

$$p(\underline{x},\varepsilon) = \varepsilon p_c(\underline{x}) + \varepsilon^2\delta p(\underline{x},\varepsilon) \tag{4.1}$$

$$R(\varepsilon) = R_c + \varepsilon^2\delta R(\varepsilon) \quad .$$

Here $\delta\underline{u}$, $\delta\theta$, δp are to be of the form (2.4) and $\delta\underline{u}$, $\delta\theta$ are orthogonal to $\underline{u}_c$, θ_c in the sense of $(\, , \,)_o$. The parameter ε may be thought of as the amplitude of the solution. For convergence of the scheme as presented below we need $|\varepsilon|$ small.

Substituting (1) into (2.1), we find:

$$\Delta\delta\underline{u} - \nabla\delta p + R_c\delta\theta\underline{e} = [(\underline{u}_c + \varepsilon\delta\underline{u})\cdot\nabla](\underline{u}_c + \varepsilon\delta\underline{u}) - \varepsilon\delta R(\theta_c + \varepsilon\delta\theta)\underline{e} \tag{4.2}$$

$$\Delta\delta\theta + w = P[(\underline{u}_c + \varepsilon\delta\underline{u})\cdot\nabla](\theta_c + \varepsilon\delta\theta) \tag{4.3}$$

$$\nabla \cdot \delta\underline{u} = 0 \tag{4.4}$$

where $\delta\underline{u}$, $\delta\theta$ satisfy the boundary conditions (2.2).

We set up an iteration scheme to solve these equations:

$$\delta\underline{u}_o = 0 \quad , \quad \delta\theta_o = 0$$

$$\Delta\delta\underline{u}_{n+1}-\nabla\delta p_{n+1}+R_c\delta\theta_{n+1}\underline{e}=[(\underline{u}_c+\varepsilon\delta\underline{u}_n)\cdot\nabla](\underline{u}_c+\varepsilon\delta\underline{u}_n)-\varepsilon\delta R_n(\theta_c+\varepsilon\delta\theta_n)$$

$$\Delta\delta\theta_{n+1}+\delta w_{n+1}=P[(\underline{u}_c+\varepsilon\delta\underline{u}_n)\cdot\nabla](\theta_c+\varepsilon\delta\theta_n) \tag{4.5}$$

$$\nabla \cdot \delta\underline{u}_{n+1} = 0 \quad .$$

Since the equations (4.5) are of the form (3.21), we cannot solve them unless the right hand side satisfies the orthogonality conditions (3.23). However we have a free parameter δR_n. Thus we determine δR_n by requiring that the right hand side of (4.5) satisfy (3.23). We can so obtain δR_n provided that on forming the integral (3.23) the coefficient of R_n is nonzero. But this coefficient is $-\varepsilon\int(\theta_c+\varepsilon\delta\theta_n)w_c d\underline{x}$. Now

$$\int_{C}\theta_c w_c d\underline{x} = \int_{-1}^{1}\int_{0}^{2\pi/a}\int_{0}^{2\pi/b} D(z,a^2+b^2)C(z,a^2+b^2)\cos^2 ax\cos^2 by d\underline{x}>0$$

since $D,C > 0$ for $z\varepsilon(-1,1)$. The remaining term in the coefficient is of order ε. In the course of the iteration we keep a pointwise bound on $\delta\theta_n$. Thus the coefficient of δR_n is nonzero if $|\varepsilon|$ is sufficiently small so we can assume the right hand side of (4.5) satisfies (3.23). It is easily seen that if $\delta\underline{u}_n$, $\delta\theta_n$, δp_n are of the form (2.4), then so is the right hand side of (4.5). Thus by Theorem 3 we can iterate and $\delta\underline{u}_{n+1}$, $\delta\theta_{n+1}$, δp_{n+1} also are of the form (2.4). Since $\underline{u}_c$, θ_c are infinitely differentiable, the same is true of $\delta\underline{u}_n$, $\delta\theta_n$, δp_n by Theorem 3 and the Sobolev inequality.

In §5 we shall show that the iteration scheme

converges for ε sufficiently small. Assuming that, we have shown:

Theorem 4: There exists a nontrivial solution to (2.1), (2.2), of the form (4.1) for $0 < \varepsilon < \varepsilon_0$. The solution is infinitely differentiable.

Corollary: $\delta R(\varepsilon) > 0$.

Proof: By the uniqueness theorem of Joseph (2.1), (2.2) possesses only the trivial solution for $R \leq R_c$.

Before going on to §5, we make a more detailed analysis of our iteration scheme. We recall that we imposed the normalization:

$$\int_{\mathcal{C}} (|\nabla \underline{u}_c|^2 + R_c|\nabla\theta|^2)d\underline{x} = 1 \qquad .$$

Since $-\underline{u}_c$, $-\theta_c$ satisfy this normalization together with $\underline{u}_c$, θ_c, we can find a second nontrivial solution to (2.1), (2.2) by using $-u_c$, $-\theta_c$ as starting point instead of $\underline{u}_c$, θ_c. Thus we have.

Theorem 5: (2.1), (2.2) possess at least two nontrivial solutions of the form (2.4) for $0 < \varepsilon < \varepsilon_0$.

We distinguish between the two solutions by denoting the first by $\underline{u}^+(\varepsilon)=\varepsilon\underline{u}_c+\varepsilon^2\delta\underline{u}^+(\varepsilon),\theta^+(\varepsilon)=\varepsilon\theta_c$ $+\varepsilon^2\delta\theta^+(\varepsilon),p^+(\varepsilon)=\varepsilon p_c+\varepsilon^2\delta p^+(\varepsilon),R^+(\varepsilon)=R_c+\varepsilon^2\delta R^+(\varepsilon)$ and replacing + by - to get the second. We have suppressed an explicit mention of the x,y,z dependence of the solutions.

Let S denote the linear transformation from $u(x,y,z), v(z,y,z), w(x,y,z), \theta(x,y,z), p(x,y,z)$ to $u(x,y,-z)$, $v(x,y,-z)$, $-w(x,y,-z)$, $-\theta(x,y,-z), p(x,y,-z)$.

Lemma 9: If $\underline{u}$, θ, p is a solution of (2.1), (2.2) so is $S\underline{u}$, $S\theta$, Sp (with the same R).

Proof: This is verified immediately by a calculation.

According to Lemma 9, from each of our previous solutions to (2.1), (2.2) we can obtain a new solution via the transformation S. This leads to no new solutions, however, as these are functionally related to our previous solutions.

Lemma 10: $S\underline{u}^-(\varepsilon)=\underline{u}^+(\varepsilon), S\theta^-(\varepsilon)=\theta^+(\varepsilon), Sp^-(\varepsilon)=p^+(\varepsilon)$, and $R^-(\varepsilon) = R^+(\varepsilon)$. We omit the proof.

Remark: Since $R(\varepsilon)$ is an even function of ε, it follows even without the uniqueness theorem for (2.1), that solutions to (2.1) can bifurcate from the zero solution only on one side of R_c.

5. The Convergence Proof.

In this section we complete our existence proof by showing the iteration scheme (4.5) converges for small $|\varepsilon|$. We essentially use a contracting mapping argument employing the estimates (3.25) of linear theory.

We work with the $\underline{u}^+$ solution but drop the +. The proof for the $\underline{u}^-$ solution is the same.

For technical reasons we need pointwise estimates as well as square integral estimates. Therefore let $||\phi(\underline{x})|| \equiv ||\phi|| = \sup_{\underline{x}\varepsilon} |\phi(\underline{x})|, ||\phi||_1 = ||\phi|| + ||\phi_x|| + ||\phi_y|| + ||\phi_z||, ||\underline{u}|| = \max(||u||, ||v||, ||w||)$. We also will employ the following lemma:

Lemma 11: $|\phi\psi|_m < \alpha(||\phi||\ |\psi|_m + ||\psi||\ |\phi|_m)$ where $m \geq 3$ and α is a constant depending on m.

Proof: The proof is essentially the same as a related inequality in [22]. It involves the use of appropriate interpolative inequalities and is omitted here.

Proof of Theorem 4: Assume we have shown

$$|\delta\underline{u}_j|_{m+2} + |\delta\theta_j|_{m+2} + |\delta p_j|_{m+1} \leq K_n \quad , \quad j = 1,\ldots,n \tag{5.1}$$

where K_n is a constant and $m \geq 3$. We show that if $|\varepsilon|$ is taken small enough, we can choose $K_n = K$ independent of n so that $\{\delta\underline{u}_n, \delta\theta_n\}$ and $\{\delta p_n\}$ is bounded in H_{m+2}, H_{m+1} respectively.

$$\delta R_j = \left(\varepsilon\int_{\mathcal{C}} w_c(\theta_c+\varepsilon\delta\theta_j)d\underline{x}\right)^{-1}\int_{\mathcal{C}} \{\underline{u}_c\cdot[(\underline{u}_c+\varepsilon\delta\underline{u}_j)\cdot\nabla](\underline{u}_c+\varepsilon\delta\underline{u}_j)$$
$$+R_c\theta_c[\underline{u}_c+\varepsilon\delta\underline{u}_j)\cdot\nabla](\theta_c+\varepsilon\delta\theta_j)\}d\underline{x}.$$

Let $\beta = \int_{\mathcal{C}} w_c \theta_c d\underline{x}$. We can estimate $|\int_{\mathcal{C}} w_c \delta\theta_j d\underline{x}|$ from above by $|w_c||\delta\theta_j| \leq |w_c| K_n$.

Letting $\gamma = 2 \max(||\underline{u}_c||_1, R_c||\theta_c||, |\underline{u}_c|_{m+1}, |\theta_c|_{m+1})$ and using (5.1), we can estimate (δR_j) by:

$$|\delta R_j| < \frac{\gamma}{\beta} (4\gamma K_n + 2\varepsilon K_n^2) \quad . \tag{5.2}$$

From (3.25) we have:

$$|\delta\underline{u}_{n+1}|_{m+2} + |\delta\theta_{n+1}|_{m+2} + |\delta p_{n+1}|_{m+1} \leq \alpha\{|[(\underline{u}_c + \varepsilon\delta\underline{u}_n)\cdot\nabla](\underline{u}_c + \varepsilon\delta\underline{u}_n)$$

$$+ \varepsilon\delta R_n(\theta_c + \varepsilon\delta\theta_n) + P|(\underline{u}_c + \varepsilon\delta\underline{u}_n)\cdot\nabla(\theta_c + \varepsilon\delta\theta_n)|_m\} \tag{5.3}$$

The Sobolev inequality [23] states

$$||\phi||_j \leq \alpha|\phi|_{m+j} \quad , \quad m \geq 2 \tag{5.4}$$

Letting $\sigma = \alpha(|(\underline{u}_c\cdot\nabla)\underline{u}_c|_m + P|(\underline{u}_c\cdot\nabla)\theta_c|_m$ and using (5.1), (5.2), (5.4), and Lemma 11 to estimate (5.3), we find

$$|\delta\underline{u}_{n+1}|_{m+2} + |\delta\theta_{n+1}|_{m+2} + |\delta p_{n+1}|_{m+1} \leq \gamma + |\varepsilon|\gamma_1 K_n + \varepsilon^2\gamma_2 K_n^2 + |\varepsilon|^3\gamma_3 K_n^3 \tag{5.5}$$

where γ_1, γ_2, γ_3 are polynomials in α, β^{-1}, γ.

Therefore if we further take $|\varepsilon|\max(2\gamma, \gamma_1, \gamma_2, \gamma_3) < \frac{1}{4}$, set $K_1 = 2\gamma$ and $K_n = 2\gamma$, we get

$$|\delta\underline{u}_{n+1}|_{m+2} + |\delta\theta_{n+1}|_{m+2} + |\delta p_{n+1}|_{m+2} < 2\gamma \tag{5.6}$$

Thus we can take $K_{n+1} = 2\gamma$ and $\{\delta\underline{u}_n, \delta\theta_n\}, \{\delta p_n\}$ are bounded in H_{m+2}, H_{m+1} respectively. Also $\{\delta R_n\}$ is a bounded set of real numbers. By standard compactness theorems we can find a subsequence of our above sequence which converges to a solution of (2.1). Actually the whole sequence converges to this solution of (2.1). To see this, let

$\delta \underline{U}_n = \delta \underline{u}_{n+1} - \delta \underline{u}_n$, $\delta\Theta_n = \delta\Theta_{n+1} - \delta\Theta_n$, $\delta P_n = \delta p_{n+1} - \delta p_n$.

By (5.6), it follows

$$|\delta \underline{U}_n|_{m+2} + |\delta\Theta_n|_{m+2} + |\delta P_n|_{m+1} \le 4\gamma$$

It is not difficult using the equations satisfied by $\delta \underline{U}_n$, $\delta\Theta_n$, δP_n and the technique used above to show that

$$|\delta \underline{U}_n|_2+|\delta\Theta_n|_2+|\delta P_n|_1<(|\varepsilon|\gamma_4+\varepsilon^2\gamma_5+|\varepsilon|^3\gamma_6)(|\delta \underline{U}_{n-1}|_1+|\delta\Theta_{n-1}|_1) \tag{5.8}$$

where $\gamma_4,\gamma_5,\gamma_6$ are polynomials in $\alpha,\beta^{-1},\gamma,P,R_c$. Thus if we further choose $|\varepsilon|$ so small that

$$|\varepsilon|\gamma_4 + \varepsilon^2\gamma_5 + |\varepsilon|^3\gamma_6 < \frac{1}{2}\text{ , then}$$

$$|\delta \underline{U}_n|_2+|\delta\Theta_n|_2+|\delta P_n|_1 \le \frac{1}{2}(|\delta \underline{U}_{n-1}|_1+|\delta\Theta_{n-1}|_1) \tag{5.9}$$

which implies that $\delta \underline{u}_n \to \delta \underline{u}$, $\delta\Theta_n \to \delta\Theta$ in H_2 and $\delta p_n \to \delta p$ in H_1.

Since by (5.7) we have bounds for the higher derivatives of $\delta \underline{U}_n$, $\delta\Theta_n$, δP_n, by using the interpolative inequality [23]:

$$|\phi|_j \leq \alpha|\phi|^{1-j/k}|\phi|_k^{j/k} \tag{5.10}$$

it follows that $\delta\underline{u}_n \to \delta\underline{u}$, $\delta\Theta_n \to \delta\Theta$ in H_{m+1}, and $\delta p_n \to \delta p$ in H_m. Actually by the Banach-Saks theorem $\delta\underline{u}, \delta\Theta \varepsilon\ H_{m+2}$, and $\delta p \varepsilon H_{m+1}$.

Once we have shown that $(\delta\underline{u}, \delta\Theta)\varepsilon H_{m+2}, \delta p\varepsilon H_{m+1}$, by a standard bootstrap argument it follows that $\delta\underline{u}$, $\delta\Theta$, δp are infinitely often differentiable. More precisely, the known differentiability of $\delta\underline{u}$, $\delta\Theta$, Lemma 5 and Lemma 11 imply that the right hand side of (4.2) is in H_{m+1} which implies that $(\delta\underline{u}, \delta\Theta)\varepsilon H_{m+3}$, $\delta p\varepsilon H_{m+2}$ via theorem 3, etc.

Thus our proof of theorem 4 is complete.

* * *

This lecture is based on [24] where further details may be found. See also [25] for further results.

BIBLIOGRAPHY

[1] Krishnamurti, R., Finite amplitude thermal convection with changing mean temperature: The stability of hexagonal flows and the possibility of finite amplitude instability, dissertation, UCLA, 1967.

[2] Kosmieder, E. L., On convection on a uniformly heated plane, Beiträge zur Physik der Atmosphäre, 39, 1966, pp. 1-11.

[3] Pearson, J. R. A., On convection cells induced by surface tension, J. Fluid Mech., 4, 1958, pp. 489-500.

[4] Chandrasekhar, S., Hydrodynamic and hydromagnetic stability, Oxford University Press, 1961.

[5] Malkus, W. V. R. and Veronis, G., Finite amplitude cellular convection, J. Fluid Mech., 4, 1958, pp. 225-260.

[6] Busse, F., Das Stabilitätsverhalten der Zellularkonvection bei endlicher Amplitude, dissertation, University of Munich, 1962. (Translation from the German by S. H. Davis, Rand Corp., Santa Monica, Calif. 1966).

[7] Segel, L. A., The structure of nonlinear cellular solutions of the Boussinesq equations, J. Fluid Mech., 21, 1965, pp. 345-358.

[8] Chorin, A. J., Numerical study of thermal convection in a fluid layer heated from below, New York University, Courant Institute of Mathematical Sciences technical report, 1966.

[9] Joseph, D. D., On the stability of the Boussinesq equations, Arch. Rational Mech. Anal., 20, 1965, pp. 59-71.

[10] Velte, W., Stabilitätsverhalten und Verzweigung stationärer Lösungen der Navier-Stokesschen Gleichungen, Arch. Rational Mech. Anal., 16, 1964, pp. 97-125.

[11] Velte, W., Stabilität und Verzweigung stationärer Lösungen der Navier-Stokesschen Gleichungen beim Taylorproblem, Arch. Rational Mech. Anal., 22, 1966, pp. 1-14.

[12] Iudovich, V. I., Example of the generation of a secondary stationary or periodic flow when there is loss of stability of the laminar flow of a viscous incompressible fluid, Jrnl. of Applied Math. and Mechanics (translation of PMM) 29; 1965, pp. 527-544.

[13] Ladyzhenskaya, O. A., The mathematical theory of viscous incompressible flow, Gordon and Breach, 1963, New York.

[14] Courant, R. and Hilbert, D., Methods of mathematical physics, V. 1, Interscience, 1953, New York.

[15] Kirchgässner, K., Die Instabilität der Strömung zwischen zwei rotierenden Zylindern gegenüber Taylor-Wirbeln für beliebige Spaltbreiten, Z. A. M. P., 12, 1961, pp. 14-30.

[16] Karlin, S., Total positivity and applications, Stanford University Press, Stanford, Calif., to appear.

[17] Krein, M. G. and Rutman, M. A., Linear operators leaving invariant a cone in a Banach space, Translations of the A. M. S., series 1, 10, 1962, pp. 199-325.

[18] Reid, W. H. and Harris, D. L., Some further results on the Bénard problem, Phys. Fluids, 1, 102-110, 1958.

[19] Dunford, N. and Schwartz, J. T., Linear Operators, Part I: General Theory, Interscience, 1958, New York.

[20] Rabinowitz, P. H., Periodic solutions of nonlinear hyperbolic partial differential equations, Comm. Pure Appl. Math., 20, 1967, pp. 145-205.

[21] Nirenberg, L., On elliptic partial differential equations, Ann. Scuola Norm. Super. Pisa, Ser. 3, 13, 1959, pp. 1-48.

[22] Douglis, A. and Nirenberg, L., Interior estimates for elliptic systems of partial differential equations, Comm. Pure Appl. Math., 8, 1955, pp. 503-538.

[23] Rabinowitz, P. H. Nonuniqueness of Rectangular solutions of the Bénard Problem, Stanford University

technical report.

[24] Rabinowitz, P. H., Existence and Nonuniqueness of Rectangular Solutions of the Bénard Problem, to appear Arch. Rational Mech. Anal.

XlV. Exchange of Stability in Couette Flow

H. F. Weinberger

1. Introduction

We consider the flow of a viscous incompressible fluid between two rotating cylinders. The inner cylinder has radius $\eta < 1$ and angular velocity Ω and the outer cylinder has radius 1 and angular velocity $\mu\Omega$ with $\mu > 0$. See Fig. 1.

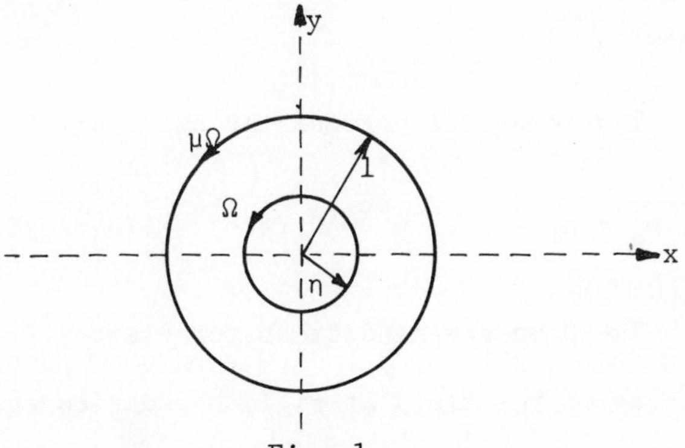

Fig. 1

In cylindrical coordinates having dimensions adjusted so that the viscosity $\nu = 1$, the Navier-Stokes equations for such fluids are

$$\frac{\partial u_r}{\partial_t} + (\underset{\sim}{u}\cdot\nabla)u_r - \frac{u_{\theta}^2}{r} = -\frac{\partial}{\partial r}(\frac{p}{\rho}) + (\Delta u_r - \frac{2}{r^2}\frac{\partial u_\theta}{\partial \theta} - \frac{u_r}{r^2}) \tag{1.1a}$$

$$\frac{\partial u_\theta}{\partial_t} + (\underset{\sim}{u}\cdot\nabla)u_\theta + \frac{u_r u_\theta}{r} = -\frac{1}{r}\frac{\partial}{\partial \theta}(\frac{p}{\rho}) + (\Delta u_\theta + \frac{2}{r^2}\frac{\partial u_r}{\partial \theta} - \frac{u_\theta}{r^2}) \tag{1.1b}$$

$$\frac{\partial u_z}{\partial_t} + (\underset{\sim}{u}\cdot\nabla)u_z = -\frac{\partial}{\partial z}(\frac{p}{\rho}) + \Delta u_z \tag{1.1c}$$

where

$$\underset{\sim}{u}\cdot\nabla = u_r\frac{\partial}{\partial r} + \frac{u_\theta}{r}\frac{\partial}{\partial \theta} + u_z\frac{\partial}{\partial z} \quad ,$$

$$\Delta = \frac{\partial^2}{\partial r^2} + \frac{1}{r}\frac{\partial}{\partial r} + \frac{1}{r^2}\frac{\partial^2}{\partial \theta^2} + \frac{\partial^2}{\partial z^2} \; .$$

The continuity equation is

$$\frac{\partial u_r}{\partial r} + \frac{u_r}{r} + \frac{1}{r}\frac{\partial u_\theta}{\partial \theta} + \frac{\partial u_z}{\partial z} = 0 \quad . \tag{1.2}$$

Here u_r, u_θ, u_z are physical components of velocity and p is the pressure.

The equations possess the exact solution

$$u_r = 0,\ u_\theta = A_r + B/r,\ u_z = 0, (p/\rho) = \int (u_\theta{}^2/r)dr \quad . \tag{1.3}$$

The boundary conditions for viscous flow are that the velocity of the fluid at rigid boundaries equal the velocity of the boundaries. For our problem, these boundary conditions on the cylinders $r = \eta$ and $r = 1$ are met by taking

$$A = -\Omega \frac{\eta^2-\mu}{1-\eta^2}, \quad B = \Omega\eta^2 \frac{1-\mu}{1-\eta^2} . \tag{1.4}$$

If the cylinders have finite length, say $|z| \leq L$, then (1.3) and (1.4) furnish a solution to the boundary value problem described in Fig. 1 only if u_θ at $z = \pm L$ is prescribed to be the value given by (1.3) and (1.4).

The flow given by (1.3) and (1.4) is called Couette flow. We wish to examine the conditions under which this flow is infinitesimally stable.

2. The perturbation problem.

We set

$$u_r = \varepsilon u, \quad u_\theta = Ar + B/r + \varepsilon v, \quad u_z = \varepsilon w,$$

$$(p/\rho) = \int [(Ar + B/r)^2 /r]dr + \varepsilon\pi. \tag{2.1}$$

We seek solutions u, v, w, π that are rotationally symmetric i.e. independent of θ.

We substitute (2.1) into (1.1) and (1.2). By equating the coefficients of ε to zero, we obtain the equations governing the axisymmetric perturbations.

$$[\frac{\partial}{\partial t} - \Delta + \frac{1}{r^2}]u - 2(A+B/r^2)v = -\frac{\partial \pi}{\partial r} \tag{2.2a}$$

$$[\frac{\partial}{\partial t} - \Delta + \frac{1}{r^2}]v + 2Au = 0 \tag{2.2b}$$

$$[\frac{\partial}{\partial t} - \Delta]w = -\frac{\partial \pi}{\partial z} \tag{2.2c}$$

$$\frac{\partial}{\partial r}(ru) + r\frac{\partial w}{\partial z} = 0 \tag{2.3}$$

If we operate on (2.2a) with $(\partial^2/\partial z^2)$, operate on (2.2c) with $-(\partial^2/\partial r\partial z)$, add the results, and use (2.3), we obtain the fourth order equation:

$$(\Delta - \frac{1}{r^2})[\frac{\partial}{\partial t} - (\Delta - \frac{1}{r^2})]u - 2(A + \frac{B}{r^2})\frac{\partial^2 v}{\partial z^2} = 0 \tag{2.4}$$

We assume that the cylinders are infinite.

The adherence boundary conditions require that the perturbations u and v satisfy

$$u = \partial u/\partial r = v = 0 \qquad \text{at } r = \eta, 1. \tag{2.5}$$

(The conditions that $\partial u/\partial r = 0$ at the $r = \eta$, 1 comes from (2.3) and the fact that $w = 0$ at $r = \eta, 1$.)

Our boundary value problem is to find functions $u(r,z,t)$ and $v(r,z,t)$ that satisfy (2.2b), (2.4) and (2.5). We seek such solutions in the Hilbert space L_2.

By performing a Fourier transform in z on these equations, we obtain

$$(L - \lambda^2 - \frac{\partial}{\partial t})\ (L - \lambda^2)\hat{u} - \lambda^2 T(\frac{1}{r^2} - K)\hat{v} = 0 \qquad (2.6)$$

$$\hat{u} + (L - \lambda^2 - \frac{\partial}{\partial t})\hat{v} = 0 \qquad (2.7)$$

with

$$\hat{u}(r,t,\lambda) = -2A \int_{-\infty}^{\infty} e^{i\lambda z} u(r,z,t)dz \quad ,$$

$$\hat{v}(r,t,\lambda) = \int_{-\infty}^{\infty} e^{i\lambda z} v(r,z,t)dz \quad ,$$

$$L \equiv \frac{\partial^2}{\partial r^2} + \frac{1}{r}\frac{\partial}{\partial r} - \frac{1}{r^2} \quad , \qquad (2.8)$$

$$T = -4AB, \qquad K = -A/B \quad . \qquad (2.9)$$

J. L. Synge [1] has shown that the flow is always stable for $\mu > \eta^2$. We therefore consider the case when $\mu < \eta^2$. From (1.4) it follows that $A < 0$, and hence $T > 0$. Moreover, $K < 1$ so that $1/r^2 - K > 0$. Under these circumstances we ask whether there are initial values that cause instability.

We now take the Laplace transform of (2.6) and (2.7) with respect to t. We get

$$(L - \lambda^2 - s)(L - \lambda^2)U - \lambda^2\ T(\frac{1}{r^2} - K)V = I \quad . \qquad (2.10)$$

$$U + (L - \lambda^2 - s)V = J \quad . \qquad (2.11)$$

Here s is the Laplace transform variable, U amd V are the

transforms of $\hat{u}$ and $\hat{v}$, and I and J are prescribed initial values.

We seek conditions under which solutions of (2.6) and (2.7) grow, i.e. conditions under which the eigenvalues s of the nonself-adjoint system (2.10) and (2.11) have positive real parts. For small enough T, it is known that the eigenvalues have negative real parts. Thus, incipient instability occurs when T is just large enough for s to be pure imaginary. Experimentally, however, it is found that incipient instability actually occurs when s = 0. We are thus led to formulate the

Principle of Exchange of Stability for Couette Flows: If the real half line is in the resolvent set for the operator corresponding to the homogeneous form of (2.10), (2.11), then the real half plane is also in the resolvent set. cf. Fig. 2).

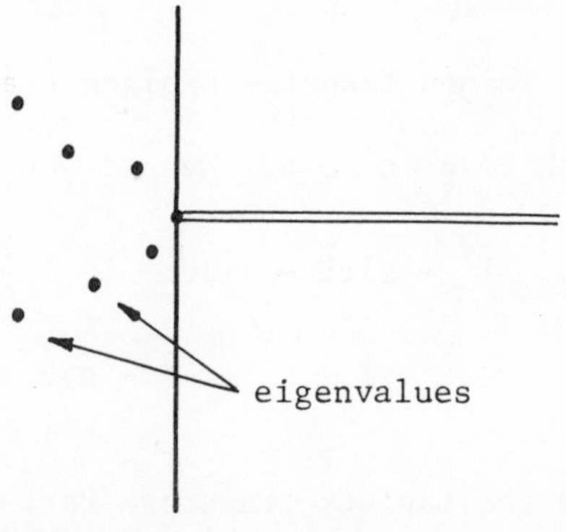

Fig. 2. s-plane

The rest of this lecture will be devoted to the development of methods for the mathematical justification of this principle.

3. Nonnegative operators.

Let A be a matrix all of whose elements are nonnegative. We term such a matrix nonnegative. We can expand the resolvent operator of A formally thus:

$$(A - sI)^{-1} = -s^{-1}(I-A/s)^{-1} = -s^{-1}(I + A/s + A^2/s^2+\dots). \tag{3.1}$$

The last expression in (3.1) is a power series in 1/s having nonnegative coefficients. We can now invoke the following theorem of Pringsheim: If a power series with nonnegative coefficients has radius of convergence R, then R is a singular point of the function represented by the power series. Hence it follows that there is a real positive eigenvalue s_1 of A such that

$$\{s: |\tfrac{1}{s}| < \tfrac{1}{s_1}\} = \{s: |s| > s_1\} \tag{3.2}$$

is in the resolvent set of A, i.e., the spectrum of A is restricted to lie in the disk $|s| \le s_1$ of the s plane. See Fig. 3. This result is part of the Perron-Frobenius Theorem for nonnegative matrices. (Cf. [2].)

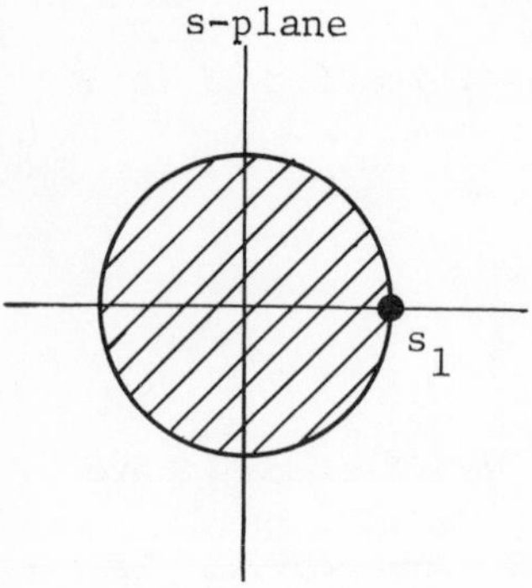

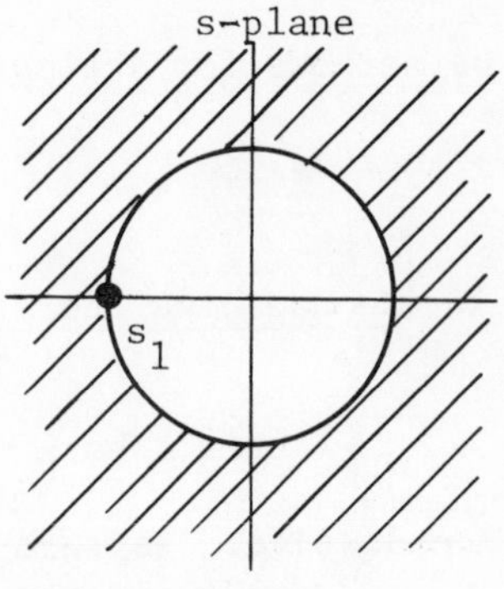

The Spectrum is in the shaded regions

Fig.3. Fig.4.

Similarly, if B is a matrix such that $-B^{-1}$ is nonnegative, then

$$(B-sI)^{-1}=B^{-1}[I-(-s)(-B^{-1})]^{-1}=B^{-1}[I+(-s)(-B^{-1})+(-s)^2(-B^{-1})^2+\dots]. \tag{3.3}$$

Since the power series in (3.3) has nonnegative coefficients, it follows that there is a real eigenvalue $s_1 < 0$ such that the disk

$$\{s: |s| < -s_1\} \tag{3.4}$$

is in the resolvent set of B. See Fig. 4.

Now let a be some prescribed real number and let C be a matrix such that $-(C - s_oI)^{-1}$ is nonnegative for all real $s_o > a$. Then

$$(C - sI)^{-1} = (C - s_oI)^{-1}\{I - (s_o-s)[-(C - sI)^{-1}]\}^{-1} \tag{3.5}$$

Using the same arguments as before, it follows that there is a real eigenvalue $s_1 < s_0$ such that the disk

$$\{s: |s_0 - s| < s_0 - s_1\} \tag{3.6}$$

is in the resolvent set of B. See Fig. 5.

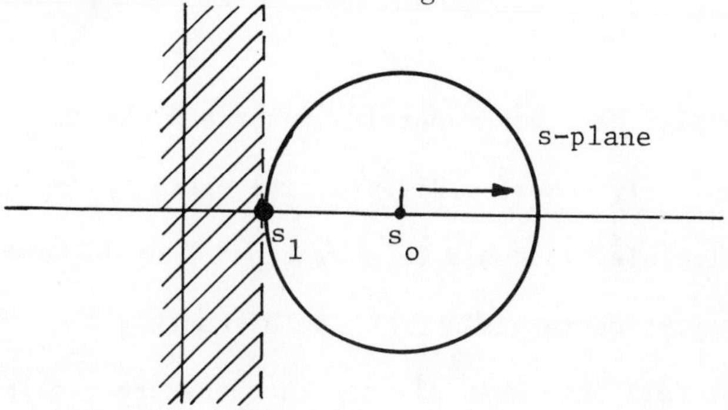

Fig. 5

Since this result holds for all $s_0 > a$ we can move s_0 to the right while the eigenvalue s_1 remains fixed. It follows when $s_0 \to \infty$ that the half-plane

$$\{ s: \operatorname{Re} s > s_1\} \tag{3.7}$$

is in the resolvent set of C.

The natural generalization of a matrix operator with nonnegative elements is an integral operator with nonnegative kernel. Jentzsch [3] and Karlin [4] used the Pringsheim theorem in the above way to show that the Perron-Frobenius theorem also holds for such integral operators. (For an abstract treatment of such operators, see [4] and [5].)

The result (3.7) is just the sort of conclusion we need to establish the principle of exchange of stability. Thus, if we can cast (2.10) and (2.11) in the form

$$[C - sI]u = f \tag{3.8}$$

where C has the properties described above, our task is done. If C were a differential operator having a maximum principle, it could be shown that C would have the requisite properties to yield(3.7). Unfortunately our problem does not fall into this class. We therefore require more delicate results.

4. Special Results.

We return to equations (2.10) and (2.11). Let

$$\Gamma(s) = -[L - \lambda^2 I - sI],^{-1} \tag{4.1}$$

$$G(s) = [(L - \lambda^2 I)(L - \lambda^2 I - sI)]^{-1} . \tag{4.2}$$

We can formulate the homogeneous problem corresponding to (2.10) and (2.11) as

$$U - K(s)U = 0 \quad , \tag{4.3}$$

where

$$K(s) = \lambda^2 TG(s)[(1/r^2 - K)\Gamma(s)] \quad . \tag{4.4}$$

$K(s)$ depends nonlinearly but analytically on s.

We examine the resolvent of $K(s)$.

$$[I-K(s)]^{-1}=\{I-[I-K(s_o)]^{-1}[K(s)-K(s_o)]\}^{-1}[I-K(s_o)]^{-1} \tag{4.5}$$

Now if for all real s_o greater than some a,

(i) $[I - K(s_o)]^{-1}$ is nonnegative, and

(ii) $K(s)$ has a power series expansion about s_o in $(s_o - s)$ with nonnegative coefficients, i.e. $(-\frac{d}{ds})^k K(s_o)$ is nonnegative for all k, (4.6)

then the right-hand side of (4.5) has an expansion in $(s_o - s)$ with nonnegative coefficients and we may apply the methods of Section 3 to assert that there exists a real eigenvalue s_1 such that the spectrum of $K(s)$ lies in the set $\{s: \text{Re } s \leq s_1\}$. This result is equivalent to the principle of exchange of stability.

Condition (i) can readily be established for our operator. To verify condition (ii), we first note that $\Gamma(s)$ is an integral operator whose kernel $\Gamma(r,\rho;s)$ is the Laplace transform of the Green's function $\Gamma^*(r,\rho,t)$ for the problem

$$(L - \lambda^2 - \frac{\partial}{\partial t})u = -f$$

$$u(\eta,t) = u(1,t) = u(r,0) = 0 \quad .$$

It is easily seen that there is a maximum principle associated with this problem, so that $f \geq 0$ implies $u \geq 0$. Consequently, $\Gamma^*(r,\rho,t) \geq 0$. Since

$$\Gamma(r,\rho;s) = \int e^{-st}\Gamma^*(r,\rho,t)dt,$$

we see that

$$(-\frac{d}{ds})^k\Gamma(r,\rho;s) = \int s^k e^{-st}\Gamma^*(r,\rho,t)dt \geq 0$$

for all k and for all $s > -\lambda^2$.

We must now examine the operator $G(s)$. We can represent $G(s)$ by an integral operator whose kernel $G(r,\rho;s)$ is the Green's function for the problem $(L-\lambda^2)(L-\lambda^2-s)u = f$ with appropriate boundary conditions. Moreover,

$$G(r,\rho;s) = \int e^{-st}G^*(r,\rho;t)dt \qquad (4.7)$$

where G^* is the Green's function of the time-dependent problem

$$(L-\lambda^2)(L-\lambda^2-\frac{\partial}{\partial t})u = f \qquad (4.8)$$

$$u = \frac{\partial u}{\partial r} = 0 \text{ at } r = \eta \text{ and } r = 1,$$

$$u = 0 \text{ at } t = 0 \quad .$$

As in the above argument, the inequalities $(-d/ds)^k G(s) > 0$ will follow if it can be shown that the Green's function G^* of the problem (4.8) is positive. Once this is done, it follows easily from the product rule for differentiation that the operator $K(s) = \lambda^2 TG(s)[(\frac{1}{r^2} - K)\Gamma(s)]$ has the property (ii).

The Green's function $G(r,\rho;s)$ can be written explicitly in terms of Bessel functions. The expression is unfortunately too complicated to verify condition (ii) directly. However, by using asymptotic expansions for $s \sim +\infty$, we can show that there is a $t_1 > 0$ such that the Laplace transform G^* satisfies $G^* > 0$ for $t < t_1$.

It is possible to expand $G^*(r,\rho,t)$ in terms of the eigenfunctions of the problem

$$(L - \lambda^2)(L + \gamma^2)w = 0$$

$$w = w' = 0 \qquad \text{at } r = \eta \text{ and } r = 1$$

in the series

$$G^* = \sum_1 w_n(r)w_n(\rho)e^{-(\gamma_n^2 + \lambda^2)t} .$$

The functions w_n can again be expressed in terms of Bessel functions, and in particular it can be shown that $w_1 > 0$. It follows that there is a value t_2 such that $G^* > 0$ for $t > t_2$.

A computation shows that for each fixed λ there is an η_o sufficiently near 1 so that for $\eta > \eta_o$, $t_2 < t_1$.

That is, $G^* > 0$ for all t when the gap is sufficiently small. (However, as $\eta \to 1$, the critical wave number λ approaches infinity, and more computations are needed to show that the condition $G^* > 0$ holds uniformly in λ for sufficiently large η.)

As $\eta \to 0$, it can be shown that G^* approaches the Green's function for the problem

$$(L - \lambda^2)(L - \lambda^2 - \frac{\partial}{\partial t})u = f$$

$$u(1,t) = \frac{\partial u}{\partial r}(1,t) = u(r,0) = 0$$

for the whole cylinder $0 \leq r \leq 1$. For this problem it can be shown that $G^* > 0$. Since the critical wave number remains finite, it follows that the principle of exchange of stability holds when the inner cylinder is sufficiently small.

5. Conclusion.

For an integral operator $K(s)$ with the kernel $K(s;x,y)$, the conditions (i) and (ii)(Section 4) can be weakened to the following set

(i) $[I - K(s)]^{-1}$ is nonnegative for all sufficiently large real s.

(ii) $K(s)$ and $-\frac{d}{ds} K(s)$ are nonnegative for real $s \geq 0$.

(iii) $|K(s+i\tau; x,y)| \leq K(s;x,y)$ for all real τ and real $s \geq 0$.

However, the verification of these conditions in the problem of Couette flow appears to be no easier than that of our previous conditions.

The problem of establishing the principle of exchange of stability in the general case is still open. Whether more refined estimates or different techniques are required is not clear.

Bibliography

[1] J.L. Synge, On the stability of a viscous liquid between rotating coaxial cylinders, Proc. Roy. Soc. (London) A, 167, 250-256, (1938).

[2] F.R. Gantmacher, Matrix Theory, Vol.1, (transl.) Chelsea, N.Y. 1959.

[3] R. Jentsch, Ueber Integralgleichungen mit positivem Kern. Crelle's J. 141, 235-244, (1912).

[4] S. Karlin, Positive Operators, J. of Math and Mech, 8, 907-937, (1959).

[5] M.A. Krasnosel'skii, Positive Solutions of Operator Equations (transl.), Noordhoff, Groningen, 1964.

XV. Perturbation Solutions of Some Nonlinear Boundary Value Problems

M. Millman

1. Introduction.

In this lecture we treat three nonlinear eigenvalue problems for partial differential equations arising from physics. We employ formal perturbation schemes to analyze the qualitative behavior of the solutions in the neighborhood of a known solution. We obtain explicit expressions for the first few terms of our perturbation expansions and specialize our results to concrete examples.

2. Steady-State Temperature in a Body Containing a Nonlinear Heat Source.

Let T(x) be the steady-state temperature distribution in a region D containing a heat source of magnitude $S(T)$. If D is bounded by an insulating surface B, then T satisfies the equations

$$\nabla^2 T = \lambda S(T) \qquad \text{in } D \tag{2.1}$$

$$\frac{\partial T}{\partial n} = 0 \qquad \text{on } B. \tag{2.2}$$

Here $S(T)$ is proportional to the local rate of heat production and λ is a source strength parameter. We wish to solve (2.1) and (2.2) for $T(x)$ when $S(T)$ is a nonlinear function.

Suppose $S(T)$ were of one sign for all T. Then since B is impervious to heat flow, we would expect T to be a monotone function of the time, with no steady-state possible. Therefore we expect that $S(T)$ must change sign for a steady state to exist. Consequently we assume the existence of at least one constant temperature T_o such that

$$S(T_o) = 0. \tag{2.3}$$

Then for arbitrary λ, a solution of (2.1) and (2.2) is

$$T(x) = T_o. \tag{2.4}$$

We now seek solutions other than (2.4). (Another approach to this problem is given in Lecture VIII.)

We seek a solution $T(x,\varepsilon)$ and $\lambda(\varepsilon)$ of (2.1) and (2.2) which depends differentiably on a parameter ε and which reduces to (2.4) when $\varepsilon = 0$. We attempt to represent

$T(x,\varepsilon)$ and $\lambda(\varepsilon)$ by Taylor series in ε about $\varepsilon = 0$:

$$T(x,\varepsilon) = T_o + \varepsilon\dot{T}(x) + \frac{1}{2}\varepsilon^2\ddot{T}(x) + \dots \tag{2.5}$$

$$\lambda(\varepsilon) = \lambda_o + \varepsilon\dot{\lambda} + \frac{1}{2}\varepsilon^2\ddot{\lambda} + \dots . \tag{2.6}$$

Equations governing the coefficients in these expansions can be obtained most efficiently by differentiating (2.1) and (2.2) repeatedly with respect to ε and then setting $\varepsilon = 0$.

By differentiating (2.1) and (2.2) once with respect to ε and setting $\varepsilon = 0$, we obtain

$$[\nabla^2 - \lambda_o S'(T_o)]\,\dot{T} = 0 \tag{2.7}$$

$$\frac{\partial\dot{T}}{\partial n} = 0 \qquad \text{on } B. \tag{2.8}$$

We assume that $S'(T_o) \neq 0$, so that (2.7) and (2.8) constitute a linear eigenvalue problem for λ_o and $\dot{T}(x)$, which is just the problem obtained by linearizing (2.1). This problem has a set of orthonormal eigenfunctions $\phi_n(x)$, with corresponding eigenvalues λ_{on}, $n = 0,1,2,\dots$. If λ_{on} is not degenerate, then (2.7) and (2.8) have the nontrivial solutions

$$\dot{T}_n = A_n\phi_n, \tag{2.9}$$

when

$$\lambda_o = \lambda_{on},\ n = 0,1,2,\dots . \tag{2.10}$$

Here A_n is an undetermined constant.

It is important to note that

$$\lambda_{oo} = 0 \tag{2.11}$$

is always a non-degenerate eigenvalue, with corresponding eigenfunction

$$\phi_o = V^{-1/2}. \tag{2.12}$$

Here V is the volume of D. The case of a degenerate eigenvalue is discussed below.

We next differentiate (2.1) and (2.2) twice with respect to ε and then set $\varepsilon = 0$ to obtain

$$[\nabla^2 - \lambda_o S'(T_o)]\,\ddot{T} = \lambda_o S''(T_o)\dot{T}^2 + 2\dot{\lambda}S'(T_o)\dot{T} \tag{2.13}$$

$$\frac{\partial \ddot{T}}{\partial n} = 0 \qquad \text{on B.} \tag{2.14}$$

The homogeneous problem corresponding to (2.13), (2.14) is just (2.7), (2.8). Thus (2.13), (2.14) has a solution if and only if the right side of (2.13) is orthogonal to ϕ_n, the eigenfunctions of the self-adjoint homogeneous problem (2.7), (2.8). By solving the orthogonality condition for $\dot{\lambda}$, employing (2.9) and (2.10), we obtain

$$\dot{\lambda}_n = -\frac{\lambda_{on}A_n S''(T_o)}{2S'(T_o)}\int_D \phi_n^3 dx. \tag{2.15}$$

We can now insert this value of $\dot{\lambda}_n$ into (2.13) and solve for $\ddot{T}_n$. We see that $\ddot{T}_n$ will be proportional to A_n^2 if the arbitrary additive multiple of ϕ_n in $\ddot{T}_n$ is eliminated by redefining ε appropriately.

Let us now suppose that the eigenvalue λ_{on} is k-fold degenerate, with corresponding eigenfunctions $\phi_{n1},\ldots,\phi_{nk}$, so that

$$\dot{T}_n = \sum_{j=1}^{k} A_{nj}\phi_{nj} \tag{2.16}$$

Here the A_{nj} are constants. The k solvability conditions corresponding to (2.16) are

$$0 = \lambda_{on} S''(T_o) \sum_{i,j}^{k} a^n_{mij} A_{ni} A_{nj} + 2\dot{\lambda} S'(T_o) A_{nm}, \quad m=1,\ldots,k. \tag{2.17}$$

Here

$$a^n_{mij} = \int \phi_{nm}\phi_{ni}\phi_{nj}\,dx. \tag{2.18}$$

Equations (2.17) determine the A_{nj} and $\dot{\lambda}$ within an arbitrary common multiplicative constant M_n, but the solution may not be unique. We write the solution in the form

$$\dot{\lambda}_n = M_n\mu_n, \quad A_{nj} = M_n C_{nj}, \qquad j = 1,\ldots,k, \tag{2.19}$$

and then we have

$$\dot{T}_n = M_n \sum_{j=1}^{k} C_{nj}\phi_{nj} \tag{2.20}$$

The determination of the C_{nj} in the degenerate case is analogous to the problem of finding the "correct" linear combination of unperturbed eigenstates in the theory of perturbation of a degenerate eigenvalue by a linear operator, as in quantum mechanics.

Finally, we differentiate (2.1), and (2.2) three

times with respect to ε and then set ε = 0 to obtain

$$[\nabla^2 - \lambda_o S'(T_o)]\, \dddot{T} = 3\lambda_o S''(T_o)\dot{T}\ddot{T} + \lambda_o S'''(T_o)\dot{T}^3 + 3\ddot{\lambda} S'(T_o)\dot{T}$$
$$+ 3\dot{\lambda} S'(T_o)\ddot{T} + 3\dot{\lambda} S''(T_o)\dot{T}^2 \qquad (2.21)$$

$$\frac{\partial \dddot{T}}{\partial n} = 0 \qquad \text{on B.} \qquad (2.22)$$

Again this is an inhomogeneous form of (2.7), (2.8). If λ_{on} is assumed to be non-degenerate, the solvability condition requires that

$$\ddot{\lambda}_n = \frac{A_n^2}{S'(T_o)} \Big[\frac{\dot{\lambda}_n}{A_n} S'(T_o) \int \phi_n \frac{\ddot{T}}{A_n^2} dx + \frac{\dot{\lambda}_n}{A_n} S''(T_o) \int \phi_n^3 dx$$
$$+ \lambda_{on} S''(T_o) \int \phi_n^2 \frac{\ddot{T}}{A_n^2} dx + \frac{1}{3} \lambda_{on} S'''(T_o) \int \phi_n^4 dx\Big] \qquad (2.23)$$

We see that $\ddot{\lambda}_n$ is proportional to A_n^2.

We now summarize our results:

For each integer $n \geq 0$, we have determined a solution of (2.1) and (2.2) of the form

$$T_n(x,\varepsilon) = T_o + \varepsilon A_n \phi_n + \frac{1}{2} \varepsilon^2 \ddot{T}_n + 0(\varepsilon^3) \qquad (2.24)$$

$$\lambda_n(\varepsilon) = \lambda_{on} + \varepsilon \dot{\lambda}_n + \frac{1}{2} \varepsilon^2 \ddot{\lambda}_n + 0(\varepsilon^3). \qquad (2.25)$$

We have shown that $\dot{\lambda}_n$, given by (2.15), is proportional to A_n and that $\ddot{\lambda}_n$, given by (2.23), and $\ddot{T}_n$ are proportional to A_n^2. Therefore (2.24) and (2.25) are expansions in powers of εA_n, the amplitude of the linearized solution. A sketch of

εA_n versus λ with $S''(T_o) = 0$ for simplicity, is shown in Figure 1.

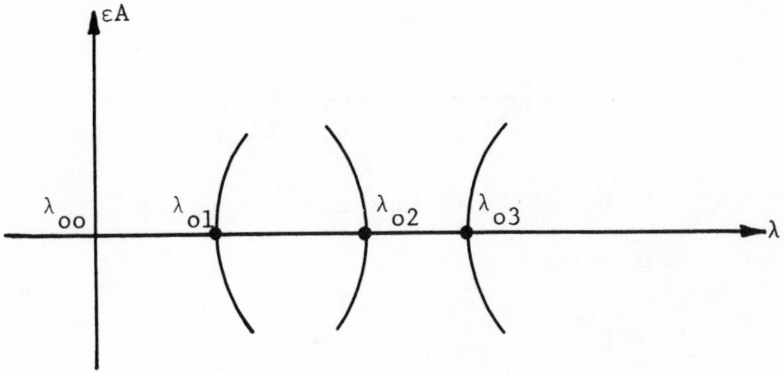

Figure 1.

To order $(\varepsilon A_n)^2$ the n-th curve is a parabola with its vertex at the bifurcation point λ_{on}. It is concave to the right or left according as $\ddot{\lambda}_n$ is positive or negative. The only exception is the n = 0 curve, which is a vertical line because $\lambda_o(\varepsilon) \equiv 0$.

The curves are to be interpreted as follows: Corresponding to each choice of the source strength λ, there are a certain number of solutions $T(x,\lambda)$. The amplitude εA of the "linear part" of $T(x,\lambda)$ is shown in the figure for each λ sufficiently near a bifurcation value λ_{on}.

Example.

Let D be a rectangular parallelepiped with edge lengths L_1, L_2 and L_3 and let $S''(T_o) = 0$. The solution of (2.7) and (2.8) is

$$\dot{T}_{nmp} = A_{nmp}\left(\frac{8}{L_1L_2L_3}\right)^{1/2}\cos\frac{n\pi x}{L_1}\cos\frac{m\pi y}{L_2}\cos\frac{p\pi z}{L_3} \tag{2.26}$$

$$\lambda_{0(nmp)} = \frac{-\pi^2}{S'(T_0)}\left[\frac{n^2}{L_1^2} + \frac{m^2}{L_2^2} + \frac{p^2}{L_3^2}\right]. \tag{2.27}$$

Here A_{nmp} is an arbitrary constant and $m,n,p = 0,1,2,\ldots$. Then (2.15) yields

$$\dot{\lambda}_{nmp} = 0. \tag{2.28}$$

When (2.28) is inserted on the right side of (2.13), that equation becomes homogeneous and identical with (2.7), which is satisfied by $\dot{T}$. Therefore $\ddot{T}$ is proportional to $\dot{T}$ and, by suitably redefining ε, we can take

$$\ddot{T}_{nmp} = 0. \tag{2.29}$$

By inserting (2.26)-(2.29) into (2.23), we obtain finally

$$\ddot{\lambda}_{nmp} = \frac{9\pi^2 S'''(T_0)}{8L_1L_2L_3[S'(T_0)]^2}\left[\frac{n^2}{L_1^2} + \frac{m^2}{L_2^2} + \frac{p^2}{L_3^2}\right]. \tag{2.30}$$

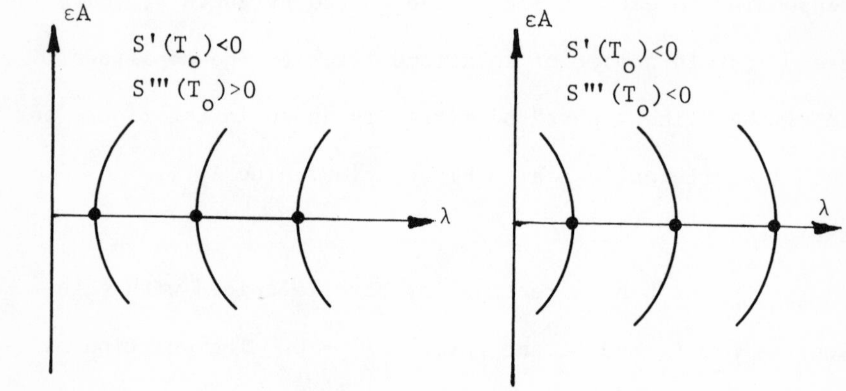

Figure 2

Equation (2.27) shows that all the $\lambda_{o(nmp)}$ are of one sign and (2.30) shows that the εA versus λ curves are either all concave to the right or all concave to the left, depending upon the sign of $S'''(T_o)$. (Figure 2.) Moreover, the eigenvalues are simple if L_1, L_2, L_3 are rationally independent.

3. Self-Sustained Oscillations.

We consider the nonlinear equation

$$u_{tt} - u_{xx} + u = \varepsilon f(u_t); \qquad 0 < x < \pi, \tag{3.1}$$

Here ε is a small parameter and $f(u_t)$ is a nonlinear "damping force" which is of the same sign as u_t for small u_t and of the opposite sign for large u_t. When u is independent of x, and $f(u_t) = u_t - \frac{1}{3}(u_t)^3$, (3.1) is the van der Pol equation. For this ordinary differential equation, it is known that all motions tend toward a single periodic motion characterized by a unique amplitude and frequency, independent of the initial conditions. Therefore we seek solutions $u(x,t)$ of (3.1) periodic with some angular frequency ω:

$$u(x,t + \frac{2\pi}{\omega}) = u(x,t). \tag{3.2}$$

We also require $u(x,t)$ to satisfy the boundary conditions

$$u(0,t) = u(\pi,t) = 0. \tag{3.3}$$

It is convenient to introduce $t' = \omega t$ in (3.1)-(3.3) and then to omit the primes. This yields

$$\omega^2 u_{tt} - u_{xx} + u = \varepsilon f(\omega u_t); \quad 0 < x < \pi \tag{3.4}$$

$$u(x,t + 2\pi) = u(x,t) \tag{3.5}$$

$$u(0,t) = u(\pi,t) = 0. \tag{3.6}$$

We now seek $u(x,t,\varepsilon)$ and $\omega(\varepsilon)$, which we represent by Taylor series in ε about $\varepsilon = 0$ as follows:

$$u(x,t,\varepsilon) = u_o(x,t) + \varepsilon\dot{u}(x,t) + \frac{1}{2}\varepsilon^2 \ddot{u}(x,t) + \ldots \tag{3.7}$$

$$\omega(\varepsilon) = \omega_o + \varepsilon\dot{\omega} + \frac{1}{2}\varepsilon^2 \ddot{\omega} + \ldots . \tag{3.8}$$

Equations for the zero order quantities in these expansions can be obtained by setting $\varepsilon = 0$ in (3.4)-(3.6). Equations for the higher order quantities can be obtained by differentiating (3.4)-(3.6) repeatedly with respect to ε and then setting $\varepsilon = 0$.

Setting $\varepsilon = 0$ in (3.4)-(3.6) yields

$$\omega_o^2 u_{ott} - u_{oxx} + u_o = 0 \tag{3.9}$$

$$u_o(x,t+2\pi) = u_o(x,t), \; u_o(0,t) = u_o(\pi,t) = 0. \tag{3.10}$$

This system has solutions

$$u_{on} = A_n \sin nx \cos t + B_n \sin nx \sin t \quad n = 1,2,\ldots \tag{3.11}$$

for $\omega_{on} = (1 + n^2)^{1/2}$. (3.12)

The amplitudes A_n and B_n are not yet fixed. By fixing the origin of t we may take $B_n = 0$. Thus

$$u_{on} = A_n \sin nx \cos t. \tag{3.13}$$

We differentiate (3.4)-(3.6) once with respect to ε and set $\varepsilon = 0$ to obtain

$$\omega_o^2 \dot{u}_{tt} - \dot{u}_{xx} + \dot{u} = -2\omega_o \dot{\omega} u_{ott} + f(\omega_o u_{ot}) \tag{3.14a}$$

$$\dot{u}(x,t+2\pi) = \dot{u}(x,t),\ \dot{u}(0,t) = \dot{u}(\pi,t) = 0 \tag{3.14b}$$

The inhomogeneous problem (3.14) has a solution if and only if the right side of (3.14a) is orthogonal to (3.11), the eigenfunctions of the self-adjoint homogeneous problem (3.9), (3.10). This solvability criterion thus requires

$$\omega_o \dot{\omega} \pi^2 A_n + \int_0^{2\pi} \int_0^{\pi} \sin nx \cos t\ f(-\omega_o A_n \sin nx \sin t) dxdt = 0 \tag{3.15}$$

$$\int_0^{2\pi} \int_0^{\pi} \sin nx \sin t\ f(-\omega_o A_n \sin nx \sin t) dxdt = 0. \tag{3.16}$$

Here we have evaluated u_{ot} and u_{ott} from (3.13). Condition (3.15) determines $\dot{\omega}$ in term of A_n and (3.16) determines A_n.

In order to obtain explicit results, we take

$$f(v) = v - \frac{1}{3} v^3. \tag{3.17}$$

Then (3.16) yields

$$A_n = 0,\ \pm \frac{4\sqrt{3}}{3\omega_o}. \tag{3.18}$$

We choose $A_n = + \frac{4\sqrt{3}}{2\omega_o}$ since the other sign would just change the phase of the solution. The integral in (3.15) is zero, so we obtain

$$\dot{\omega} = 0. \tag{3.19}$$

We now insert (3.18) and (3.19) into the right side of (3.14a) and find

$$\omega_o^2 \dot{u}_{tt} - \dot{u}_{xx} + \dot{u} = \frac{4\sqrt{3}}{27} [\sin 3nx \sin 3t - 3 \sin 3nx \sin t \\ -3\sin nx \sin 3t]. \tag{3.20}$$

The solution of (3.20), (3.14b) is

$$\dot{u} = -\frac{\sqrt{3}}{54} \sin 3nx \sin 3t + \frac{\sqrt{3}}{18(1+n^2)} \sin nx \sin 3t \\ - \frac{\sqrt{3}}{18n^2} \sin 3nx \sin t + D \sin nx \sin t + E \sin nx \cos t. \tag{3.21}$$

Here D and E are arbitrary constants.

We differentiate (3.4)-(3.6) twice with respect to ε, set $\varepsilon = 0$, and use (3.19) to obtain

$$\omega_o^2 \ddot{u}_{tt} - \ddot{u}_{xx} + \ddot{u} = -2\omega_o \ddot{\omega} u_{ott} + 2\omega_o \dot{u}_t f'(\omega_o u_{ot}), \tag{3.22}$$

$$\ddot{u}(x,t+2\pi) = \ddot{u}(x,t), \quad \ddot{u}(0,t) = \ddot{u}(\pi,t) = 0 .$$

The solvability condition for (3.22) in conjunction with (3.12), (3.13) and (3.21) now implies

$$E = 0 \tag{3.23}$$

$$\ddot{\omega} = -\frac{\sqrt{1+n^2}}{72} \left(1 - \frac{1}{n^2} + \frac{9}{1+n^2}\right). \tag{3.24}$$

We collect our results and reintroduce the original t variable. For each integer n there is a mode of vibration given by

$$u_n(x,t,\varepsilon) = \frac{4\sqrt{3}}{3\sqrt{1+n^2}} \sin nx \cos \omega_n t \tag{3.25}$$

$$+ \varepsilon[- \frac{\sqrt{3}}{54} \sin 3nx \sin 3\omega_n t + \frac{\sqrt{3}}{18(1+n^2)} \sin nx \sin 3\omega_n t$$

$$- \frac{\sqrt{3}}{18n^2} \sin 3nx \sin \omega_n t + D \sin nx \sin \omega_n t] + 0(\varepsilon^3)$$

$$\omega_n(\varepsilon) = \sqrt{1+n^2} - \frac{\varepsilon^2\sqrt{1+n^2}}{144}\left(1 - \frac{1}{n^2} + \frac{9}{1+n^2}\right) + 0(\varepsilon^3). \tag{3.26}$$

This is an oscillation which bifurcates at $\varepsilon = 0$ from that particular solution of the linearized problem which has amplitude $4\sqrt{3}\,/3\sqrt{1+n^2}$. From (3.26) we see that as ε increases the frequency of each mode decreases due to the presence of the nonlinear damping force.

4. Forced Vibrations of a "String" with a Nonlinear Restoring Force.

We consider periodic small vibrations of a model equation for a uniform string fixed at one end and harmonically driven at the other, under the action of a nonlinear restoring force. The relevant equations are

$$u_{tt} - u_{xx} = \varepsilon F(u), \qquad 0 < x < \pi \tag{4.1}$$

$$u(0,t) = 0, \qquad u(\pi,t) = A \cos \omega t \tag{4.2}$$

$$u(x,t + \frac{2\pi}{\omega}) = u(x,t) \tag{4.3}$$

$$\frac{1}{2}\int_0^\pi [u_x^2 + u_t^2 - 2\varepsilon \int_0^u F(u)du]_{t=0} dx = E. \tag{4.4}$$

In (4.1) we have explicitly written the restoring force small of order ε, so that our development will be in the neighborhood of the linear forced vibration. Below we also treat the case in which the forcing function is in the differential equation, rather than in the boundary condition.

It seems natural in (4.2) to regard ω as prescribed in advance, but $u(x,t,\omega,\varepsilon)$ is not analytic in ε for ω near a resonance frequency. Therefore we prescribe the energy E in (4.4) and consider ω and u to be functions of E, A and ε. Then u and ω are both analytic in ε, as we shall see. Equation (4.3) expresses the requirement that the response have the same period as the excitation. It is convenient to introduce $t' = \omega t$ in (4.1)-(4.4) and then to omit the primes. This yields

$$\omega^2 u_{tt} - u_{xx} = \varepsilon F(u), \qquad 0 < x < \pi \tag{4.5}$$

$$u(0,t) = 0, \qquad u(\pi,t) = A \cos t \tag{4.6}$$

$$u(x,t+2\pi) = u(x,t) \tag{4.7}$$

$$\frac{1}{2}\int_0^\pi [u_x^2+\omega^2 u_t^2-2\varepsilon\int_0^u F(u)du]_{t=0} dx = E. \tag{4.8}$$

We represent $u(x,t,\varepsilon)$ and $\omega(E,A,\varepsilon)$ by their Taylor series in ε about $\varepsilon = 0$ as follows:

$$u(x,t,\varepsilon) = u_o(x,t) + \varepsilon u_1(x,t) + \ldots \tag{4.9}$$

$$\omega(E,A,\varepsilon) = \omega_o^2(E,A) + \varepsilon\omega_1^2(E,A) + \ldots \, . \tag{4.10}$$

Equations for the first coefficients in these expansions can be obtained by setting $\varepsilon = 0$ in (4.5)-(4.8), for the next coefficients by differentiating with respect to ε and putting $\varepsilon = 0$, etc.

Setting $\varepsilon = 0$ in (4.5)-(4.8) yields

$$\omega_o^2 u_{ott} - u_{oxx} = 0, \qquad 0 < x < \pi \tag{4.11}$$

$$\frac{1}{2}\int_o^\pi [u_{ox}^2 + \omega_o^2 u_{ot}^2]_{t=o} dx = E, \tag{4.12}$$

and (4.6), (4.7) with u_o in place of u. The solution of (4.11), (4.6) and (4.7) is

$$u_o = \frac{A}{\sin \omega_o \pi} \sin \omega_o x \cos t. \tag{4.13}$$

Insertion of (4.13) into (4.12) then yields the following linear response relation between E and ω_o:

$$\frac{4\pi E}{A^2} \left(\frac{\sin \omega_o \pi}{\omega_o \pi}\right)^2 = 1 + \frac{\sin 2\omega_o \pi}{2\omega_o \pi} \, . \tag{4.14}$$

Figure 3 shows a graph of E versus ω_o based on (4.14). It can be seen that for given E there are no roots for ω_o unless

$$E \geq \frac{A^2}{2\pi} . \tag{4.15}$$

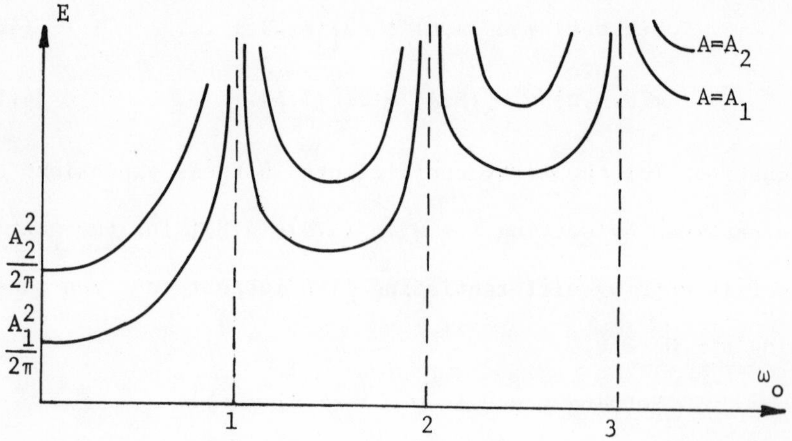

Figure 3.

As $E \to \infty$, the number of roots increases monotonically and they draw closer to the values $\omega_o = 1,2,\ldots$. Thus for each E satisfying (4.15) there is at least one root for ω_o which is not an integer, and corresponding to this root there is a finite u_o given by (4.13).

We next differentiate (4.5)-(4.8) once with respect to ε and set $\varepsilon = 0$ to obtain

$$\omega_o^2 u_{1tt} - u_{1xx} = -\omega_1^2 u_{ott} + F(u_o), \quad 0 < x < \pi \tag{4.16}$$

$$\int_0^\pi [u_{ox}u_{1x} + \omega_o^2 u_{ot}u_{1t} + 2\omega_1^2 u_{ot}^2 - \int_0^{u_o} F(u)du]_{t=o} dx = 0, \tag{4.17}$$

and (4.6), (4.7) with u_1 in place of u. The homogeneous form of (4.16) has no solution satisfying (4.6) so (4.16) has a unique solution. It is readily found to be

$$u_1 = \frac{A\omega_1^2 \cos t}{\sin\omega_o\pi} \sum_{k=1}^{\infty} \frac{B_k}{k^2-\omega_o^2} \sin kx + \sum_{\substack{k=1 \\ j=o}}^{\infty} \frac{C_{jk}}{k^2-\omega_o^2 j^2} \cos jt \sin kx. \tag{4.18}$$

Here the coefficients B_k and C_{jk} are defined by

$$\sin \omega_o x = \sum_{k=1}^{\infty} B_k \sin kx \tag{4.19}$$

$$F(u_o) = \sum_{\substack{k=1 \\ j=o}}^{\infty} C_{jk} \cos jt \sin kx, \quad 0 < x < \pi . \tag{4.20}$$

Insertion of (4.18) into (4.17) then yields

$$\omega_1^2 = \frac{\sin\omega_o\pi}{A} \; \frac{\frac{2}{\pi}\int_0^{\pi}\left(\int_0^{u_o} F(u)du\right)_{t=o} dx - \sum_{j,k} \frac{kc_{jk}D_k}{k^2-\omega_o^2 j^2}}{\sum_k \frac{kB_kD_k}{k^2-\omega_o^2}}. \tag{4.21}$$

Here D_k is defined by

$$\frac{A\omega_o}{\sin\omega_o\pi} \cos \omega_o x = \sum_{k=o}^{\infty} D_k \cos kx, \qquad 0 < x < \pi. \tag{4.22}$$

We collect our results and reintroduce the original t variable. We have determined the periodic modes of vibration in the form

$$u(x,t,\varepsilon) = \frac{A}{\sin\omega_o\pi} \sin \omega_o x \cos \omega t \tag{4.23}$$

$$+ \varepsilon\left[\frac{A\omega_1^2}{\sin\omega_o\pi} \sum_{k=1}^{\infty} \frac{B_k}{k^2-\omega_o^2} \sin kx \cos \omega t\right.$$

$$+ \sum_{\substack{j=o \\ k=1}}^{\infty} \frac{C_{jk}}{k^2-\omega_o^2 j^2} \sin kx \cos j\omega t] + O(\varepsilon^2)$$

$$\omega^2(E,A,\varepsilon) = \omega_o^2 + \varepsilon\omega_1^2 + O(\varepsilon^2). \tag{4.24}$$

In (4.23) and (4.24) ω_o and ω_1 are given as functions of E, A and ε by (4.14) and (4.21) respectively. Therefore (4.23) gives $u(x,t,E,A,\varepsilon)$ and (4.24) gives $\omega(E,A,\varepsilon)$. We may consider these equations to be parametric equations for $u(x,t,\omega,A,\varepsilon)$ with E being the parameter. From (4.23) we see that the nonlinearity introduces harmonics of the applied frequency. The relation (4.24) can be viewed as a response relation which determines E, the energy at $t = 2\pi n/\omega$, as a function of ε, A and ω.

Example.

Let us choose

$$F(u) = -u^3, \tag{4.25}$$

Then for $|\omega_o - n| < < 1$, $n = 1,2,\ldots$, we can can simplify (4.21) and use the result in (4.24) to obtain

$$\omega^2 \simeq \omega_o^2 + \frac{9\varepsilon A^2}{16\pi^2} \frac{1}{(\omega_o - n)^2} + O(\varepsilon^2). \tag{4.26}$$

The qualitative behavior of ω as a function of ω_o for $\varepsilon > 0$ based on (4.26), is indicated in Figure 4.

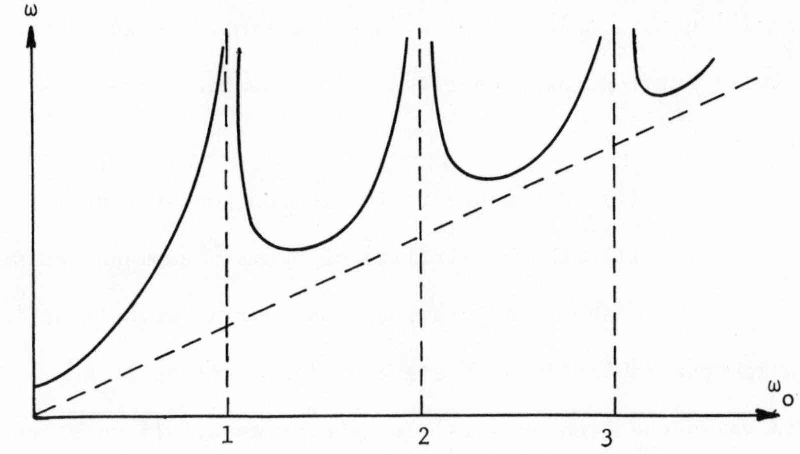

Figure 4. ($\varepsilon > 0$)

We now eliminate ω_o between (4.14) and (4.26), or between Figures 3 and 4, to obtain E as a function of ω. The result is the nonlinear response relation shown in Figure 5. The nonlinearity has bent the linear response

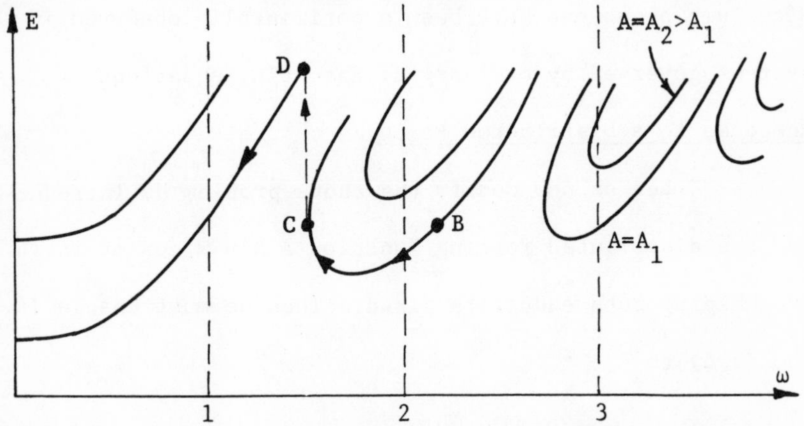

Figure 5.

curves to the right, just as it does for an ordinary differential equation involving a "hard" spring. We note the following interesting properties of the nonlinear response curves:

(i) Resonance infinities no longer occur.

(ii) The possibility of "jump phenomena" arises.

To show the jumps, we consider an experiment in which the amplitude of the excitation is fixed at A_1, and in which the frequency is slowly decreased. If we start at point B in Figure 5, we see that the energy E gradually decreases as ω decreases and then E slowly increases until point C is reached, where the tangent is vertical. With a further decrease in ω, there occurs a sudden jump in the energy to point D, after which E gradually decreases again. Such jump phenomena have been experimentally observed in systems governed by ordinary differential equations.

Response to a Distributed Force.

Let us now modify the above problem by introducing the distributed forcing function A sin x cos ωt in (4.1) and keeping both endpoints fixed. Then we must change (4.5) and (4.6) to

$$\omega^2 u_{tt} - u_{xx} - \varepsilon F(u) = A \sin x \cos t, \qquad 0 < x < \pi \tag{4.27}$$

$$u(0,t) = u(\pi,t) = 0. \tag{4.28}$$

Thus we must solve (4.27), (4.28), (4.7) and (4.8). By setting $\varepsilon = 0$, we find for the solution of (4.27), (4.28) and (4.7) the result

$$u_o = \frac{A}{1-\omega_o^2} \sin x \cos t. \qquad (2.29)$$

Upon introducing (4.29) into (4.8), we obtain the linearized response relation (See Figure 6)

$$E = \frac{A^2}{4(1-\omega_o^2)} . \qquad (4.30)$$

There is only one resonance because the driving force, being proportional to sin x, excites only the lowest mode of the free system.

We next differentiate (4.27) and (4.8) once with respect to ε and then set $\varepsilon = 0$ to obtain

$$\omega_o^2 u_{1tt} - u_{1xx} = -\omega_1^2 u_{ott} + F(u_o) \qquad (4.31)$$

$$\int_o^\pi [u_{ox}u_{1x} + \omega_o^2 u_{ot}u_{1t} + 2\omega_1^2 u_{ot}^2 - \int_o^{u_o} F(u)du]_{t=o} dx = 0. \qquad (4.32)$$

Differentiation of (4.28) and (4.7) at $\varepsilon = 0$ merely replaces u by u_1 in them. The solution of (4.31), (4.28) and (4.7) **is**

$$u_1 = \frac{\omega_1^2 A}{(1-\omega_o^2)^2} \sin x \cos t + \sum_{\substack{k=1 \\ j=o}}^{\infty} \frac{c_{jk}}{\omega_o^2 j^2 - k^2} \sin kx \cos jt. \qquad (4.33)$$

Here the coefficients c_{jk} are defined by (4.20). Insertion of (4.33) into (4.32) then yields

$$\omega_1^2 = \frac{(1-\omega_o^2)^2}{A} \sum_{j=o}^{\infty} \frac{c_{j1}}{1-\omega_o^2 j^2} - \frac{2(1-\omega_o^2)^3}{\pi A^2} \int_o^{\pi} \int_o^{\frac{A}{1-\omega_o^2}\sin x} F(u)du\, dx. \tag{4.34}$$

Again our result is $u = u_o + \varepsilon u_1 + O(\varepsilon^2)$ and $\omega^2 = \omega_o^2 + \varepsilon\omega_1^2 + O(\varepsilon^2)$. To exemplify it let us take $F(u)=u^3$. Then after some algebra we can simplify (4.34), for ω_o near unity, and obtain the approximate result

$$\omega^2 \simeq \omega_o^2 + \frac{9A^2\varepsilon}{16(1-\omega_o^2)^2} + \cdots, \quad |\omega_o - 1| < < 1. \tag{4.35}$$

The qualitative behavior of ω as a function of ω_o is shown in Figure 7.

We now eliminate ω_o between (4.30) and the relation $\omega^2 = \omega_o^2 + \varepsilon\omega_1^2 + O(\varepsilon^2)$, or between Figures 6 and 7, to obtain E as a function of ω. This is the nonlinear response relation shown in Figure 8. Again, we find a behavior analogous to that of a "hard" spring.

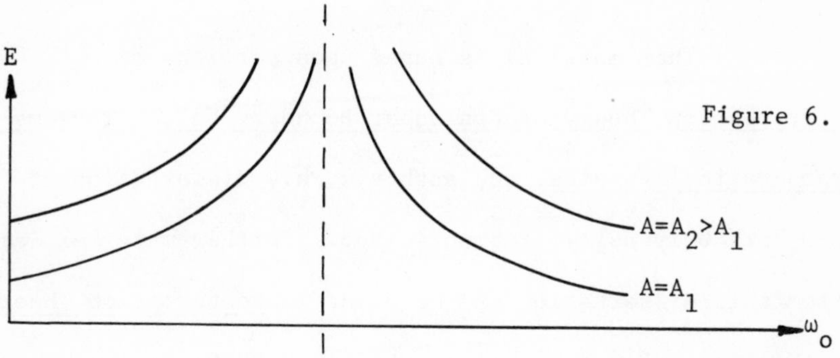

Figure 6.

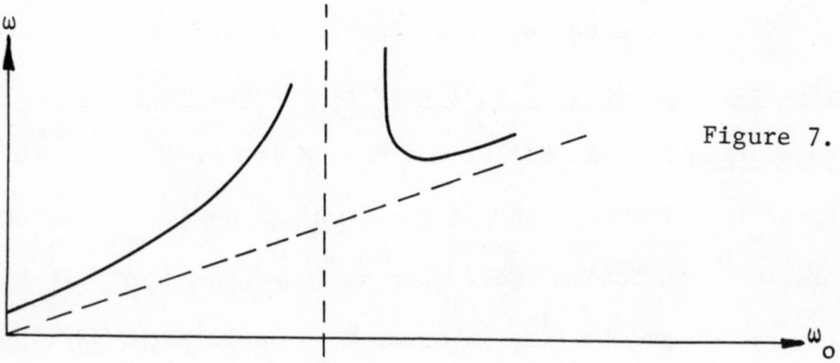

Figure 7.

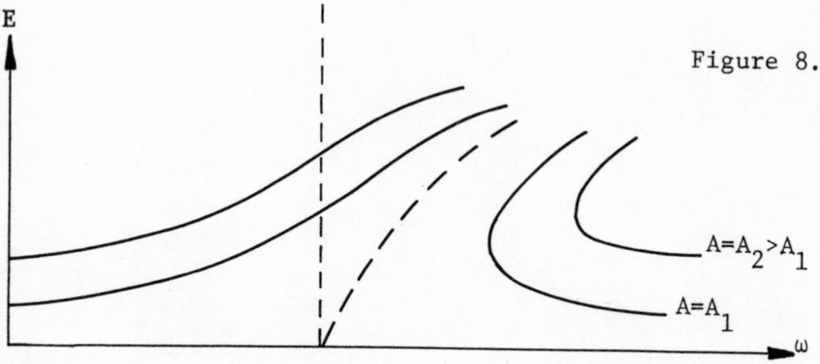

Figure 8.

5. References.

This material is based upon portions of Perturbation Theory of Nonlinear Boundary Value Problems in Mathematical Physics, the author's Ph.D dissertation at New York University, February 1968. Further material drawn from this dissertation may be found in Perturbation Theory of Nonlinear Boundary Value Problems by M.H. Millman and J.B. Keller, Journal of Math. Phys., January 1969 and Perturbation Theory of Nonlinear Electromagnetic Wave Propagation by J.B. Keller and M.H. Millman, which is to appear in a future issue of the Physical Review. Related work in perturbation theory can be found in an article by J.B. Keller and L. Ting in Comm. Pure Appl. Math. 19 (1966).